Interstellar Communication

PHYSICAL INVESTIGATIONS OF THE UNIVERSE

A. G. W. Cameron, Editor

Interstellar Matter in Galaxies *L. Woltjer, Editor*

Interstellar Communication *A. G. W. Cameron, Editor*

Gravitation and Relativity *H. Y. Chiu and W. F. Hoffmann, Editors*

INTERSTELLAR
COMMUNICATION

A Collection of Reprints
and Original Contributions

*

A. G. W. Cameron, Editor

Institute for Space Studies
Goddard Space Flight Center, NASA

W. A. Benjamin, Inc.
1963   *new york*   *amsterdam*

INTERSTELLAR COMMUNICATION
A Collection of Reprints and Original Contributions

Library of Congress Catalog Card Number: 63-11724
Manufactured in the United States of America

The last chapter of the manuscript was received on December 17, 1962, and this volume was published on May 15, 1963

The publisher is pleased to acknowledge the assistance of Cecilia Duray-Bito, who produced the illustrations, and William Prokos, who designed the cover and dust jacket

W. A. BENJAMIN, INC.
2465 Broadway, New York 25, New York

EDITOR'S FOREWORD

While astronomy and geology have traditionally been sciences involving observation and classification of phenomena in the universe, the other physical sciences have been largely restricted to laboratory investigations of the laws of nature and their manifestations in simple forms of matter. In recent years, however, immense progress has been made in understanding how the laws of nature operate in the universe itself—in the cosmic laboratory—where man cannot perform simple experiments but must attempt to analyze nature as he finds it. Progress has been particularly vigorous in such fields as astrophysics, geophysics, geochemistry, and meteoritics. In particular, the space research program has stimulated large numbers of people from various physical disciplines to participate in the physical exploration of the solar system.

This series of books will be concerned with any line of scientific inquiry which attempts to achieve a better understanding of the physical mechanisms that operate in the universe. Pure investigations of the laws of nature, and laboratory investigations of the properties of matter, will not be included. If a laboratory scientist turns his experimental and theoretical talents to the investigation of his physical environment, the results of his investigations are of interest for this series.

The primary aim of the series will be to further communication between scientists investigating nature, and the mode of publication will be varied to minimize the diversion of a scientist's energy from his active participation in teaching and research. The series will include monographs on various specialized topics, proceedings of conferences and symposia, collections of scientific reprints with critical commentary, and publication of lecture-note volumes.

A. G. W. CAMERON

New York, New York
February 1963

THE AUTHORS

Marcia Ascher, Department of Mathematics and Physics, Ithaca College, New York

Robert Ascher, Department of Sociology and Anthropology, Cornell University

R. N. Bracewell, Radio Astronomy Institute, Stanford University

Melvin Calvin, Department of Chemistry, University of California, Berkeley

A. G. W. Cameron, Institute for Space Studies, Goddard Space Flight Center, National Aeronautics and Space Administration, New York, New York

Giuseppe Cocconi, CERN, Geneva, Switzerland

Frank D. Drake, National Radio Astronomy Observatory, Green Bank, West Virginia

Freeman J. Dyson, Institute for Advanced Study, Princeton

M. J. E. Golay, Technische Hogeschool, Eindhoven, Netherlands

Su-Shu Huang, Goddard Space Flight Center, National Aeronautics and Space Administration, Greenbelt, Maryland

Philip Morrison, Physics Department, Cornell University

B. M. Oliver, Hewlett-Packard Company, Palo Alto, California

J. P. T. Pearman, Space Science Board, National Academy of Sciences —National Research Council, Washington, D.C.

Edward Purcell, Physics Department, Harvard University

R. N. Schwartz, Institute for Defense Analyses, Washington, D.C.

Iosif S. Shklovskiy, Shternberg State Astronomical Institute, Moscow, U.S.S.R.

C. H. Townes, Provost, Massachusetts Institute of Technology

Sebastian von Hoerner, Astronomisches Rechen-Institut, Heidelberg, Germany

J. A. Webb, Lockheed Georgia Company, Marietta, Georgia

PUBLICATION HISTORY
OF THE PAPERS

The editor and publishers are very grateful to the above authors and publications for granting permission for the reprinting of material in this book.

CONTENTS

xii : Contents

Interstellar Communication

Great Nebula in Andromeda

A. G. W. Cameron

✳ INTRODUCTION

This book is a scientific anthology in which are reprinted some of the more important articles that have dealt with what is currently the greatest question in scientific philosophy. This question can be asked in the form, "How many technologically advanced societies exist in our galaxy and how can we communicate with them?" Or we could simply say, "Where is everybody?"

Only a few years ago we tended to think that we were unique in the universe. The solar system was thought to have resulted from a close passage of two stars: an exceedingly rare event. But more recently we have tended to think that the formation of planetary systems is a usual event accompanying star formation. We have also begun to think that the spontaneous generation of life is a natural and normal occurrence on a primitive planet if the composition is earth-like and the temperature reasonable. Hence we are now completing the Copernican intellectual revolution and admitting the probability not only that we are not unique in the universe but that there may be millions of societies more advanced than ourselves in our galaxy alone. If we can now take the next step and communicate with some of these societies, then we can expect to obtain an enormous enrichment of all phases of our sciences and arts. Perhaps we shall also receive valuable lessons in the techniques of stable world government.

Harlow Shapley set the stage for our discussions in his book *Of Stars and Men*. In attempting to answer the question, "Are we alone?", he suggested that we take an overly cautious view of the probabilities of life in the universe and do some simple computations. Suppose one star in a thousand has planets. Suppose only one in a thousand of these planetary systems has a planet suitably placed with a favorable temperature to support life. Let us further suppose that only one in a thousand of these is big enough to hold an atmosphere. Let us further

I

suppose that only one in a thousand of these has a suitable chemical composition. Thus only one star in 10^{12} may have conditions suitable for the origin of life. But since there are more than 10^{20} stars in the universe, we can expect that more than 10^8 stars will have developed life.

We are less cautious today, and we estimate that far more stars than these have developed life. But we now wish to enquire further: How many of the stars with life also have advanced civilizations with which we can communicate? We shall encounter some estimates of this toward the end of our book.

We start in Chapter 1 with a review of the problem by the Russian astrophysicist I. S. Shklovskiy. Not only is it useful to have a Russian point of view included here, but it is also useful to take a preliminary look at the various subjects of our discussion.

The following chapters deal with some of the background material necessary to place our discussion in its proper perspective. These include questions of galactic history, of the origin of our solar system, and of the history of the earth, discussed by myself. Then Melvin Calvin discusses the chemical evolution on the earth that led to the origin of life and its early development.

Su-Shu Huang in Chapters 6 through 9 examines the conditions in the universe under which planets are likely to become abodes of life. In Chapter 10 I have a few words to say on this subject.

Chapters 11 and 12, by Freeman J. Dyson, discuss some of the possible activities that a very advanced civilization might undertake. The interest of this to our present discussion is that some of the suggested activities may result in a sufficient modification of a normal stellar environment that we might be able to detect advanced civilizations by looking for such modifications.

In Chapter 13 Edward Purcell presents in a vivid and stimulating lecture some of the reasons why we cannot expect space travel between the stars to be a suitable means of interstellar communication, and he advocates signalling with radio waves. Sebastian von Hoerner further demolishes the myth of interstellar travel in Chapter 14.

Chapter 15 is the important pioneering paper of Giuseppe Cocconi and Philip Morrison, in which they analyzed quantitatively the problem of interstellar communication with radio waves and suggested that the wavelength region of the 21-cm waves emitted by interstellar hydrogen would be a natural region to use in signalling toward other stars.

Chapter 16 is the paper in which Frank Drake explained how he was going to search for 21-cm signals from two solar-type stars about

11 light-years away: τ Ceti and ϵ Eridani. Chapter 17 is a brief report of his negative results. He does not mention a fantastic coincidence that happened during this search. He listened for a few days to his first presumed source, ϵ Eridani, and heard nothing. Then he turned to τ Ceti, and, a minute and a half after turning on his receiver, unmistakably strong signals came in. You can imagine his excitement at hearing an unmistakably intelligent signal. But as his antenna tracked the source, the signals faded out. He was forced to conclude that he had picked up a terrestrial signal. τ Ceti sent nothing detectable, and after a day or two his strong interference never occurred again.

Further discussions of radio communication are given in Chapters 18 through 21, by J. A. Webb, M. J. E. Golay, R. N. Bracewell, and Su-Shu Huang.

In Chapters 22 and 23 the possibilities of interstellar signalling with the new laser technology are discussed by B. M. Oliver, R. N. Schwartz, and C. H. Townes. One of the interesting aspects of this technology is that it seems to be a historical accident that it was not developed much sooner. Perhaps some advanced societies consider lasers the most promising means of communication.

In Chapters 24 and 25 R. N. Bracewell introduces the interesting concept that advanced societies may send interstellar probes to explore nearby stars and also to wait around until civilizations develop on them. Then the probes might establish first contacts with such a new civilization.

In later chapters the discussion turns to the broader questions of calculating the likelihood of advanced societies within our galaxy. In Chapter 26 Philip Morrison discusses some of the physical, biological, and social questions associated with this problem. Sebastian von Hoerner, in Chapter 27, makes some quantitative estimates of the distance to the nearest advanced civilizations, taking into account the possible importance of the interstellar communications themselves in lengthening the life of a culture.

In Chapter 28 J. P. T. Pearman describes the discussions at the first conference on the question of extra-terrestrial intelligent life. One interesting note about this conference is that the award of the Nobel Prize to Melvin Calvin was announced during his attendance at the meeting, and the resulting barrage of phone calls somewhat disrupted the proceedings.

In Chapter 29 B. M. Oliver raises again the questions of the techniques of communication and gives a practical demonstration of the usefulness of sending television signals as a preferred form of interstellar message.

4 : Interstellar Communication

The subject of interstellar communication has now developed to the point where the participation in the discussions of social and behavioral scientists is much to be desired. The most uncertain factors governing the distance to the nearest advanced society involve the lifetime of such a society, a question that lies within their realm. A preliminary discussion of one of the factors from the point of view of anthropology is given by Robert and Marcia Ascher in Chapter 30.

Finally, in Chapters 31 and 32 I have made some closing remarks on future research on interstellar communication, within the framework of a formal statement of the various probabilities involved, and Philip Morrison has also made some remarks about the future outlook in the field.

Much of the material in this book is of a considerable technical nature. Nevertheless, the interested lay reader can peruse much of the material with profit. I would suggest he look at Chapters 1, 2, 3, 4, 5, 6, 7, 11, 13, 16, 17, 21, 24, 25, 26, 28, 29, 30, 31, and 32.

In gathering together papers for a scientific anthology of this type, I have been faced with the problem of accepting a certain amount of repetition in the articles by different authors, or of trying to edit the repetition away. If the articles were being published for the first time, I would probably adopt the latter course. But I have felt that it would be unfair to the authors to truncate their material, especially since this book would have been only slightly smaller had I done so.

Much valuable research is now being done on the subject of interstellar communication. It is my hope that by making this assembled collection of articles available, considerably more research will be stimulated in this field. This research is likely to take place in a wide variety of disciplines and to be published in a widely scattered variety of journals. It may be that the proper interdisciplinary presentation of results will be helped by further collections such as this one. Hence I should like to suggest that authors send reprints of their material to me for possible publication in further volumes on the subject of interstellar communication.

Iosif S. Shklovskiy

I ❋ IS COMMUNICATION POSSIBLE WITH INTELLIGENT BEINGS ON OTHER PLANETS?

The actual title of this paper may appear fantastic to the reader of *Priroda*. One may wonder whether so serious a periodical should ever tackle this unusual problem, to say the least. Is this not just mystification after all? However, on second thought it seems quite natural. And yet, we must strive to demonstrate that in this era of extraordinarily rapid progress in science and technology, the approach is legitimate and timely. After all, the first steps have already been taken toward solving this far-reaching problem that confronts humanity.

Are There Other Planetary Systems?

The first question we ask is: "To what extent is there a basis in the assertion that the galaxy is constituted by a determined number of stars?" Up until very recently, planetary systems were considered to be extreme rarities in the universe. In fact, the cosmogonic hypothesis of the English astronomer Jeans generally prevailed until the middle 1930s; it asserts that the solar system was formed as a result of a catastrophic rapprochement, or a chance collision between two stars. Considering this as a most unlikely event (the magnitude of interstellar distances is enormous by comparison to the dimensions of stars), one comes to the conclusion that our solar system is an almost unique phenomenon within the galaxy.

Collapse of Jeans' Hypothesis

The inconsistency of Jeans' hypothesis gradually became evident in the 1930s. At that time, the famous American astronomer, the late H. N.

5

Russell, demonstrated in principle (qualitatively) that this hypothesis could not explain one of the basic peculiarities of the solar system—the concentration of 98 per cent of its total moment of momentum in the orbital motion of the planets. Jeans' hypothesis received a final blow from the calculations of the Soviet astronomer N. N. Pariysk, who fully confirmed Russell's deductions. It was shown that the orbits of planets, born out of the catastrophic collision between two stars, are of too small dimensions and that, consequently, the total moment of momentum of the planets is entirely insufficient.

After the collapse of Jeans' cosmogonic hypothesis, new viewpoints were developed by a series of researchers. The O. U. Schmidt hypothesis, and the works of A. I. Lebedinov and L. E. Gurevich who developed it, had a great significance. These investigations brought us closer to the understanding of the principle of gradual planet formation out of an initial gas-dust cloud surrounding the sun, which at that time already rather resembled the contemporary sun. However, the Schmidt hypothesis could not provide a sufficiently plausible answer to the main question concerning the origin of the gas-dust cloud. Different variations brought forth by Schmidt and other authors concerned with the attraction of the gas-dust, interstellar medium by the sun have met with considerable difficulties.

At present, it becomes more and more evident that the planets and sun originated simultaneously out of a common, diffused "parent" nebula. Thus, the cosmogony is now to a significant degree turning back to the original concepts of Kant and Laplace.

However, these concepts now stand at an incomparably higher level than they did a century and a half ago. Our knowledge of the universe has grown tremendously, and the researchers today make full use of the most recent achievements in theoretical physics. While the Kant and Laplace hypothesis had at that time a distinctly mechanistic character (which was quite legitimate in those times), nowadays the achievements in the fields of space electrodynamics and nuclear physics are fully used when dealing with contemporary cosmogonic hypotheses.

As a rule, twin and multiple stars form out of the original gas-dust nebula. Nearly 50 per cent of all new stars are multiple. The masses of stars entering into a multiple-star system may differ from one another. There exist rather numerous stars whose satellites have insignificant masses and consequently very weak luminosities. Such satellites cannot be observed by the most powerful telescopes. Their existence is revealed by slight periodic variations of the principal stars' positions conditioned by the attraction of an invisible satellite. As a classical example of such a celestial body we may mention the star 61 Cygni, which is one of the nearest to the sun and which was studied in detail by the Soviet astronomer A. N. Deutsch. The mass of the invisible satellite of the star is only ten times larger than that of Jupiter. However, under the circumstances, the existence of invisible satellites may only be established for close stars and only when the mass of satellites is larger by at least one order than the mass of giant planets. The existence of planetary systems comparable to ours cannot be detected by astronomical observation, even in nearest stars.

The well-known American astronomer O. L. Struve has illustrated this situation as follows: Let us suppose an imaginary observer, distant from the sun by 10 parsecs (a little more than 30 light-years), situated in Jupiter's orbital plane. Assuming he had at his disposal the necessary contemporary astronomic means of observation, could he detect the giant planet Jupiter near the sun? The Struve calculations show that in order to be able to solve this problem by astrometric methods, the observer should be in a position to measure angles in the sky with a 0.005" precision. If he resorted to the spectroscopic method, he should be able to measure the radial velocities with a precision to 10 m/sec. Such measurement precisions are not attainable in contemporary astronomy. Let us note, however, that nearly once in eleven years, he might have observed the passing of Jupiter across the solar disk, and at that time, the visible stellar magnitude of the sun would have been weakened by 0.01 of the stellar magnitude.

Such measurement is still impractical by contemporary electrophotometry. It must be borne in mind that if the direction observer–sun should only represent few angular minutes with the plane of Jupiter's orbit, the concealment of Jupiter by the sun would no longer be observable. Therefore, it is impossible to detect large planets by direct observations of even the closest stars.

But this naturally does not mean that in the process of star formation out of nebulae rather small-mass, planet-type cosmic bodies may not be formed simultaneously. The Chinese astronomer, Su-Shu Huang, working in the United States, has concluded, while analyzing this problem, that there must exist a continuous sequence of masses of cosmic bodies forming from nebulae. This may range from usual stellar masses through masses of invisible stars of the 61 Cygni type, to planetary systems of the earth, Mars, and Mercury types. The immediate conclusion is that planetary systems of the solar type must be widespread in the galaxy. This conclusion may also be reached through entirely different considerations.

What Does the Rotation of the Stars Imply?

The analysis of the rotation of various types of stars has a great significance in contemporary planetary cosmogony. The rotation of stars was discovered by means of spectroscopic methods more than thirty years ago by O. L. Struve and the late Soviet astronomer G. A. Shayn.

It appears that comparatively massive hot stars are characterized by very rapid rotation. The hottest stars (spectral classes Oe and Be), whose masses are dozens of times larger than that of the sun, are rotating with velocities of 300 to 500 km/sec (at the equator). The spectral class A stars, neither as hot nor as massive, often encountered in the galaxy, usually rotate at velocities somewhat lower than approximately 100 to 200 km/sec. The rotation speeds exceed several dozens of km/sec up to and including the spectral class F5 of the main sequence. However, a sudden, sharp break in that speed is observed in stars near the spectral class F5. For dwarf stars of G, M, and K types, whose temperatures are less than 6500° and whose masses are less than 1.2 of the solar mass, equatorial rotation speeds are very small: They are of the order of a few kilometers per second. The sun also belongs to this part of stars of the main sequence.

Here we are confronted with an exceedingly interesting and important phenomenon. While the basic characteristics of the stars (such as surface temperatures, mass, and brightness) vary continuously along the main sequence, such an important characteristic as the speed of rotation changes abruptly by a jump in the region of the F5 spectral class without any apparent reason. The low speed of rotation for stars of later spectral classes means that their moment of momentum is several dozen times smaller than that of earlier stars than F5. But the masses of the latter group differ little from those of the dwarf type G. Meanwhile, it must be borne in mind that some masses of forming stars are determined by masses of parent nebulae and their moments of momentum—by disorderly velocities of gas masses in these nebulae. It is very difficult if not altogether impossible to visualize that for sufficiently close masses, the inner motions in nebulae, from which G-type dwarfs are forming, must differ qualitatively from the inner motions in nebulae giving birth to F5-type stars. Most probably, the cause of the abnormally small moment of momentum for dwarf stars of later spectral classes is the result of a motion around them of invisible, small-mass, cosmic bodies whose orbital moment of momentum is dozens of times higher than the moment of momentum of the star connected with its rotation. Let us point out in connection with the above that if the total moment of momentum of the solar system were concentrated in the sun, its equatorial rotation speed would reach 100 km/sec and would become identical to that of the majority of A- to F5-type stars.

Multiplicity of Planetary Systems

A prominent English astronomer, W. McCrea, developed very recently a cosmogonic theory in which the above-described qualitative considerations are presented quantitatively. According to his thinking, the original nebula was broken into a series of clusters in the course of its condensation. As a result of the interaction of these clusters, a central massive body—the sun—and a certain quantity of planets were formed. At the same time, according to his calculations, 96 per cent of the moment of momentum of the system was concentrated in the orbital motion of the planets. This is in perfect agreement with the observed distribution of the solar system's moment of momentum.

Although it is certain that McCrea's calculations as yet cannot be considered an unquestionable proof, they nevertheless corroborate the deduction arrived at in astrophysics during recent years by purely empirical means, i.e., it may be stated with a large degree of probability that most of the G, K, and M types of dwarf stars must be surrounded by families of planets. But this implies that at least several billion stars in the galaxy must possess planetary systems. Let us recall that over 150 billion stars of all types are counted in the galaxy. As is known, our sun is located near the plane of the galactic equator, in the vicinity of one of the spiral branches. Nearly 10,000 stars are counted within a 100 light-year radius sphere, and a substantial part, if not all of them, are dwarfs of G, K, and M types.

Where Is Life Likely to Begin?

It is quite natural to assume that under favorable circumstances, life may originate and develop on planets surrounding these stars. The problem of the origin of life on earth is one of the basic problems of natural science.

A multilateral discussion of this problem took place for the first time in Moscow in 1957, during an international congress. It was indicated by a series of prominent specialists in the field that the formation of complex organic molecules—the "building blocks of life" —must of necessity take place at a comparatively early stage of the planet's evolution.

In the course of further evolution, which may have taken several hundred million or billion years, the organisms gradually developed and reached a high degree of perfection, while one series of species was continuously replaced by others. Man—the intelligent being—appeared on earth at a relatively late stage of evolution.

Since there is a basis for assuming that there are in the galaxy several billion planetary systems similar to the solar system, it is natural to admit that the process of the beginning and evolution of life there is also similar to that on earth.

It must be understood that the birth and the development of life is not possible on every planet. A series of conditions are necessary to that effect.

1. Planets on which life may begin and develop may not rotate too close or too far away from the star. Their surface temperatures must be favorable to the development of life. However, taking into account that a comparatively large number of planets, say about ten, must originate simultaneously with the star, it may be reasonably expected that at least one or two of them may rotate at distances at which the temperature range remains within the required limits.

Let us also note that as there is transfer from comparatively hot stars of the main sequence to colder ones, the zone of distance between the planets and the star under which temperature conditions are favorable to the development of life is continuously diminishing and nearing that of the surface of the star. Thus, it is hardly possible to consider the red dwarfs of the spectral class M, and even later sub-classes K, as sources for sustaining life on their planets since their radiation energy is insufficient for that effect.

2. The masses of formed planets must be neither too large nor too small. This was stressed by V. G. Fesenkov. In the first case, the gigantic atmospheres of these planets, rich in hydrogen and its combinations, exclude all possibility for the development of life. In the second case, they will disperse during the time of atmospheric evolution (Mercury is such an example). However, bearing in mind the number of forming planets, let us expect that a certain, even a very small number of them, may have the required mass. At the same time, such planets have to fulfill the first condition.

Let us note that conditions 1 and 2 are not independent. Indeed, it is not a matter of chance that relatively small-mass solar system planets (the so-called planets of the earth group) are relatively close to the sun, while giant planets, rich in hydrogen combinations, are relatively remote from the sun. Because of this, we may consider that at least a significant part of the planets with a mass suitable for the development of life must at the same time be situated at a convenient distance from the star.

3. A highly organized life may be found only on planets circling sufficiently old stars, whose ages may be estimated at several billion years, for enormous intervals of time are necessary to make the appearance of life possible during the process of evolution. Let us note that nearly all dwarf stars of spectral types of interest to us satisfy the third condition.

4. The star must not vary significantly its brightness during several billion years. The overwhelming majority of stars of interest to us meet this condition.

5. The star must not be of multiple type, otherwise the orbital motion of the planet would be substantially different from the circular, and the resulting sharp, if not catastrophic, temperature variations of the planet's surface would preclude the possibility of development of any form of life.

How Many Planets Could Be Cradles of Intelligent Beings?

Even accounting for all the above-described limitations, we may consider that there are in the galaxy at least a billion planets, rotating around dwarf stars similar to our sun, or somewhat colder, on which a highly organized and possibly intelligent life may take place.

However, attention must immediately be drawn to a very important circumstance. It is known that man appeared on the earth as a biological species several hundred thousand years ago. Can we hold, under the circumstances, that mankind, developing continuously, will exist as long as we want, say a billion years?

It seems to us that faith in the eternity of mankind on earth (since we only may speak of faith) is just as absurd and senseless as the faith in the personal immortality of the individual. Anything that was born must unavoidably perish sooner or later. And there is no reason for intelligent life on any planet to constitute an exception.

What is the length of the different world psychozoic eras, i.e., those periods during which intelligent life began to develop? This is a very difficult question to answer. It may be hundreds of thousands or even millions of years.

The limit of the psychozoic era in time on different planets reduces sensibly the number of worlds where human beings live simultaneously with us. Assuming for instance that the average duration of such an era is of say a million years, there would be in contemporary times only several million planets having intelligent life of a sufficiently high level. In this case, in a sphere of a 100 light-years radius surrounding the earth there may be only one or two planetary systems of that kind. Quite obviously the correction of the limit of psychozoic eras we just made has a rather arbitrary character. However, from our viewpoint it is quite indispensable, otherwise the estimate of the number of inhabitable worlds in the universe would be grossly exaggerated. However, the speculation that there are more worlds inhabited by intelligent beings than we assume cannot altogether be excluded. But it still is more than probable that they are fewer.

Therefore, science in the second half of the twentieth century provides a foundation for the genial ideas of the great Italian philosopher Giordano Bruno about the multiplicity of inhabited worlds. But here we might ask quite naturally the question: What are the perspectives for establishing a contact with intelligent beings of such planetary systems?

Interstellar Communications

To highly organized civilizations of certain planets our sun must appear as a star around which some planets with intelligent life may be rotating. It is quite natural that disposing of powerful technical means, they should attempt to establish some sort of a contact with the intelligent life of some other planet of the solar system. Let us suppose that they established a long time ago, perhaps several thousand years back, some sort of a communication channel and that they are patiently awaiting the answer to come.

What Is the Nature of This Communication Channel?

Giuseppe Cocconi and Philip Morrison devoted a special paper on this subject entitled "Searching for Interstellar Communications," published in the September 19, 1960, issue of *Nature* (No. 4690). Their analysis shows that such a communication channel across the galactic plasma without dispersion in direction and flight time is only practical by means of electromagnetic waves. It must be borne in mind that these waves are not expected to attenuate substantially on passing through interstellar space and planetary atmospheres. Besides, the power of transmitters must be as low as possible, and the applied technique simple and reliable. This limits outright the possible electromagnetic wave range to a radio frequency from 10 to about 10^4 mc, which corresponds to wavelengths from 30 m to about 3 cm.

The powerful interference of cosmic origin eliminates the possibility of utilizing sufficiently long waves, say $\lambda > 50$ cm. On the other hand, the thermal radio emission of planetary atmospheres excludes the possibility of using ultra-short waves. Let us note that the range may be broadened toward higher frequencies with the help of artificial satellites situated beyond the planet's atmosphere.

How Far Will the Signal Reach?

We now ask over what distances is the establishment of a direct radio communication possible today. Here we must stress the extraordinary progress in radiophysics during the past half century.

The preceding generation saw a remarkable event taking place which was of utmost importance in those times: the establishment of the trans-Atlantic radio link. In 1945, the first signal sent to the moon was bounced off and received back on earth. In 1959, the radar location of Venus was achieved; and this is a much more difficult problem than the location of the moon; since, as is known, radar location requires for the transmitter a power proportional to the fourth power of its distance to the object to be located. The sending of rockets to Mars and Venus is now being discussed in the United States and Soviet press. This will entail the establishment of reliable radio communications to distances up to 100 million kilometers. It must be borne in mind that for a series of natural reasons radio devices aboard rockets will be miniature and have low capacity.

Meanwhile, the dimensions of radiotelescope mirrors and the sensitivity of receivers over centimeter and decimeter wave bandwidths is considerably improved, owing to the introduction of new types of amplifiers (such as the molecular amplifiers). Consequently, as shown below, it is possible even now to establish radio communications over distances of approximately 10 light-years, provided the largest existing antennas and the most sensitive receiving devices are used.

How to Overcome Interferences

In computing a radio communication line between two worlds, the interference level should be taken into account. There are two types of interference which have to be considered: First, the radio-emission frequency of the star around which the planet inhabited by intelligent beings rotates. Then the intensity of the radio transmitter must be such that its signal reliability dominates the unavoidable cosmic-ray background. First of all, it is quite evident that the power of the transmitter in the required direction (toward the star with which a communication is sought) must be within a certain frequency range and greater than that of the thermal radio-frequency emission of the star. This condition may be easily fulfilled. Calculations show that the radio-frequency emission flux from the transmitter will be greater than the thermal emission of the star even for small transmitter capacities. In fact, the solar radio-frequency emission flux at distance R is equal to $10^{-15} (f^2/F^2)$ watt/mc, where f is the frequency, while that of the transmitter is $W (G^6/R^2)$, where W is the power of the transmitter and G is the coefficient of directed energy of the transmitting antenna determined by its diameter: $G = 4\pi d^2/\lambda^2$.

Thus, with d approximately 100 m for a decimetric wave band, G is about 10^5. It follows that with $f = 10^3$ mc, the radio-frequency emission flux from the transmitter will be greater than that of thermal radiation from the star with $W > 10^{-2}$ watt/cps.

The interference from the cosmic-radiation background is considerably more substantial. Here, the possible frequency range over which the establishment of the appropriate radio communication is being attempted must be more specifically determined.

Morrison and Cocconi introduced rather a novel idea that such type of radio communication should be attempted with a 21-cm wavelength. It is well known that this wavelength corresponds to the hydrogen radio-frequency line. This is precisely the wavelength intelligent beings of higher development must put to use in order to carry out intensive investigations of space. Similar investigations have already enriched astronomical science by a series of important scientific discoveries. It must be particularly stressed that they will develop unlimitedly in the future, since the success of such an investigation is closely linked with the general progress in radiophysics. Therefore, the most sensitive receiving device must be adjusted precisely to that wave. Besides, prolonged and systematic investigations of various celestial objects must be conducted over that wavelength, as this increases considerably the possibility of signal reception. Finally, hydrogen is the most widespread element in the universe and that is why its radio-frequency line constitutes a sort of a natural gauge which must unavoidably be used by any civilization in process of development.

In What Direction Is the Search to Be Conducted?

The intensity of the interstellar radio-frequency line does not surpass that of the continuous galaxy radio-frequency emission within the same spectral range which is equal to $10^{-21.5}$ cm/m^2 ster/cps for comparatively large angular distances from the Milky Way band constituting nearly two-thirds of the sky. But in the Milky Way itself the intensity of the hydrogen radio-frequency line is several dozen times greater than that magnitude. Thus, it is more advantageous to try to establish radio communication with objects situated at rather high galactic latitudes where the level of interference (determined by cosmic-radiation background) is much smaller.

Computations show that the establishment of radio communications between civilizations separated by interplanetary space are within bounds of contemporary techniques.

If, for instance, we use a reflector of a diameter d_1 as a transmitter, the power which is to be radiated in the appropriate direction (for example, toward the solar system) under the condition that the signal surpasses the cosmic background at the receiving end with a reflector of diameter d_2 will be

$$W \geqslant I_\nu \left(\frac{\lambda}{d_1}\right)^2 \left(\frac{\lambda}{d_2}\right)^2 R^2 = 10^{-24.2} \frac{R^2}{d_1{}^2 d_2{}^2} \qquad \text{watt/cps}$$

It follows that with $d_1 = d_2 = 80$ m and with $R = 10$ light-years, $W = 100$ watts/cps, which already is feasible today.

Let us note, however, that the dimensions of transmitting antennas and the transmitting capacity of highly organized civilizations may be taken much larger than our own. Besides, reflectors with 200-m diameters are already being projected on earth at present.

It may be assumed that highly intelligent beings, living on some other planet, are continuously and during long intervals of time "holding" on the ramifications of their gigantic antennas in the expectation that some return signal might come from a certain number (~ 100) of relatively close stars where intelligent life may presumably exist. Such a particular "space radio communication service" is completely within the means of a highly organized society. And the possibility of our having been for a long time within a bundle of electromagnetic radiation beamed toward us by some intelligent beings of a well-known star that is several dozen light-years distant is not excluded.

The transmitted signals must have certain properties, distinctly different from cosmic radio noises. They may represent the simplest code: for instance, the first numbers of a natural series in a continuously repeated sequence or numbers such as π or e. The frequency band used in cosmic radio communications must be relatively narrow. The orbital motion of the planet with the transmitter would entail intense periodical frequency variations because of the Doppler effect. Assuming that with such a motion the expected velocities vary within the limits of ~100 km/sec, the signal frequency variation may be within ~300 kc range from the basic hydrogen-line frequency, which is 1420.3 mc.

Obviously, the chances of establishing a radio communication with other worlds are not so numerous in the foreseeable future. Morrison and Cocconi rightly consider, however, that a discriminating search for signals deserves a considerable effort; for if no search is attempted the chances of success will be zero indeed.

The possibility of establishing radio communications with other worlds is seriously being attempted by the National Radio Astronomy Observatory of the United States, where the well-known American radio astronomer Frank D. Drake has worked out an apparatus capable of solving the problem. Its detailed description was published in the January 1960 issue of the periodical *Sky and Telescope*.

We live in an era of astonishing scientific discoveries and great accomplishments. The most incredible fantasies suddenly and unexpectedly become realized. People have dreamed from the early days about possible communication with intelligent beings in the scattered and unlimited planetary systems within the galaxy. Now we may be surprised only by the speed with which science confirms in principle the possibility of such an achievement and makes the first steps toward its realization. We must however bear in mind the magnitude of the difficulties ahead. Let us hope that these dreams may some day become a reality.

A. G. W. *Cameron*

2 ✳ THE HISTORY OF OUR GALAXY

In many ways it is easier to study the structure of other galaxies than that of our own. Because we are immersed in our own galaxy, and surrounded by clouds of dark absorbing interstellar gas and dust, many of the most interesting parts of our galaxy are obscured from our view, including the entire region at the galactic center. Because the stars have a wide range of luminosity, it is difficult to trace out the galactic structural features. Only in recent years, with the development of radio astronomy, have we been able to map the location of hydrogen gas in the interstellar medium, and thus to construct a reasonably accurate galactic model.

There are a tremendous number of structural features among the galaxies. Some consist almost entirely of stars and are spherical or ellipsoidal in shape. Others contain a significant quantity of gas, several per cent of the total galactic mass, and this gas is usually flattened into a relatively thin disk. Many of the stars in such galaxies also have this flattened distribution; such stars have evidently formed after the gas had flattened to the disk. These galaxies are called "spirals," a term describing the further concentration of gas and bright stars into spirally-wound arms within the disk. Still other galaxies have of the order of half their mass in uncondensed form. Because such galaxies do not have nearly so high a degree of flattening, or even of regularity, they are called "irregulars." Our own galaxy appears to be a reasonably typical spiral.

There is also a tremendous variety in the characteristics of the stars in our galaxy. However, much progress has been made in recent years in the understanding of many of these variations as late stages in the evolution of old stars. Such classes of stars often have very different distributions in our own galaxy. These differences provide clues from which we can attempt to deduce the age and evolutionary history of our galaxy.

Some of the oldest stars in our galaxy form what is termed the "halo" population. These stars have a nearly spherical distribution about the center of the galaxy, and their orbits have strong radial components. Since the sun is moving in a nearly circular orbit, the halo stars coming into the solar vicinity are usually observed to have a large velocity relative to the sun. The halo stars appear generally to be deficient in heavier elements relative to hydrogen as compared to the sun. In some extreme cases this deficiency amounts to a factor of a hundred or more.

The stars formed more recently have distributions considerably flattened toward the plane of the galaxy. They tend to have more circular orbits. These stars have heavy element abundances quite comparable with those in the sun; the very recent stars may in fact be slightly enriched in heavy elements.

These differences in composition are understandable in the light of modern theories of the formation of the elements. In the course of its evolution, the interior of a star becomes progressively hotter and denser. During the longest period of their active lifetime they derive their energy from the thermonuclear conversion of hydrogen into helium. Hydrogen is the most abundant element in the universe, and these thermonuclear reactions release more energy than any subsequent nuclear reaction. After the exhaustion of hydrogen in the central regions, further heating destroys the helium with the production of carbon and oxygen, and these in turn disappear at still higher temperatures. Eventually the material at the stellar center is converted largely into iron and no further nuclear energy release is possible. However, the central heating continues and the star undergoes a catastrophic implosion, followed by a huge release of energy which explodes away the overlying layers in a spectacular event we call a supernova.

All these nuclear reactions seem to form as products those nuclei that we find in the earth and in meteorites, and the products are formed in approximately the correct relative proportions. Thus it seems probable that at one time the galaxy was largely or entirely composed of hydrogen. As stars formed from this gas, evolved, and returned many of the products of their nuclear evolution back into space, a significant abundance of heavy elements built up in the remaining interstellar gases. Stars continuing to form from such gases thus showed a progressively increasing content of heavy elements. The galaxy now contains only a few per cent of its mass in the form of interstellar gases, and hence the rate of stellar activity is less, and the rate of enrichment of new stars with heavy elements has accordingly declined.

Not all stars undergo supernova explosions as described above. However, it appears that all stars lose mass before they end their lives in quantum mechanical degenerate configurations known as white dwarf stars or neutron stars. Furthermore, after a star finishes converting hydrogen into helium, it appears that its luminosity undergoes a considerable increase. This brightening process can be expected to destroy life on any accompanying planets unless that life can employ means for its survival that lie far beyond the present technological comprehension of the human race.

One of the important questions connected with the presence of mature civilizations in the galaxy is the time which such societies have had in which to develop. The age of the galaxy is still an extremely uncertain number. Only a few years ago it was thought to be just two billion years. Recently some estimates as high as 25 billion years have been made. Probably the bulk of the evidence currently points toward ten to fifteen billion years.

These estimates are made by trying to account for the distribution of luminosities and colors of stars in clusters by empirical and theoretical methods. The reasonable assumption is made that all the stars in a given cluster were formed at the same time, and hence that the present dispersion in luminosities and colors results from the effects of stellar evolution for stars of different mass during the age of the cluster. Such age estimates suffer both from the observational uncertainties in the determination of the *absolute* luminosities of the stars in the cluster and from uncertainties in the theory of stellar evolution.

One of the principal concerns of this book is the probability that other stars within the galaxy may contain advanced societies. Clearly we may exclude the very oldest stars that are composed of nearly pure hydrogen. The gases from which these stars condensed are unlikely to have contained sufficient heavy elements for planets to have formed. However, this prohibition is unlikely to apply once a star can form with a significant content of nonvolatile elements, perhaps more than 10 per cent the content of the sun. Such a condition was probably achieved quite quickly in the history of the galaxy, owing to the extensive stellar activity we expect to have occurred in the early stages.

The solar system is 4.5 billion years old. This figure has been rather reliably established by radioactive dating methods. The galaxy thus is probably two or three times the age of the solar system. Thus, if the time required for the emergence of the human race is typical of that required for the emergence of advanced societies generally, we can expect that in the majority of stars in the galaxy such societies appeared several billion years ago, if conditions for their appearance were favorable.

Bibliography

D. J. K. O'Connell, *Stellar Populations*, North-Holland, Amsterdam, 1958.

E. M. Burbidge, G. R. Burbidge, W. A. Fowler, and F. Hoyle, *Rev. Mod. Phys.*, **29**, 547 (1957).

A. G. W. Cameron, *Ann. Rev. Nucl. Sci.*, **8**, 299 (1958).

A. Sandage, *Astrophys. J.*, **135**, 349 (1962).

N. J. Woolf, *Astrophys. J.*, **135**, 644 (1962).

A. G. W. Cameron

3 ✳ THE ORIGIN

OF THE SOLAR SYSTEM

Probably the oldest unsolved problem of scientific philosophy is that of the formation of the solar system. René Descartes appears to have been the first to publish serious scientific speculations on the subject, in 1644. This was at a time when the scientific method of investigation was being formulated, and before Newton found his general law of gravitation.

Descartes postulated that in a universe filled with ether and primordial matter, only vortex motion would be possible. These vortices formed eddies of all sizes; friction between these eddies would file down the rough shape of the primordial matter. The filings go to the center of the largest vortex and form the sun, while the coarser pieces become the planets at the center of secondary vortices, with still further pieces of matter forming the satellites. These ideas have some degree of resemblance to the modern cosmogonical ideas of von Weizsäcker.

In the three centuries from Descartes' time to the present day, a multitude of scientific writers have proposed solutions to this central problem. None of these has been a satisfactory solution, although most of them claimed to be satisfactory. The basic difficulty with the problem of the origin of the solar system is that a wide variety of physical and chemical processes were involved. If one attempts to describe any one of these processes, it is of course necessary to assume certain boundary conditions within which the process can take place. These boundary conditions necessarily involve assumptions about all the other physical and chemical processes with which one is not directly concerned. Thus, even if one displays immense ingenuity in working out the consequences of one's assumptions, this is of no avail if the assumptions are incorrect, as they are very likely to be. Evidently we can only make progress slowly, as more and more people consider the various processes that may have been involved, and as we obtain observational evidence about the boundary conditions from studies of such diverse subjects as stellar and galactic evolution, the chemical and physical properties of meteorites, and the physics and chemistry of the planets.

During the history of the problem two different but principal lines of thought have been followed. One class of theories, called "dualistic," has postulated that the solar system formed as a result of an encounter of the sun with another star. Since such encounters must be rare, it follows as a consequence of such a theory that there will be very few planetary systems in the galaxy. Such authors as Buffon, Bickerton, Arrhenius, See, Chamberlin, Moulton, Jeffreys, and Jeans have been among the principal contributors to these theories. The second class of theories, called "monistic," has postulated that the planets formed by condensation from a gaseous nebula about the sun, possibly as part of the process in which the sun itself was formed. With the latter qualification, it would follow that planetary systems must be very common in the galaxy. Among the principal contributors to these theories we may mention Descartes, Kant, Laplace, Birkeland, Berlage, Alfvén, von Weizsäcker, Whipple, Kuiper, ter Harr, Schmidt, and Urey.

In the more modern form of dualistic theory, as proposed by Chamberlin and Moulton and developed by Jeffreys and Jeans, the passage of another star close to the sun is supposed to raise a large tidal bulge and to draw out from this a filament of gas in the direction of the intruder. The filament is then supposed to break up into gas spheres from which the planetary bodies condensed. Many aspects of these ideas have come in for serious criticism. Among the difficulties pointed out are that the different parts of the filament do not have the desired angular momentum, that the inevitable high temperature of the filament immediately after ejection from the sun must cause its dispersal in space rather than its condensation, and, even if this were not sufficient, shearing in the tidal field of the sun would cause such a dispersal. Since there seems to be no satisfactory answer to these criticisms, all forms of dualistic theory have now been abandoned by most scientific workers.

There are several major questions that must be answered by a successful monistic theory. These include the following:

1. How was the solar nebula formed?

2. How did the planets form from the solar nebula and how did they obtain their present characteristics?

3. How was the solar nebula dissipated?

We consider first the formation of the solar nebula. There have been two general lines of thought on this point. On the one hand it has been postulated that the sun has captured a cloud of gas from space. In particular Alfvén and Lyttleton have proposed theories of this kind. Such theories suffer from the difficulty that any such capture process must be rather inefficient and it seems much too difficult to sweep up from space in a reasonable time enough material to make the planets. This leaves as a second alternative the formation of a solar nebula as part of the general condensation process in which the sun itself was formed.

There are at present two general suggestions as to how this condensation took place. One suggestion, due to Fred Hoyle, provides a solar nebula with the minimum possible amount of mass and the minimum possible angular momentum. The other suggestion, due to me, provides a solar nebula that is far more massive and has a great deal more angular momentum.

In developing his theory, Hoyle argued as follows. All the planets, except possibly Jupiter and Saturn, represent a collection of nonvolatile elements from which the most abundant volatile elements, particularly hydrogen and helium, have escaped. Let us restore to the planets the volatile gases that escaped, putting them back in proportion to the composition of the sun. Let us then see what the total angular momentum of the planets would become. Now imagine this angular momentum transferred to the sun, with the sun rotating rigidly, and ask at what radius the contracting sun would become rotationally unstable at the equator. It turns out that the sun, during its contraction phase, would become rotationally unstable when its radius becomes approximately equal to the radius of the orbit of Mercury.

Hoyle then postulated that the sun was formed from a contraction of interstellar gases, and that at the time it had shrunk to dimensions of the order of the orbit of Mercury it had the angular momentum calculated in the above manner. He noted that this angular momentum is much less than the sun would typically have had as part of the interstellar medium, and he assumed that most of the original angular momentum was lost somehow. He then pointed out that any further contraction of the sun would have to be accompanied by loss of mass in the equatorial plane in order to conserve angular momentum.

After the necessary amount of mass has been shed to form the planets, Hoyle suggests that the angular momentum remaining in the sun is then transferred to the nebular disk by means of the magnetic coupling that exists between the two, utilizing the magnetic field that was compressed out of the interstellar medium with the condensing gases. This causes the nebular disk to move outward from the general region inside the orbit of Mercury to the general region of the outer planets.

Together with Fowler and Greenstein, Hoyle proposed that solid bodies condensed and accumulated to a size of several meters radius while the nebula was still inside the orbit of Mercury. As the nebula moves outward these planetesimals are dropped in the region of the inner planets, where they eventually collect to form the few large bodies that now exist. No theory of this collection process is given. However, Fowler, Greenstein, and Hoyle suggest that while the planetesimals are of metric size, they will be heavily bombarded by charged particles accelerated by the dissipation of magnetic energy that is occurring. This bombardment should, in their view, be the principal source of production of the light elements deuterium, lithium, beryllium, and boron in the earth and meteorites.

Their theory is completed by postulating that the outer planets contain largely ice, in the cases of Uranus, Neptune, and Pluto, and ice, helium, and hydrogen in the cases of Jupiter and Saturn. The excess hydrogen and helium was supposed to evaporate into space from the outer boundary of the solar system.

The Fowler, Greenstein, and Hoyle theory suffers the deficiency that no mechanisms are provided for depleting the original interstellar material of most of its angular momentum, and for accumulating rather than shattering the metric planetesimals when they collide in space. There are also some inconsistencies between the results of chemical and isotopic analyses of meteorites and the results that would be expected to be produced by the charged-particle bombardment described above.

My own discussion of the problem starts with the initial process of star formation. The average density of gas in the interstellar medium is about one hydrogen atom per cubic centimeter, but the medium is greatly inhomogeneous, and "clouds" with densities commonly of ten and occasionally as high as one thousand hydrogen atoms per cubic centimeter are known to exist. In order that one of these clouds can become gravitationally unstable and undergo collapse, its gravitational potential energy must exceed in magnitude twice the internal thermal energy plus other forms of internal energy. It appears that this condition is likely to be achieved when the densest clouds are subjected to an external pressure and compressed to some critical density, which depends on the cloud mass but is of the order of one thousand hydrogen atoms per cubic centimeter. The angular momentum of such clouds is likely to be given by the consideration that the galactic magnetic field will constrain the cloud to rotate once per orbital revolution around the center of the galaxy. A cloud of this sort that becomes gravitationally unstable is likely to have a mass of several thousand times that of the sun.

As a cloud collapses, the various cooling mechanisms within it, which depend upon atomic collisions to radiate away energy, become much more efficient. Hence the compression of the gas will not build up a high thermal pressure inside the cloud; instead the collapse will be roughly isothermal. This has the important consequence that as time goes by smaller subunits of the cloud will individually become unstable against gravitational collapse, and so the cloud can fragment into smaller pieces about its density fluctuations. Fragmentation will continue as the density increases.

The process of collapse and fragmentation can be halted only when the opacity of the material would become high enough to halt the escape of radiation and to allow the internal thermal energy of the fragments to become high enough that the bodies can reach approximate hydrostatic equilibrium. J. Gaustad has recently shown that the opacity of the material will remain too small to allow the collapse to be halted at the time that the central temperature of the fragments rises far enough to initiate the dissociation of hydrogen molecules.

The dissociation of all the hydrogen molecules and the complete ionization of the hydrogen and helium in such an object requires far more energy than the available gravitational potential energy can provide at this stage of the collapse. Hence, in a fragment with no rotation, the purely thermal energy cannot rise sufficiently to enable hydrostatic equilibrium to be reached until the ionization process is nearly complete. Recent calculations by Dilhan Ezer and myself show that a star of one solar mass first reaches hydrostatic equilibrium at a radius of 0.27 astronomical units, well inside the orbit of Mercury.

However, there appears to be no way for the collapsing cloud or its fragments to transmit any significant portion of its angular momentum to the surroundings that do not partake of the collapse. The cloud will be linked with the surroundings by the galactic magnetic field, but the collapse in free fall takes place sufficiently rapidly that very little magnetic torque can be exerted on the surrounding interstellar medium. Hence it appears very likely that the fragments of the cloud will possess the same angular momentum that they did before the collapse commenced. Then one readily finds that the fragments will become rotationally unstable long before they can collapse to a radius of 0.27 astronomical units.

It is unlikely that the fragments can develop significant central condensations while they are collapsing. Hence it is useful to consider the kind of thin disks that can develop from the collapse of a uniformly rotating, uniformly dense sphere. Leon Mestel has discussed this problem in connection with the collapse of gas spheres to form galaxies. It appears that two different disks can be formed that have radically different mass distributions. One disk has a surface mass density in the form

$$m = m_0[1 - (r/R)^2]^{1/2}$$

where m_0 is a constant, R is the disk radius, and r is a radial distance. This disk has a uniform angular velocity and we shall refer to it as the "uniform" disk in view of the slow variation of surface mass density near the center. The other disk is "axially condensed." In this the surface mass density is approximately inversely proportional to the radial distance, and the angular velocity varies similarly.

The reason for the existence of two solutions is that in one case, the axially condensed disk, the potential governing the motion of a particle depends only on the mass interior to the particle, whereas for the uniform disk the potential depends on the mass distribution both interior to and exterior to the particle. We do not yet have any insight into how either one of these disks can be the natural result of the collapse of the fragment under discussion. As we shall see, it seems useful to postulate that some fragments form one kind of disk and some the other.

From consideration of the conservation of angular momentum, it appears likely that the uniform disk would be formed with a radius of several tens of astronomical units. There are no obvious forces that would promote a further condensation toward the center. On the other hand, the nuclei of two stars can be formed by an azimuthal displacement of mass around its orbit toward any diameter of the disk. It seems likely that such disks will thus give rise to binary star systems. About 80 per cent of the stars in the solar neighborhood are in binary systems. The situation here does not seem propitious for the formation of planets circling these stars.

The axially condensed disk is also likely to be formed with a radius of several tens of astronomical units. However, as we have seen, the disk possesses nonuniform rotation. The shear between gas at adjacent radii will thus stretch out the lines of force of the original interstellar magnetic field that was compressed with the gas. This increases the magnetic energy at the expense of the energy of differential rotation, thus causing a redistribution of the mass in the disk. The majority of the mass will be forced to spiral inward, while a small portion of the mass moves outward but carries with it most of the angular momentum in the disk.

I have no detailed mechanisms to suggest for the manner in which planets can be formed from such a disk. However, it is evident that unless fairly large bodies (asteroidal in size) can be formed fairly quickly by some sort of chemical condensation and accumulation within the gaseous nebula, the inward motion of the nebular gas will sweep solid condensations into the forming sun. The mass of the disk is, of course, greatly increased over that postulated by Hoyle, and its angular momentum is correspondingly greater also. The present planets thus represent a very inefficient utilization of the nonvolatile material in the nebula, consistent with the idea that most of the finely divided condensed material was carried inward to the sun, except near the outskirts of the solar system, where the flow was outward, and hence where the solids would be dropped at several tens of astronomical units from the sun.

We finish the description of this picture by noting that when the sun is able to form a hot corona, a flow of the solar wind will be set up that will probably dissipate the remainder of gas in the nebular disk. Evry Schatzman has shown that the interaction between the solar magnetic field and the outflowing solar wind is likely to transmit enough angular momentum to the outgoing plasma to slow down the rotation of the sun.

The calculations of Dilhan Ezer and myself, referred to above, confirm predictions of Hayashi that the early contracting sun was highly luminous and fully convective. The luminosity probably exceeded a factor of one hundred greater than the present luminosity of the sun for at least several thousands of years. Hence the nascent planets were evidently subjected to a brief high-temperature environment.

A great deal of uncertainty and contradictory evidence surrounds the manner in which condensation from the solar nebula occurred. H. C. Urey has pointed out that the moon seems to have a different composition from the earth and meteorites in one important respect: It appears to have a deficiency of iron relative to neighboring elements. The sun has a similar deficiency of iron. Also, if one wishes to interpret the large distortions of the lunar figure as indicating that the interior of the moon is cold enough to be highly rigid, then the moon must be deficient in potassium relative to the earth and meteorites. It is a considerable challenge to determine how such differences could have come about.

Another very important question is the nature of the heat source responsible for heating the interiors of meteorite parent bodies sufficiently at least to melt iron. Fish, Goles, and Anders have suggested, following an earlier idea of Urey, that an extinct radioactivity, probably Al^{26}, was responsible for this heating. The radioactivity might be a survivor of the supernova activity in the interstellar medium prior to the condensation to form the solar system, or it might have been formed directly in the solar nebula by charged-particle bombardment.

However, Urey argues that the presence of extinct radioactivities simply makes the problem of having the lunar interior relatively cold more difficult. Hence he has suggested that the gas in the solar nebula broke up into self-gravitating spheres, each with about a lunar mass of nonvolatile material. This nonvolatile material would settle to the center and be heated as the gas was compressed. Planets are supposed to have formed by collisions of these gas spheres in which the gas would be dissipated and the solids amalgamated. He suggests that the moon is a surviving central body of such a gas sphere. J. A. Wood would like to make the small glassy inclusions found in chondritic meteorites at the high pressures and temperatures to be expected in such gas spheres.

The difficulty with the formation of gas spheres of this sort is to see how the planets that are formed can have lost so completely all the very heavy gases, such as krypton and xenon, that would be present in the spheres. Relative to neighboring elements, the earth has lost these by a factor of a million or more. On the other hand, collisions between bodies in empty space will generally tend to shatter them rather than cause amalgamation. Recent studies of hypervelocity collisions have suggested that collisions of meteorites and micrometeorites with the surface of the moon will lead to a net loss of mass by the moon. Plainly the details of the accumulation problem are some of the most important unsolved problems associated with the origin of the solar system.

It is when we attempt to generalize our ideas about the origin of the solar system to the question of the formation of other planetary systems that we discover how imperfect is our understanding of what took place. Since many of our conjectures are qualitative in character rather than quantitative, we do not know how much intrinsic variability there may be in the planetary systems associated with other stars similar to the sun, let alone that associated with different types of stars. Hence the following conjectures on this topic are necessarily strongly weighted by my own views on the origin of the solar system as outlined above.

The best candidates for planetary systems are the 20 per cent of stars that appear to be single in space. I do not believe the presence or absence of fast rotation in these stars distinguishes between those without or with planetary systems, respectively. This distinction is suggested by several authors in this book. Probably all single stars have planetary systems of some sort.

There will necessarily be a considerable variation in the size of the nebula formed about single stars. This is an inevitable consequence of variations in the density and angular velocity of the interstellar clouds that become gravitationally unstable. The size of the final flat disk is quite sensitive to these quantities. These size variations will probably lead not only to great variations in the distribution and masses of the condensed planets, but also in the amount of matter that becomes centrally condensed to form the star. Because both surface density and radius of the disk can vary almost independently, we can expect no simple relation between the size and orbit distributions of the planets and the mass of the star. However, because the angular velocity of gas clouds closer to the center of the galaxy is much larger than in our vicinity, it follows that on the average the nebular disks formed in such regions are likely to be considerably larger than those in our region of space. Thus, again on the average, it seems likely that the planets may be smaller than those in the solar system. Hence a smaller fraction of such systems may be a suitable abode for the development of life.

It should be noted that the above discussion of star formation refers specifically to the processes occurring in the gas clouds of the spiral arms of our galaxy. The conditions for star formation were obviously very different when the dense globular and rich galactic clusters of stars were formed. Hence it is a completely open question as to how many planetary systems such clusters contain.

Bibliography

R. Jastrow and A. G. W. Cameron (eds.), *Proceedings of the Conference on the Origin of the Solar System,* Academic, New York, in press.

F. Hoyle, *Quart. J. Roy. Astron. Soc.,* **1,** 28 (1960).

W. A. Fowler, J. L. Greenstein, and F. Hoyle, *Geophys. J.,* **6,** 148 (1962).

A. G. W. Cameron, *Icarus,* **1,** 13 (1962).

A. G. W. Cameron

4 ✳ THE EARLY DEVELOPMENT
OF THE EARTH

We have seen how uncertain are our ideas on the origin and development of the solar system. In particular, the manner in which the planets were amalgamated from the gas and dust of the solar nebula is especially controversial. About the only feature of the process that seems to be reasonably well established is that the amalgamation did not take place at too high a temperature. H. C. Urey was an early advocate of the "cold accretion" idea; he advanced it on the grounds that at high temperatures such elements as arsenic become volatile and would be lost by a large factor from the earth.

Once the earth had formed, it underwent a thorough chemical differentiation. The details of this process are almost completely obscure. The earth was formed 4.5 billion years ago. The oldest surface rocks that have been dated were formed about 3.5 billion years ago. So the first billion years of terrestrial history are not recorded. Differentiation certainly took place in this interval, but we do not know how long the bulk of it took.

Seismologists have found that the earth has a regular layered structure. At the top lies a thin crust, then a rocky mantle largely composed of such substances as magnesium silicate, and finally a liquid core largely composed of iron. The properties of transmission of seismic waves change very close to the center of the earth, and this has been interpreted as indicating the presence of a solid inner core, although with less certainty. Clearly this layered structure could not have been formed without extensive melting in the interior of the earth. Calculations indicate that the heat output from such natural radioactivities as potassium, thorium, and uranium is quite adequate to provide the necessary amount of melting.

The outer crust of the earth is mainly composed of materials that melt at relatively low temperatures and that have relatively low density. This material was apparently extruded from cracks in the mantle, but details are obscure. There are two schools of thought about the state of the mantle. One school holds that the mantle is quite static and crustal material is mainly brought up through pores as in volcanos. The other school interprets a number of geological phenomena as indicating that the mantle is undergoing a convective turnover. In this picture crustal material is continually being brought to the surface at the upflowing edges of the convection cells, and the convective motion induces wandering of the continents.

The atmosphere of the earth is greatly deficient in the rare gases. The meteorites not infrequently have two orders of magnitude more rare gases per gram than does the earth in its entirety, including the atmosphere. The element xenon is particularly interesting. The isotopic composition of atmospheric xenon is entirely different from that of meteoritic xenon. Two sources of difference are the decay of the extinct radioactivities I^{129} and Pu^{244}, which have half-lives of 17 and 76 million years, respectively. The former decays to Xe^{129} and the latter occasionally undergoes spontaneous fission with the formation of the neutron-rich xenon isotopes. I interpret the differences in abundance of the neutron-deficient xenon isotopes as being produced by neutron irradiation of xenon in the sun during the deuterium-burning phase of its contraction. This analysis indicates that most of the xenon in the atmosphere was once in the sun, and the earth has perhaps captured it out of the solar wind. This conclusion is controversial, but if correct it shows that we have no evidence that any constituent of the atmosphere is a direct survivor of the primitive solar nebula.

Meteoritic xenon frequently has a large variation in the content of Xe^{129}. This indicates that the meteorite parent bodies contained significant amounts of I^{129} when they were formed and became cool enough to retain rare gases. However, despite having much less xenon per unit mass, the earthly xenon has very little excess of Xe^{129}. I interpret this as indicating that the earth was unable to retain xenon emitted from the interior until about 100 million years after the meteorite parent bodies cooled, and the amounts of decay products of Pu^{244} are consistent with this interpretation. Anders has reached a similar conclusion by a slightly different chain of reasoning.

Harrison Brown pointed out many years ago that the earth is much less deficient in the chemically reactive volatile gases such as H_2O, CO_2, and N_2 than in the rare gases. Therefore it is evident that carbon, nitrogen, and oxygen compounds were accumulated into the earth in solid form and that these elements have subsequently been emitted into the atmosphere and have formed the oceans. Only after this has happened is the stage set for the chemical evolution that can lead to the formation of life.

This chemical evolution is discussed by Melvin Calvin in the following chapter, which is a reprint of his Condon Lectures at the University of Oregon. His point of departure for such evolution is the assumption of an early terrestrial reducing atmosphere. A common assumption for this atmosphere is a composition of fully hydrogenated compounds assumed to be retained from the primitive solar nebula. We have seen above that such a direct retention is somewhat unlikely. However, even the much less fully hydrogenated compounds that would be retained in the earth's interior would still form a reducing atmosphere.

Bibliography

Sir H. Jeffreys, *The Earth,* 4th ed. with additions, Cambridge University Press, New York, 1962.

H. Brown, *in* G. P. Kniper (ed.), *The Atmospheres of the Earth and Planets,* 2nd ed., University of Chicago Press, Chicago, 1952.

E. Anders, *Rev. Mod. Phys.,* **34,** 287 (1962).

A. G. W. Cameron, *Icarus,* **1,** 13 (1962).

Melvin Calvin

5 ✳ CHEMICAL EVOLUTION

I. From Molecule to Microbe

The word "evolution" has connotations which have been elaborated in earlier Condon Lectures: the evolution of the stars by Otto Struve, the chemical basis of heredity by George W. Beadle, and the evolution of man by W. E. Le Gros Clark. The area I wish to discuss lies somewhere between the first and the last. There is a very broad gap between these two areas of knowledge. To try and bridge that gap! It wasn't possible even to make any serious scientific attempt to bridge it until the last decade or two.

What Is Life?

The question of the *origin of life on the earth* is one which has stimulated the minds of men since they first were able to think about their own place on the earth and in the universe. It has been answered in many ways, by many different kinds of people. I propose to try to answer it within the scope of modern science, and wherever possible to bring these answers to the point where some kind of experimental, or observational, test of the kind of answer we propose may be made.

This is not to say that this is the only way in which this question can, or should, be answered. There are other ways, and to many people these answers are not only adequate but very satisfying. Here, however, we will be limited to the scientific type of answer. For almost a hundred years, until, perhaps, this last decade, it has not been scientifically respectable to broach this subject. In order to describe this hiatus, how it came about and how it was broken, it is necessary to go into a bit of recent history.

The word "evolution" in the title of this paper is the key to our subject, because what we are going to do is to extrapolate the Darwin-

33

ian idea as far back as we can go. In 1858 Darwin and Wallace published jointly in the Linnaean Society in London their well-known tract (*1*). Separately, Wallace had written, prior to the joint publication, another one which bore the title "On the Tendency of Varieties to Depart Indefinitely from Original Types" (*2*). This title describes precisely the nature of organic evolution, but the paper was not then published under that title. It is still possible to find transcriptions of this manuscript, but it has never appeared, as far as I know, in a scientific periodical. It advances the idea that species (or types) which today are totally different were at one time two varieties of a single species, and that with each step backward there will again be two different organisms which once were two varieties of a single species. And so on, back in time. Quite obviously once this essential notion of evolutionary transformation is accepted, one can go backward in time to the point at which there were only *two* species of living things. Eventually these two become varieties of a single species of living matter. This "living" species was in turn one of a variety of organizations of organic molecules, some of which gave rise to the stem which we now call living things. The others later vanished in the construction of the more rapidly growing organization.

Darwin recognized this—the implication of the basic notion of evolution—at the start in his earliest writings. Recently there appeared a hitherto unpublished letter from Charles Darwin to George Charles Wallich, dated March 28, 1882, which Sir Gavin de Beer thinks may have been the last which Darwin dictated and signed before he died (*3*).

You expressed quite correctly my views where you say that I had intentionally left the question of the Origin of Life uncanvassed as being altogether *ultra vires* in the present state of our knowledge, and that I dealt only with the manner of succession. I have met with no evidence that seems in the least trustworthy, in favour of so-called Spontaneous Generation. I believe that I have somewhere said (but cannot find the passage) that the principle of continuity renders it probable that the principle of life will hereafter be shown to be a part, or a consequence, of some general law. . . .

The statement to which Darwin refers and which he had forgotten was written much earlier, in another letter, sometime prior to 1871:

It is often said that all the conditions for the first production of a living organism are now present, which could ever have been present. But if (and oh! what a big if!) we could conceive in some warm little pond, with all sorts of ammonia and phosphoric acid salts, light, heat, electricity, etc., present, that a proteine compound was chemically formed ready to undergo still more complex changes, at the present day such matter would be instantly devoured or absorbed, which would not have been the case before living creatures were formed.

Here, in these two remarks of Darwin, lies all the essential foundation of today's speculation of the origin of life on the earth. To students of science, I emphasize that the basic ideas that I present here are, and must remain for some time, speculation. I will bring to bear on them, here and there, experimental, or observational, facts which may be interpreted in the light of the principal idea, but the idea itself is, for the time being, speculation until, perhaps, we make a trip to some planet in our solar system (or elsewhere) and are able to see this process of chemical evolution either more or less advanced than on our planet. That day fortunately (or unfortunately) is not too distant, and it is for this reason that we must concern ourselves with as much of the available information and the concepts of the origin of life on the earth so that we will have a broader idea of what to look for when we go elsewhere. And we are going—in the very near future!

Development of the Concepts of the Origin of Life

Why is it that in spite of this quite clear idea that Darwin expressed, it was not pursued for almost a hundred years? The answer lies in the work of a chemist which was published two or three years after Darwin's paper, early in 1863. This was the work of Louis Pasteur. There had been periodically in the previous several centuries reports on spontaneous generation at various levels, ranging from men to mice to flies to microbes, and at each one of these levels eventually a proper experiment had been done which demonstrated that these living things came from prior living things. It remained for Pasteur to do it most elegantly for microbes, which was the last frontier in this succession of retreats from the idea of spontaneous generation. He did it very conclusively and unequivocally in his experiments reported in 1862. Pasteur showed—and stated—categorically that no life could arise under the present conditions (as he defined them) save from previously existing living things. In the state of over-all scientific knowledge at that time, this was an unassailable conclusion. Therefore, although the Darwinian idea really demanded a backward extrapolation, there were only a few brave men immediately following Darwin's publication who attempted this thing in the middle 1860s. One of them was the first professor of geology at the University of Michigan, Alexander Winchell, who wrote a book *Sketches of Creation* (4), but there were not many after that.

The attacks on Winchell were very severe. He went from Michigan to Tennessee, where he became professor of geology. Two years later he was asked to resign but refused unless the trustees would give publicly the reason for his resignation. This they would not do, so they abolished his job. Winchell went back to Michigan, wrote his book, and Michigan has continued to be a productive source of zoological and geological training.

Between the publication of Winchell's *Sketches of Creation* in 1870 and the statements by J. B. S. Haldane, the English biologist, in 1928 (5) and those by the Russian biochemist, Oparin, in the middle thirties (6), there appear to be few serious attempts to answer the question of the origin of life within the context of the science of this period.

Definition of Life

We now have a much more sophisticated knowledge of the nature of the materials of which life is made. In the last two decades particularly it has become possible to try to devise a sequence of events (which are in consonance with our present state of knowledge) that will give rise by the normal physical-chemical progressions to those things which we think of as "living." The recognition of life at the level of a man or even an amoeba presents few problems. It becomes a little more difficult, however, as one goes to simpler and simpler organisms. The definition of life at the higher levels is very easy, but at the borderline it becomes very difficult.

Before we consider the finer points of defining what we are going to evolve, let us look at one of the simpler units of living materials, at least for the higher organisms: a single cell. Figure 1 shows such a cell structure in all its complicated glory. This is a nucleated human red cell, containing all sorts of structural elements within it. The drawing on the right is a diagrammatic representation of the actual cell on the left and shows the names of the various components. What cannot be shown in such a photograph is the fact that the ground substance itself, the material in which the obvious visible structural elements are embedded, is highly structured also. Not only are the nucleus and the mitochondria and the various other elements of structure within the cell minutely ordered, but all the protein material inside the cell is also highly structured. This "structure" is one of the essential and dramatic features of all living things. It is the development of this kind of order which we must trace from nonliving physical elements.

We may say several other things about the living cell which can perhaps summarize in the simplest way the kinds of things we have to

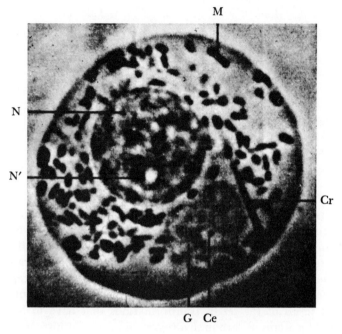

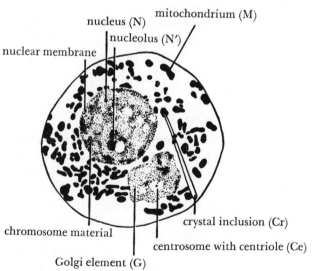

Figure 1

Structure of a nucleated human red cell. (Photo by P. H. Ralph from Greep's Histology.)

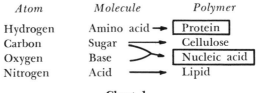

Atom	*Molecule*	*Polymer*
Hydrogen	Amino acid →	Protein
Carbon	Sugar	Cellulose
Oxygen	Base	Nucleic acid
Nitrogen	Acid ⟶	Lipid

Chart 1

Diagrammatic representation in chemical terms of the set of transformations which have to be accomplished from the atom to produce the structure of the cell.

accomplish. First, we must make the organic molecules which ultimately go into making up the structure of the cell. Then we need to put them together in these highly structured ways. Finally, they must be able to accomplish their own reproduction and energy transformation. These are the essential features we have to be able to reproduce. To outline a sequence, Chart 1 gives a diagrammatic representation in chemical terms of the set of transformations that have to be accomplished. The atoms of carbon, hydrogen, oxygen, and nitrogen in their most reduced combinations must be transformed first into small molecules of varied type; then these molecules have to be transformed into giant molecules which go on to make the structured features which are shown in the cell (Figure 1). We will discuss each of these steps in turn.

The Time Scale

The time period available for accomplishing the transformation from simple elements to the simplest living organisms is quite long. We have about five billion years, or thereabouts, to do the job. From the time scale in Figure 2 it is apparent that man occupies an extremely small part of the evolutionary period. A jagged edge represents the period of the formation of the present earth, some $4\frac{1}{2}$ billion years ago. Following the formation of the earth is a period labeled chemical evolution, which goes on until such time as life appears, at which point organic evolution, that is, the evolution of living things, begins. This point continues into modern time, in which there is no longer any chemical evolution in the old sense because there are no more organic chemicals left except those that are handled by living organisms. Today we may

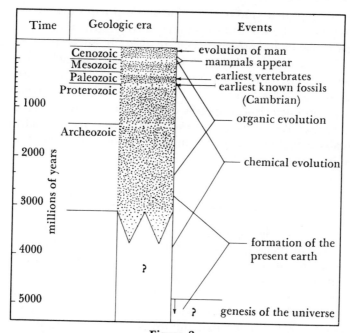

Figure 2

Time scale for total evolution.

even be adding to organic evolution a new type which has been called, among other things, psycho-social evolution.

We are concerned here only with the period of chemical evolution, that early stage following the formation of the earth in its present form and leading up to the very simplest of what we would call living things (7).

The basic notion of evolution contains in it the definition of the nature of a living thing. I have avoided defining a particular point in this scheme of events before which there was no living thing and after which there was. I do not think it possible to define such a point in time, let alone with that degree of precision. The reason is that the aggregation of qualities—of chemicals, of organization, and of inter-action—which we require to be associated with a single region of space before we call that region a living thing may differ from person to person. A geneticist may be quite satisfied to say that the moment he has a replicating molecule he has a "living" thing; a zoologist is not so prone to accept that kind of definition and will require more metabolic processes before he will call something "alive." Still others will require not only metabolic processes and replication but cell membranes. There is a variety of such properties which, when brought together in sufficient number in a specific region of space, will permit many of us to call the aggregate "alive" (8, 9, 10). Therefore, I have avoided laying down an unequivocal, specific definition for what we are attempting to evolve: We are trying to evolve all these various qualities and eventually bring an "adequate" number of them together in a single region in space.

The Primitive Atmosphere

In order to make the molecules in the first place, we need to have the atoms. The principal atoms of living material are carbon, nitrogen, oxygen, hydrogen, and a few others. Where do they come from? First of all, hydrogen is the commonest element in the universe; carbon, nitrogen, and oxygen were present on the surface of the earth (and are present throughout the solar system) primarily in combination with hydrogen. It is presumed that the primeval atmosphere of the earth consisted essentially of these four substances (or four molecules): hydrogen, carbon combined with hydrogen in the form of methane, oxygen combined with hydrogen in the form of water, and nitrogen combined with hydrogen in the form of ammonia. It is from these substances that we must make everything; this is our starting point, our primeval atmosphere from which we must make the primitive molecules of which living things were ultimately constructed.

Here we have a chance of doing an experiment. We can see what kinds of conditions are required to start the transformation of these four or five primeval substances into more complex substances. It is observable that almost any process which tears the atoms from each other will give rise to more complex molecules after a new separation has occurred, and there are various ways in which these atoms can be torn from each other (6, 8). Ultraviolet light from the sun, ionizing radiation from cosmic rays or radioactive elements of the primitive earth (reconstructed experimentally in our cyclotrons), and lightning are the three principal ways in which molecules of this kind can be torn apart in order to see if the atoms can regroup themselves into more complex substances.

It turns out that indeed they can. We did one of the earliest ex-

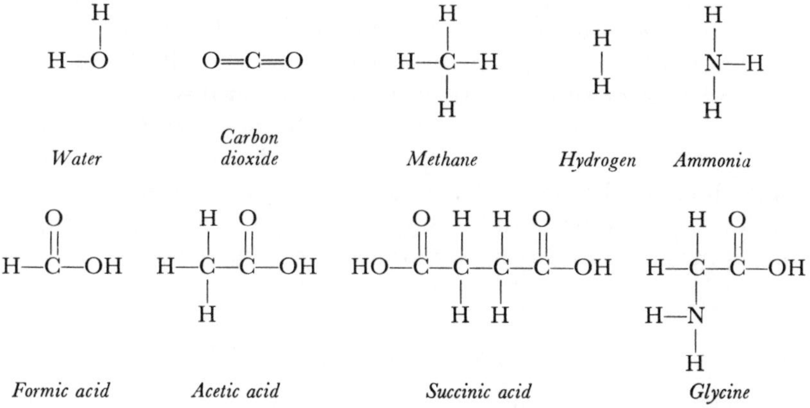

Figure 3

Primeval and primitive organic molecules.

periments in 1950, using the cyclotron as a source of ionizing radiation, in order to discover if such transformations would occur. We started with carbon dioxide (instead of methane) and hydrogen, and we were able to get reduced carbon compounds, such as formic acid and formaldehyde (*11*). Since that time, the completely reduced theory of the primeval atmosphere has become increasingly accepted (*6, 8*), and a wide variety of experiments have been performed, using ionizing radiation, ultraviolet light, and the electric discharge (lightning); these simple molecules have been converted into more complex ones (*6, 8, 12, 13*). Figure 3 shows the primeval molecules (water, methane, hydrogen, ammonia, and carbon dioxide) from which, after the molecules are torn apart by lightning, by ionizing radiation, or by ultraviolet light, more complex molecules of the type in the bottom row of Figure 3 are obtained. These molecules are formed from those of the upper row when they are subjected to electric discharge or ionizing radiation. Ultraviolet light is not as productive, a subject which will be discussed later. It is important to note that these changes were made in the laboratory for elements existing on the primitive earth by means of forces which also existed on the primitive earth.

These molecules (formic acid, acetic acid, succinic acid, and glycine) are the very ones of which living things today are constructed. We have passed now from the atoms to the primitive molecules—the amino acids (of which glycine is one), the sugars (which are in the same class as formaldehyde), and the fats (in the same class as acetic acid). The bases are not shown here because when this illustration was drawn we did not know if bases could be made in this way. We now know that they can be, and we will discuss this more thoroughly later.

We have taken the first step, a random juggling of the atoms, which shows us that we can experimentally change the simple things which accreted to the earth in its primeval atmosphere into the beginning of molecules of which living things are made today.

Evolution of Catalysts

The next thing is to evolve more efficient ways of transforming these molecules in a manner which will be selective. If we transform all the primitive elements—carbon, hydrogen, nitrogen, and oxygen in their combinations with hydrogen—into the more complex molecules such as formic acid, acetic acid, succinic acid, and glycine, eventually the same forces which tear apart the primitive molecules will start tearing apart the more complex ones. Unless there is some way of selecting among the processes which occur, the more complex molecules will again be decomposed to the smaller ones, with more random reconstructions.

A way of selection among the processes which can occur is through autocatalysis, shown in its simplest form in Figure 4. If substance A has a choice of going to substances B, C, or D, and if it turns out that substance D is such a one which accelerates the rate of the transformation from A to D, then A will automatically go more rapidly to D than to C or B. This is what we mean by autocatalysis: D is a catalyst for its own formation, and any random appearance of such materials will automatically select among all the random transformations that can occur, preferring those leading to autocatalysts.

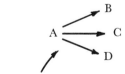

This transformation catalyzed by D

Figure 4

Autocatalysis.

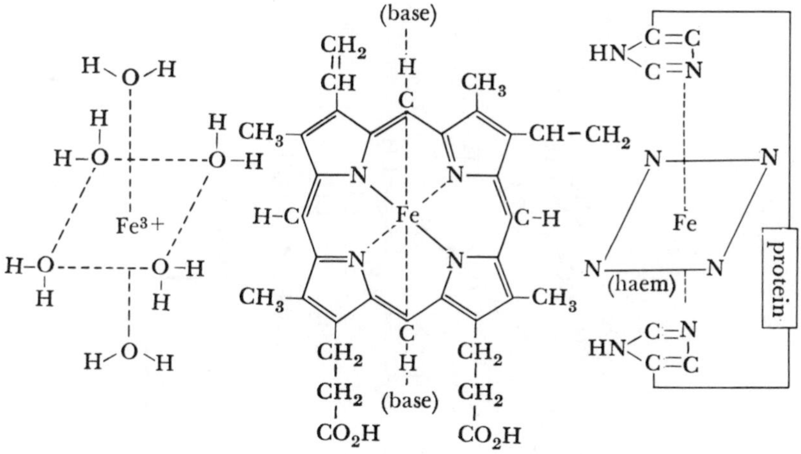

	aqueous ferric ion	*haem*	*catalase*
catalytic activity $ml^{-1}\ sec^{-1}$ at 0°C.	10^{-5}	10^{-2}	10^{5}

Figure 5

Evolution of a catalyst for the reaction $H_2O \rightarrow H_2O + \frac{1}{2}O_2$.

Figures 5, 6, and 7 show the development of such autocatalysts. Figure 5 shows the development of the catalytic function of the iron ion which is present in the sea as a catalyst for the decomposition of hydrogen peroxide, which is formed by the same irradiations that make the other molecules. A very closely related catalytic mechanism, the peroxidase function, may make hydrogen peroxide useful in the construction of some of the catalytic types. In the very early development of organic materials some mechanism had to be found for decomposing (and/or using) the hydrogen peroxide, and iron was the way to do it, particularly when iron is built into a more complex molecule. Here, as a simple iron ion, it has an efficiency of only one part in 100,000. When it is built into the heme molecule, it has an efficiency of one part in 100, so obviously heme will soon displace the aqueous ferric ion. When it is finally built into the modern molecule (catalase) which does the same job, its efficiency is ten thousand million times as great as the original aqueous ferric ion. It is possible to transform molecules with simple rudimentary functions to very refined behavior, such as is represented by the catalase (*14, 15*).

Figure 6 shows the possible opportunity for the evolution of the catalytic function of iron and the biosynthesis of porphyrin. Here is a

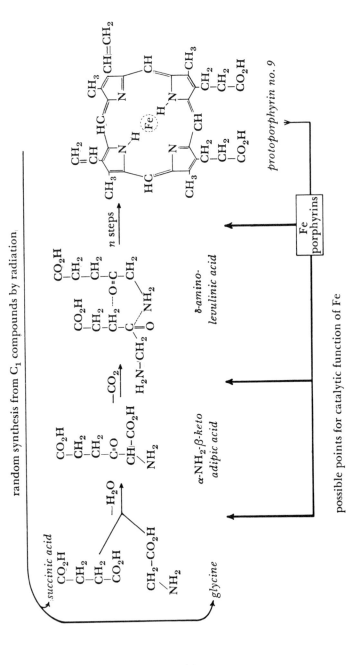

Figure 6

Evolution of the catalytic functions of iron and the biosynthesis of porphyrin.

sequence of reactions, leading from the compounds which we saw were randomly synthesized by radiation (succinic acid and glycine) to the porphyrins. The sequence of reactions involves simple condensation, followed by decarboxylation and another condensation, which, in turn, is followed by a series of oxidation steps, leading finally to the tetra-pyrrole. If any of these steps is catalyzed by iron and if the iron por-phyrin structures turn out to be better catalysts for any of these steps than the bare iron itself, then once this process begins (as it would have begun by random synthesis and condensation) autoselection of this sequence would enhance the transformation of the succinic acid and glycine into delta-aminolevulinic acid and finally into the porphyrin. There is already evidence that in the presence of iron and oxygen and ionizing radiation, or even ultraviolet light, one can actually synthesize small amounts of porphyrin by the primitive catalytic abilities of the iron and the iron porphyrins themselves (*16*).

Molecular Crystallization

Protein Structure

We have passed from random synthesis to selective synthesis and are now in the era in which we have a large number of small molecules. We have to devise ways of making polymers (giant molecules) from the more complex ones, and amino acids constitute one of the principal classes of compounds in which giant molecules can be made by hooking small ones together, end to end. There is an amino (basic) end and an acid end, and these can combine indefinitely to make a long chain which is called polypeptide and which constitutes one of the principal structural materials (protein) of all living things. Figure 7 shows a protein structure as a linear array of these amino acids: R_1, R_2, R_3, R_4 are simply different atom groups, but the "backbone" is always the same. Each protein has a specific arrangement of the functional groups (R groups), at least in the present-day organisms.

In recent years, the biochemist S. W. Fox has shown that by taking some of the simple amino acids under what he calls prebiological con-ditions they could be converted into protein-like materials (*17*). He took a mixture of 18 or 20 amino acids, heated them up in molten glu-tamic acid, a little above the boiling point of water, and got the amino acids to hook together, one to another, and make polypeptides.

Today, of course, living organisms are made up of a very large number of these long polypeptide chains, each one of a specific order. This bears repeating, because one of our main problems is to deter-mine how this specific order is achieved. The long polypeptide chains

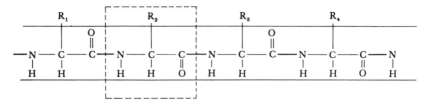

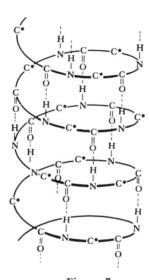

Figure 7

Protein structure. Simple structural principles; variety of chemical reactivity.

exist in a specific type of coil, called an alpha-helix, and this coil is the result of the fact that all polypeptides have certain structural elements in common built into them. The hydrogen bonding in the alpha-helix, together with the specific angles of the carbon and nitrogen atoms, leads to the internal structure of the protein molecule. This protein is one type of macromolecule (giant molecule) which we now know can be made by these random processes, chemical selection, and internal structure determination.

Of the other materials listed in Chart 1, the one made from sugar (cellulose) and the one made from fat (lipid) are not, at least at this stage of our knowledge, in the center of the stage for the evolution of living things. The two that are in the center are the protein and the fourth one, the nucleic acid, which is made up of a heterocyclic base and sugar phosphate molecules tied together in a long chain.

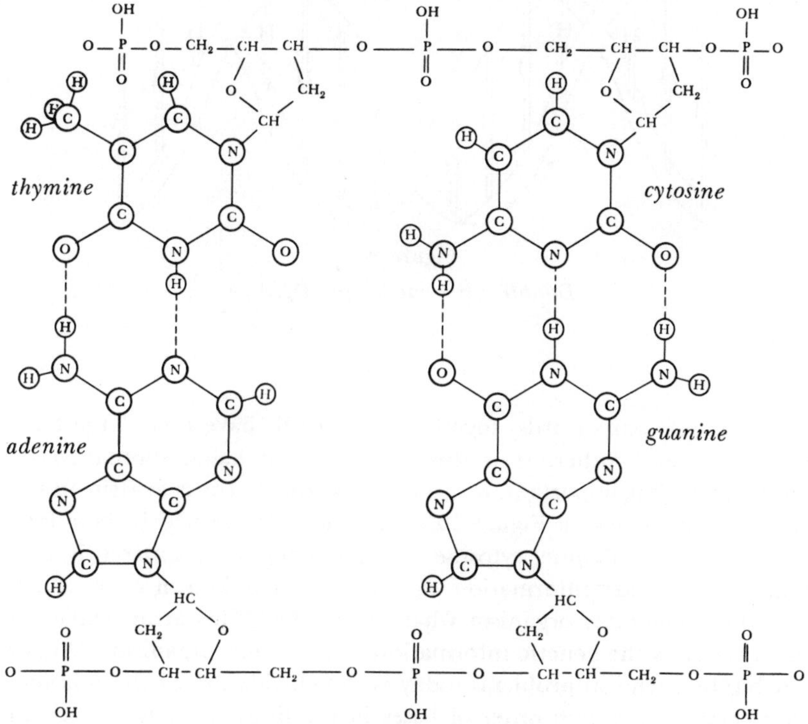

Figure 8

Molecular drawing of components of deoxyribonucleic acid.

Nucleic Acid Structure

Figure 8 shows the structure of the nucleic acids. The shaded atoms form the base molecules—thymine, adenine, cytosine, and guanine. They are held together in pairs by hydrogen bonds. On the outside of these bases are sugar molecules strung along, held together by phosphate groups. It is as though two ribbons were tying together the edges of a row of playing cards. If these ribbons are twisted, the playing cards instead of lying flat will turn sideways and stack up. And indeed flat molecules do stack up under certain conditions in water solution. The molecules do this spontaneously under proper conditions; it is a molecular crystallization phenomenon. Figure 9 shows how this occurs: the two ribbons, and the H's representing the hydrogen bonds which

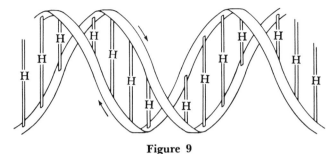

Figure 9
Double helix model for DNA.

hold the base pairs (cards) together. The cards have their large faces parallel to each other. It is this long stack of bases, spontaneously formed, which is important, for today we know that it is evident in the arrangement shown in Figure 10 (*18*). The order in which these four bases (thymine, adenine, cytosine, and guanine) occur apparently contains the necessary information, in some as yet unknown code, which tells the present-day organism what to become. This arrangement of bases contains the genetic information of a modern organism. One of our big biochemical problems today is the elucidation of the relationship between a certain order of bases in the linear nucleic acid chain and a particular order of amino acids in the linear protein chain.

From Chaos to Order

To reconstruct a sequence of events which might have given rise to present-day living organisms, we must solve the problem not only of what the relationship is between this linear array of amino acids and the linear array of bases in the genetic material which determines what an organism will become, but also of how the relationship arose. It is quite clear that there is a connection between these two structures, and thoughts on how it evolved may very well give us a clue to what that connection is, if we can visualize the mechanisms of this evolution. This would be a subject for long discussion in itself; it is one of the frontiers of modern biochemistry.

The essential features to be pointed out are that the structure of nucleic acid is something which comes about as a result of its components, and the structure of its components is something which comes

DNA

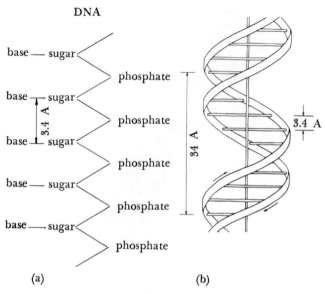

(a)   (b)

Figure 10

Arrangement of bases and sugar phosphate chains in DNA according to Watson and Crick. (a) Chemical formula of a single chain of deoxyribonucleic acid. (b) The figure is purely schematic. The two ribbons symbolize the two sugar phosphate chains, and the horizontal rods the pairs of bases holding the chains together. The vertical line marks the fiber axis. [From J. D. Watson and F. H. C. Crick, Nature, 171, 964 (1953).]

about as a result of the chemical behavior of the four particular atoms of which the components are made: carbon, hydrogen, nitrogen, and oxygen.

We have a route from the atoms themselves with their particular chemical properties, through the molecules, to at least the giant molecules of which the living material is made. We have not yet devised processes for organizing these giant molecules into the organized cells which one can see. One cannot ordinarily see these giant molecules; they are much below the level of visibility of the structured elements of the cell shown in Figure 1. The question is, in evolutionary terms, How did these giant molecules become organized into bigger structures reaching into the range of the visible?

Again, I believe that this organization is a process of crystallization

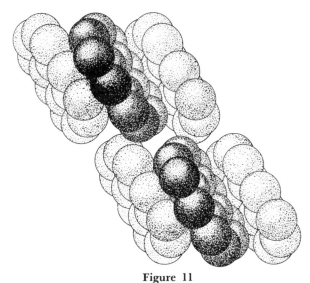

Figure 11

Packing of flat molecules of the anthracene structure projected on its b face.

and that we can trace this crystallization from small molecules to big ones in Figures 11, 12, 13, and 14. Figure 11 shows how anthracene molecules tend to pack; the round balls represent individual atoms and the distinguishable groups of these balls are individual molecules. They tend to pack face-on to each other, which is exactly the type of packing mentioned earlier. Figure 12 shows the structure of aggregates of dye stuff molecules (a cyanine dye) which do not have to drop out of solution as crystals to pack face-on. Even in a very dilute aqueous solution they tend to line up with their flat faces parallel to each other, as a stack of cards (*19*). This is without any help from the ribbon on the side, such as the nucleic acid structure has. These dyestuff structures do this spontaneously, in very dilute solutions. Thus available to us are the structural principles which are built into the structure of the molecules with which we are concerned (*20*).

Figure 13 shows a crystal made up of plant protein. The small spheres are individual protein molecules; when they aggregate out of solution they do so in an ordered array. They do not fall out at random; they order themselves in a very specific way (*21*). Built into the structure of the molecule itself, even in the macromolecules, is some element of order.

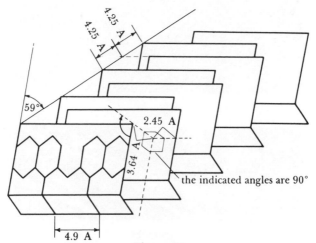

Figure 12

Packing arrangement of a cyanine dye in solution. Arrangement of the plate-like molecules of pseudo-isocyanin when they associate. [G. Scheibe, Z. Elektrochem., 52, 283 (1948).]

Figure 13

Electron micrograph of plant protein crystal (virus).

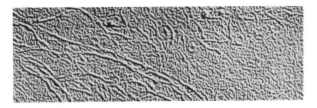

Figure 14

Structure of collagen. Top: Filaments of collagen, a protein which is usually found in long fibrils, were dispersed by placing them in dilute acetic acid. This electron micrograph, which enlarges the filaments 75,000 times, was made by Jerome Gross of the Harvard Medical School. Bottom: Fibrils of collagen formed spontaneously out of filaments such as those shown above when 1 per cent of sodium chloride was added to the dilute acetic acid. These long fibrils are identical in appearance with those of collagen before dispersion.

Finally, let us examine one other type of molecule, a long string which is the collagen molecule shown in Figure 14. Here, at the top, are the individual collagen strands, separated from each other. If one adds a bit of salt to a solution containing them, these protein molecules re-aggregate to make the fibrils and these fibrils look exactly like native collagen fibrils. These re-aggregated fibrils formed from the dissolved collagen are shown below in the same figure. So, even the macromolecules must have some elements of structure in them; the R groups, which are sticking out on the side of the helix in some particular order (see Figure 7), have in them something which tends to bring them together in an ordered array of this sort.

We have thus traced a path from the atoms, through the random synthesis, to the ordered synthesis, to the macromolecules, and eventually to structures that can be seen. But all this still does not hold the material together. It is true that these things will come out of solution as precipitates, if conditions are right. But they do not give rise in and of themselves to the confined type of structure seen in the nucleated red cell of Figure 1 and recognizable as one of the essential features of living cells. Still lacking is the cellular wall, the membrane, which separates the cell from its environment.

Concentration and Localization—The Formation of a Cell

The sight of oil films on water and the wind blowing on these oil films is a common experience. Such phenomena can be reproduced in the laboratory. If the oil film is lying on a protein layer, it is especially easy for it to roll up and form droplets, sometimes containing air and sometimes enclosing water. Figure 15 (top) shows the oil film lying on a protein film over water. The center row shows the process of collapse giving rise to enclosed bodies of water with films around them (bottom). This illustrates the fact that there are physical-chemical mechanisms for producing enclosing membranes (22). This is not the only way, however, in which one can concentrate the materials.

It is possible to take a fairly dilute solution of a synthetic polymer, polyvinylsulfonic acid, and by adding a trace of iron to it to cause the material to separate out in oily droplets which carry all the iron. Both the red oily droplets and the water layer consist primarily of water (23). This is the process of coacervation, another process that has been called upon as a primary phenomenon leading to the development of local

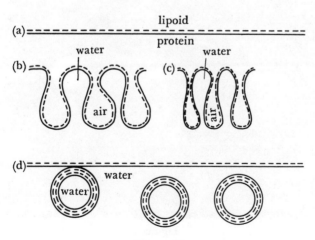

Figure 15
Droplet formation by film collapse (22).

concentration and cellular structures (6). This phenomenon is dependent on the ability of giant molecules in water solutions to separate out from a dilute water solution into relatively more concentrated phases, or droplets, suspended in the more dilute water solution around them. It is a proposal which is actively being followed, particularly in the A. N. Bakh Biochemical Institute of the Academy of Sciences in Moscow, and periodically experiments are published in which the coacervate hypothesis is tested in various ways (8). Beyond this, the giant molecules tend to pack themselves in ordered arrays, provided that they themselves have ordered structures. This is one of the areas in which a good deal more work has to be done in order to define precisely the conditions under which such phenomena as these can occur.

Relationship between Visible and Invisible Structures

Figure 16 is an electron micrograph of tobacco mosaic virus (TMV). The rods are the complete virus particles which, when spread on a to-

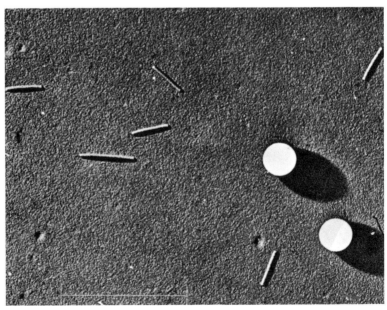

Figure 16

Native tobacco mosaic virus (TMV). (Photograph courtesy of R. C. Williams, Virus Laboratory, University of California, Berkeley.)

bacco plant, will infect the leaves and produce typical disease manifestations. This organism, to call it such, is not an organism in the sense that was shown in the cells of Figure 1 (it has no cell membrane and no nucleus) but it does have two essential features: It has both nucleic acid and protein, and it is able (1) to reproduce itself and (2) to mutate under the right circumstances. Thus it has some of the elements which we require in a living thing. This material can be broken down into its protein component and its nucleic acid component; that is, it can be separated into two parts by suitable chemical treatment. If the protein part, without the nucleic acid, is salted-out in the proper way, it will re-form rods because the protein has in it the necessary structural elements just as the collagen has (Figure 14). Figure 17 shows reconstituted TMV protein without the nucleic acid component. The rod structure does indeed appear, but the length of the rod is varied. In other words, the reconstituted TMV protein does not have the genetic information to tell the rods how long they should be; there is great

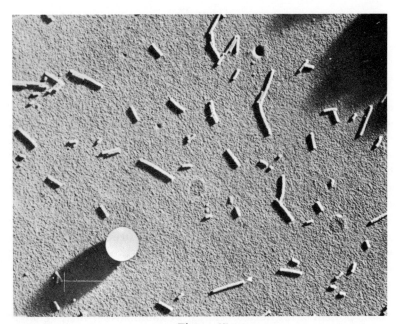

Figure 17

Repolymerized TMV protein. (*Photograph courtesy of R. C. Williams, Virus Laboratory, University of California, Berkeley.*)

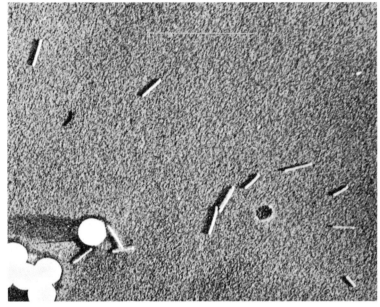

Figure 18

Reconstituted TMV protein and nucleic acid. (Photograph courtesy of R. C. Williams, Virus Laboratory, University of California, Berkeley.)

variation in length. Finally, if we now take the protein component of the TMV which gave rise to the rods of varying length and add back to it the very thin nucleic acid strand in the proper manner, we get the reconstituted material shown in Figure 18. Here are TMV particles which have been reconstituted and which are of the proper size. They know, among other things, how long to be because they have the genetic code wrapped up in the middle of them.

It is quite clear that both of these structures, the protein and the nucleic acid, are required to give the right total structure for the TMV particle. There is an interaction between these two elements to bring about the final construction; these are, if you like, molecular crystallization phenomena.

The evolutionary question can be asked in this way: Which came first, the protein or the nucleic acid? If we could answer that, we might get some clues to modern biochemistry. Until now, I have discussed ways for spontaneous generation of amino acids and proteins, nothing as yet about spontaneous generation of the bases which are necessary to give the nucleic acids. Perhaps on a trip to Venus we will find out which came first. If Venus is in an early stage of evolution, we might find which is the dominant species, protein or nucleic acid.

II. Origin of Life on Earth and Elsewhere

We have traced a sequence of chemical and physical events which might conceivably have led from the primitive molecules present on the primeval earth all the way through to what most of us would have called a living substance. In this sequence, two chemical substances emerged as especially characteristic and especially functional, both of them required to provide what we consider the essential qualities of a living organism. These two substances, these two types of organic material, were the protein and the nucleic acid (Chart 2). The proteins are made up of a sequence of amino acids represented in the chart by the backbone of peptides, each one of the R groups representing a different group of atoms. The nucleic acids, on the other hand, are a sequence, also a chain of atoms, consisting of bases represented by capital letters. (There are four different types of bases represented here by the four letters A, C, T and G.) The bases are hooked together

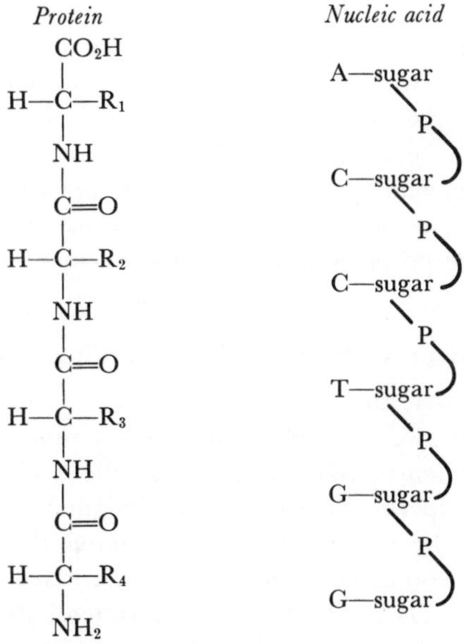

Chart 2
Structure of protein and nucleic acid.

through a sugar molecule and a phosphorous atom to another sugar molecule with another base, another phosphorous atom, and so on.

These two molecules seem to constitute the two kinds of essential structural material which we feel are required to give the aggregate of organic material the properties of living organisms. Among these properties was that of self-reproduction; this property was given to the material by virtue of the nucleic acid base sequence. Only certain bases would pair with each other: A would pair only with T, C would pair only with G. Thus another string of nucleic acid could be constructed complementary to the first one in which A matched with T and G matched with C, to form another string, in some as yet undetermined way, but which would be complementary to the first string, and would thus constitute a replication system. In addition to that, we need the variety of chemical function which the proteins can provide by virtue of the enormous variety which the varied R groups could give us: acids, bases, neutral groups, aromatic groups. All the types of chemical function could be provided by the twenty or so varieties of R groups which go to make up a protein.

Further than that, we know that today, at least, the series of bases which go to make up the nucleic acid contains coded in it all the necessary knowledge, or information, for the manufacture of all the proteins in the living organism. There seems to be, in the simplest cases at least, evidence that there is some relationship between the sequence of bases in the nucleic acid (the A,C,C, G,T) and the primary sequence of these R groups which go to make up the protein. Here is one of the frontiers of modern biochemistry (or biophysics and molecular biology, genetics, and the like). Various terms are applied to this phenomenon, depending upon where you happen to be and what your background is. The problem is always the same: What is the relationship between the proteins and the nucleic acids?

Precursor Conditions for Chemical Evolution

Knowing today that there is some close relationship between protein and nucleic acids, we ask: How could such a relationship arise in the evolutionary sequence? Which came first, the nucleic acid or the protein? Our first experiments which were designed to test the possibility of constructing the raw materials for making these giant molecules showed that we could, by random processes, make the sugar and the amino acid units (11). These early experiments did not demonstrate the random formation of anything that might be called, or related to, these nucleic bases, which seem to be essential for the initial ordering process and for the storage of replication information. But additional laboratory experiments did give some clue to the possible order in which these two substances (proteins and nucleic acids) were evolved.

Figures 7 and 8 show the protein and nucleic acid structures. Although the primary structure of the protein resides in the order of these R groups, an additional feature of the protein is its tendency to coil up in a helical structure by virtue of the very atoms of which it is made. The bond distances and directions inherent in the atoms of which it is made bring it into such a helical structure. This, in turn, leads to higher degrees of order and, finally, leads to the order which one sees in the living organism.

Figure 8 shows the basic structure of the units which go to make up the nucleic acid. The base, adenine for example, is a ring structure containing four carbon atoms and two nitrogen atoms fused to another ring made up of three carbon atoms and two nitrogen atoms, having a number of hydrogens around them. Another one is C, for cytosine; G is the guanine; and T is thymine. Their mode of specific pairing is also shown in Figure 8. Adenine, for example, cannot pair with cytosine; guanine cannot pair with thymine. This phenomenon gives rise to the specificity of replication of the order of bases in a chain and is one of the essential features of a modern living organism. The ability to reproduce itself very nearly identically, but not necessarily exactly, is an essential characteristic of a living thing. In addition to the bases in the nucleic acids, there is the sugar molecule, a five-carbon sugar, and between the sugar molecules are phosphate radicals which hook the sugar molecules together. These create the sugar phosphate ribbons which are the framework of the nucleic acid chain.

The question now is: Can we make these nucleic acid bases? Figure 3 shows that when we take a mixture of what we believe to be the primeval molecules of the earth's atmosphere—water, methane, hydrogen, and ammonia (top row of Figure 3)—and rip them apart by some suitable high energy process, they fall back together again in a random way, and among the things they form are the molecules in the lower row, including amino acids. Notice that there was no evidence on this list—in the first experiments at least—of the formation of the bases which are essential for the construction of the nucleic acid. This would lead one to suppose that the evolutionary mechanism led first to the protein and later, by some means as yet not understood, to the nucleic acid (24, 25).

Energy Sources for Chemical Conversion

However, a re-examination of the sources of energy which might be used to tear these molecules apart has led us to conclude that what was originally believed to be the primary source of energy—the ultraviolet radiations which strike the upper atmosphere—might not be the only, or even the main, source of energy for breaking up these molecules. Another important source might be the radioactivity which is found in the earth's crust, particularly in the form of radioactive potassium-40. There is a set of numbers, which is perhaps worth noting, to give some idea of the relative energies which are available for dissociating the primeval molecules and starting the terrestrial chemical evolution process (Table 1).

The energy available was in various forms, principally ultraviolet light, lightning, and radioactivity. The K^{40} decay provides to the surface of the earth 1×10^{20} cal/yr; the ultraviolet light of wavelength below 1500 A (which is very short ultraviolet, and none of which really gets to the surface of the earth today at all) provides 0.08×10^{20} cal/yr; ultraviolet light shorter than 2000 A is 4.5 (in the same units); and ultraviolet light shorter than 2500 A is 30; lightning is 0.05.

The early experiments which gave the results shown in Figure 3 were done with electrical discharge, the same energy as that of lightning. Attempts to use ultraviolet light have not been very successful in the region of 2000 A and 2500 A (27). That light is not absorbed by CH_4, H_2 or H_2O. We are thus left with the radiation from potassium

Table 1

Energy Available for Synthesis of Organic Compounds (26)

Source of energy	Energy, in 10^{20} cal/yr
Decay of K^{40} in earth's crust at present	0.3
Decay of K^{40} in earth's crust 1.3×10^9 years ago	0.6
Decay of K^{40} in earth's crust 2.6×10^9 years ago	1.2
Ultraviolet light of wavelength below 1500 A	0.08
Ultraviolet light of wavelength below 2000 A	4.5
Ultraviolet light of wavelength below 2500 A	30
Lightning	0.05

-40 in the surface of the earth as a major constituent among the various energy sources which provide energy for tearing the initial molecule apart in order to make more complex ones.

Synthesis of Nucleic Acid Bases under Primitive Earth Conditions

In the last few months we undertook to do another experiment where we would use something resembling the radiation from K^{40}, which is a high energy electron, and bombard mixtures of gases which we believed to be the primeval gases present on the surface of the earth. We wanted to see what sort of material could be formed. Among the materials we found was something which was not unexpected, hydrocyanic acid (28). This material was not unexpected for two reasons: First, it is a rather stable substance produced in the dilute gas phase and, second, it is very common in the universe, particularly in comet tails. When a comet comes close to the sun, the sun shines on the gases of a comet, and makes them glow. These gases emit light, from which we can tell that the gases contain among them large amounts of this combination of atoms—hydrogen, carbon, and nitrogen, HCN. We found a good deal of HCN in such a bombardment mixture, but more important was the observation that we get out of this mixture the bases which we need for making the nucleic acids.

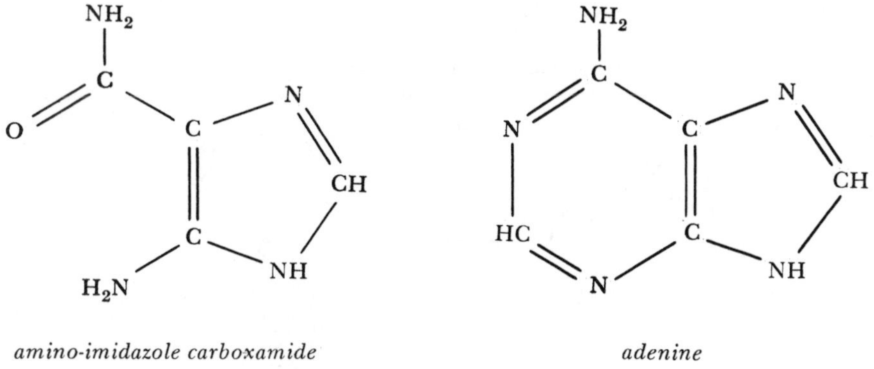

amino-imidazole carboxamide   adenine

Figure 19

Synthesis of adenine under primitive earth conditions. [From J. Oro, Biochem. Biophys. Res. Comm., 2, 407 (1960).]

It had already been found that if HCN were put into a water solution with large amounts of ammonia, which we believe to have been present in the primeval atmosphere (from the fact that it is present in the larger planets of our solar system), adenine is formed (*29, 29a, 29b, 30, 31, 32, 32a*). Figures 19 and 20 show that adenine, one of the most important of the bases, is simply a molecule made up of five HCN molecules put together—just five of them falling together in the right way to make adenine. Figure 20 shows how three of the HCN's combine to form amino-malononitrile, which has been isolated, and then by a series of other changes, a fourth HCN adds on to give the compound amino-cyanoimidazole, the hydrolytic product of which is a present-day intermediate in the formation of the bases (Figure 19). Addition of more HCN gives adenine. This work was done only in the last year. Other bases have been isolated since, from ammoniacal solutions of HCN, and adenine is one of the most important of the four heterocyclic bases which are constituents of the nucleic acids.

We know now that the electron bombardments (and even the

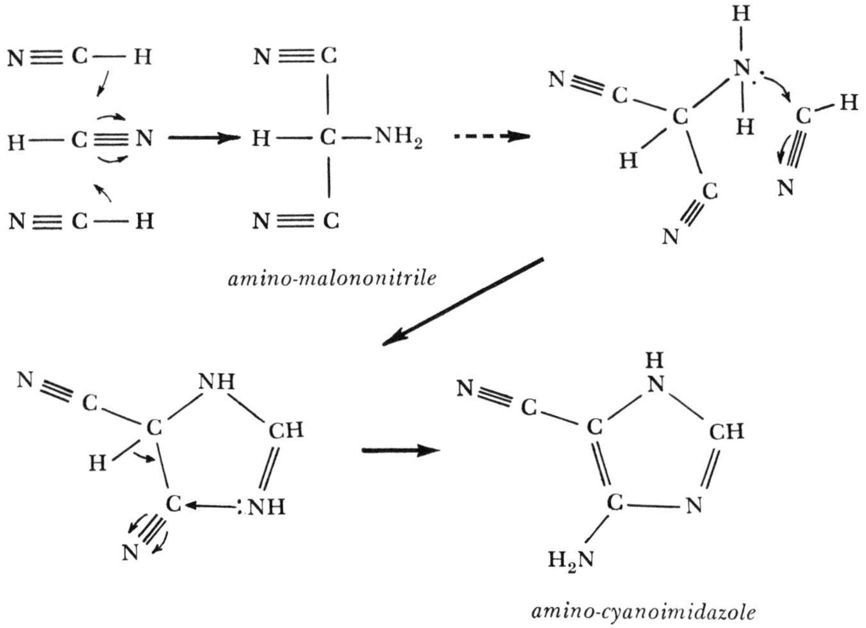

Figure 20

Synthesis of intermediates from HCN to adenine.

lightning) will produce respectable amounts of HCN and adenine and other bases as well *(28).*

Once more we have experimental data from which to draw conclusions. When methane, ammonia, water, and hydrogen are subjected to ionizing radiations which tear them apart, these primitive materials fall back together in all sorts of configurations. One might have supposed that they would fall together in random ways, but they do not. The atoms have certain qualities about them, built into their electronic structure, so they do not fall together in completely random ways but form certain specific substances. We know this by virtue of the way in which we have performed certain experiments in our laboratory.

Rather than just passing the 5 million electron volt electrons through this primitive gas mixture and then analyzing the gas mixture by ordinary chemical analysis (looking for sugar, base, HCN, amino acids, neutral substances), we wanted some method that would find all the things that the carbon from the methane had become without

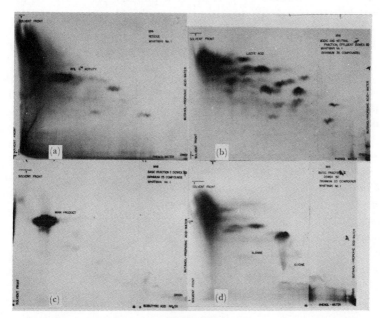

Figure 21

Radioautographs of paper chromatograms of methane irradiated with 5-Mev electrons, showing major components.

having to know ahead of time what they were. There is only one way to follow the carbon, and that is to use carbon atoms which can be traced no matter what becomes of them, namely, radioactive carbon (carbon-14). We used C^{14}-labeled methane and passed the discharge through the labeled methane, together with water, ammonia, and hydrogen. We then took the water solution containing the product from this bombardment and spread it out on a piece of filter paper in a systematic way, a technique known as paper chromatography.

Figure 21 shows the results of one of these bombardment experiments. We took a bit of the material from the bombardment, put it at one corner of the filter paper, and then passed a solvent (water and phenol) over that paper in one direction which spreads the compounds that are present on that corner of the paper out in a line along the bottom of the filter paper. Next, we dried off the paper and passed another solvent over it (butanol:propionic acid:water) in a direction normal to the first one, and the compounds which originally were overlapping were spread out further. We find the compounds on the filter paper by laying a piece of photographic film in contact with the paper; wherever there is some radioactive compound the photographic film will become dark. Figure 21 is a photograph of the darkened films: Wherever a black spot appears on the film, there a particular compound containing the radioactive carbon is located. We can tell the nature of that compound by where it is on the film with respect to its origin. This process is radioautography.

Figure 21a shows all the different radioactive compounds which result from one particular bombardment. Much of the material is smeared out; it has not separated into distinct compounds, but about a dozen of them have indeed separated out. Figure 21b, c and d are radioautographs of chromatograms of different components of the mixture resulting from preliminary chemical separation. We were able to identify in this way some half-dozen compounds, including adenine and HCN, and glycine and alanine, and various amino acids and sugars, some fatty acids, some hydroxy acids—the very things of which today's living matter is composed (see Table 2). There are many compounds which we have not yet identified, but Figure 21 shows the data in their primitive form. One of the main products formed as a result of the bombardment is urea, which in living matter today is an important biological material (28a).

This information not only describes the work in progress but shows that this apparently violent thing we are doing to what we believe to have been the primeval gases of the earth's atmosphere does indeed

Table 2

Identification of Compounds from Irradiation Experiment
from C^{14}-labeled Methane, Ammonia, and Water

Experiment M22	$^{14}CH_4$, NH_3, H_2O, PH_3 $(NH_4PO_3)_x$	
Acid fraction	= 45.5%	
Basic fraction	= 17.44%	Separation on Dowex 1 and Dowex 50
Nonionic fraction	= 21.3%	

HCN	=	0.45% of total
Adenine	=	0.203% of basic fraction
	=	0.034% of total
5-Aminoimidazole-carboxamide	=	0.105% of basic fraction
	=	0.018% of total
Lactic acid	=	2.21% of acid fraction
	=	0.99% of total

The *two* unknown other dominating acids (not including lactic) account for 29% and 17.8%, respectively, of the acid fraction.

Glycine	=	0.2% of basic fraction
	=	0.03% of total
α-Alanine	=	1.07% of basic fraction
	=	0.18% of total
Aspartic acid	=	0.2% of basic fraction
	=	0.03% of total

The *two* unknown (not urea or guanidine) dominating basic compounds (ninhydrin positive) account for 20.9% and 11.9% of the basic fraction.

produce materials which are of extreme importance today in all living things. This gives us confidence that we are experimentally progressing toward an understanding of how living things may have come into being on the surface of the earth. It is as far as we can go with the terrestrial experiments at this time.

Life on Other Planets?

The question then arises, Are such processes as these going on anywhere else, first in our own solar system and then beyond our solar system? I am concerned now only with the kind of life we know, that based on carbon. There may be other kinds of life, based on other elemental systems than carbon, hydrogen, nitrogen, oxygen, and liquid water, and one can imagine such systems. I do not feel that we are in a position to speculate about those to the extent of equating them with all the qualities we define as "living" in the system consisting of carbon, hydrogen, nitrogen, and oxygen atoms.

An anonymous article recently published in a German periodical bears the title "Is Life Possible on the Surface of the Earth?" The author, a presumed denizen of Jupiter, comes to the conclusion that it is not possible! He reasoned from the fact that Jupiter has an atmosphere consisting mostly of methane, and because it is much colder than the surface of the earth, water would be frozen. Its liquid phase would therefore be liquid ammonia. The Jovians have decided that because there is no ammonia in the earth's atmosphere and because it is much too warm to have liquid ammonia on the earth's surface, we therefore cannot have life on the surface of the earth. This is the kind of argument that a Jovian might adduce, and from his point of view it is a reasonable one.

Here I shall consider the question of earthlike life, terrestrial life, life as we know it, anywhere else in our solar system. This means that we must have the materials which we have decided are primitive on the earth and the same kinds of processes taking place, the same temperature ranges, and so on.

This question is not a completely hypothetical one but a real one since we shall have definite information very soon, at least about our three nearest neighbors. We will probably know the answer within five years, certainly within ten. In fact, we might even know something about its possibility on Venus within a few months. The Venus probe, which will give us direct information about the surface temperature as well as other properties, is on its way.

It is important to keep in mind the imminence of this knowledge. It is coming very soon and we shall have the answers to this question about extraterrestrial life that has been asked in one way or another ever since men looked at the stars and wondered if anything were alive out there. Even in ancient times the stars were assigned living functions, related always to human life, and in recent years in a more scientific way this same question has arisen.

Obviously, one of the better ways of getting an answer to this question would be to send somebody, or something, to the moon, to Venus, or to Mars, to scoop up a chunk and bring it back and examine it in the laboratory. Presumably we would then know whether or not anything was alive there.

Meteorite Experiments

Fortunately bits of our solar system are coming to us all the time in the form of meteoritic infall. Various estimates of the amount of meteoritic infall range from a minimum of 350,000 tons/year to 10,000,000 tons/year (*33*). Even 5,000,000 tons/year is a good size of meteoritic infall. Unfortunately most of it goes into the ocean. Just a few months ago one came over southern Oregon and went into the sea. There is talk of some of it having fallen into southern Oregon or northern California, but so far no recovery has been reported. In any case, there are a few meteors which fall in places from which they may be recovered.

Of these meteorites, the largest group by weight are the iron meteorites because they are the ones that are tough and survive and can be found and easily recognized. The stones are not so easily recognized, but they also comprise a large group, largest by far numerically among the falls. But among the stony meteorites there is a very small group containing carbon, called carbonaceous chondrites. Of some 900 stones listed in the 1955 catalog of meteorites, only 12 to 15 are carbonaceous chondrites, that is, stones containing appreciable amounts of carbon, between 2 and 3 per cent of their total weight.

Common belief at present is that these meteorites come from the asteroid belt, the so-called vacant space between Mars and Jupiter and presumably the home of the meteorites (*34, 35, 36*). The meteorite does represent extraterrestrial material, and if we can get it and examine it, we can obtain some idea of what extraterrestrial material is like. A good deal of inorganic analysis, mineralogical analysis, and metallurgical analysis has been made of all the types of meteorites I have described (*37, 38*). Relatively little has been done to determine the nature of the carbon compounds contained in the carbonaceous chondrites for two reasons: first, there are so few of them; second, it is only recently that our analytical methods have been sufficiently precise and delicate to tell us very much about them. The first modern complete analysis of a carbonaceous chondrite was made in 1953 by Mueller on the Cold Bokkeveld meteorite which fell in South Africa in 1838. The carbon compounds in terms of their solubility and carbon content resembled hydrocarbons (*39*).

A carbonaceous chondrite fell in Murray, Calloway County, Kentucky, in 1950, and we were able to get a sample of it from Dr. E. P. Henderson of the Smithsonian Institution (*40*). We proceeded to analyze it very carefully for the kind of carbon compounds it contained.

Does it show any signs of the compounds which we see being made by these various radiation methods? Do we see any signs of the compounds which might have formed in the primeval earth just by the condensation of carbon and hydrogen atoms in the original collection of dust and gases which aggregated to form, first, the solar system and the sun and, next, the various planets, including the earth?

We analyzed about half the sample of the Murray meteorite which we had. We have not yet identified any single compound, but we have identified certain groups, or classes, of materials (40a). For example, we were able to identify long-chain hydrocarbon materials, that is, long-chain waxlike, or petroleum-like, molecules, containing as many as from 10 to 12 carbon atoms in a string, and longer ones as well. These were identified by some of the very sensitive methods that we now have, that is, by mass spectrometry. These materials have possibly a number of abiogenic sources.*

What was more interesting, however, was an answer to the question posed at the beginning of this discussion: Are there any amino acids or heterocyclic bases present in the meteorite fragments? These are the two compounds which seem to be the ones we want to know about. Our first tests for the presence of amino acids failed. On the other hand, the extracts of the ground-up insides of the meteorite showed some materials which absorbed light in a way characteristic of the heterocyclic bases. Figure 22 reproduces a photomicrograph of the Murray meteorite. It is a very friable, soft thing, resembling no known terrestrial rock. The little chondrules (spherules) give the meteorite its name of chondrite.

The first piece of information obtained from our analytical work on the samples of Murray was the infrared absorption of the organic

* Since these lectures were presented, new information has been announced regarding the analysis of another carbonaceous chondrite, Orgueil, which fell in France in 1864. Nagy, Meinschein, and Hennessy announced in March, 1961, their analytical results which confirmed the presence of hydrocarbon-like materials in this meteorite as well (41). The distribution of normal paraffins in life forms is quite distinctive. Instead of monotonically distributed mixture of these molecules, hydrocarbons from living things show a preference for odd carbon groups, such as 21-carbon-atom-containing molecules, 23-carbon-atom-containing molecules, whereas the even number (20, 22, 24) carbon-atom-containing-molecule content is low. The meteorite hydrocarbons, according to these investigators, also show a preference for certain odd carbon normal paraffins. These workers feel that the mass-spectrometric analyses make it likely that the materials are a result of biogenic processes occurring in regions beyond the earth from which the meteorites came.

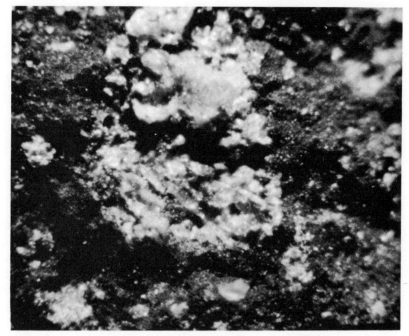

Figure 22

Photograph of meteorite Murray.

material which we extracted from the chondrite. This is shown in Figure 23, which also indicates a variety of carbon-hydrogen bonds in this extract. The troughs represent the absorption of a certain kind of light corresponding to the presence in this material of C-H bonds. There are several different kinds of C-H bonds present in the meteorite extract, indicated by the breadth and complexity of the absorption in the 2800 cm^{-1} region. More interesting, however, is the region between 1650 through 1800 wave numbers. These dips correspond to the absorption of a certain wavelength of light, which tells us that in this meteorite extract there are molecules containing carbon-oxygen double bonds and carbon-nitrogen double bonds of various kinds. This is a complex mixture, and there are several different kinds of these things present. So we know that the meteorite material is not pure, but we also know that, in general, the kinds of things we are looking for are there.

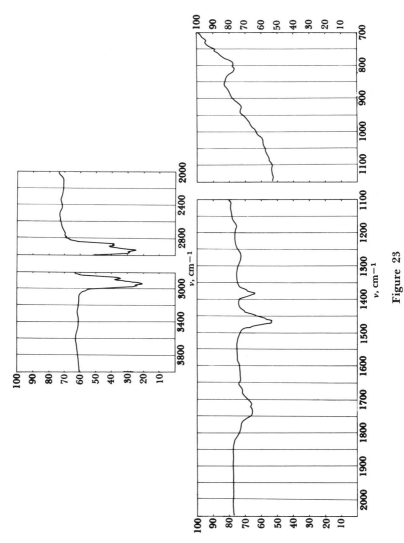

Figure 23

Infrared spectrum of carbon tetrachloride spectrum of meteorite Murray.

70

Much more specifically informative was the absorption of light at the other end of the spectrum, the ultraviolet end, which is shown in Figure 24. This shows absorption at a very short wavelength in the ultraviolet region and it changes with the acidity of the solution in a very important way. The change is highly characteristic of one of those heterocyclic bases which go to make up the nucleic acids, the one to which the name cytosine has been given. I do not claim that this material in the meteorite is cytosine, only that its absorption spectrum behaves very much like the absorption of cytosine. There seems to be evidence for the presence in the meteorites of a material which resembles the heterocyclic bases.*

This gives some idea that perhaps the nucleic acid type of fragment, the base, might have come before the amino acids. Actually, I suspect that they both came up together (42). I suspect that both the bases and the amino acids appeared at the same time; perhaps the bases came a little earlier. At this stage we cannot make assertions beyond this point.

If we can go to the moon and get a sample of moon dust collected by it as it sweeps through space, we will be able to see what has accumulated underneath the moon surface, protected alike from radiation and from the possible transformation by living organisms (43, 44, 45, 46). We can then find out what the primitive organic molecules of the solar system were. This is one of the reasons why we want to go —and we will go, very soon.

Speculation on Life Elsewhere in the Solar System

Let us now examine the situation with respect to our two nearest planetary neighbors. I have not discussed the moon particularly as a possible source of living materials, because the moon has no atmosphere (46). It is not likely that we will find any kind of living material unless it is very deeply hidden under the surface in some unknown environment which we cannot yet define. We should find on the surface of the moon large collections of carbon-containing materials such as meteorites, which presumably also contain primitive organic compounds, and from this we will perhaps be able to deduce something that we have been trying to deduce from the small fragments of meteorites available to us.

Of our two nearest neighbors, Venus is on an orbit inside the

* The presence of heterocyclic bases has been suggested in another meteorite, Mokoia. M. H. Briggs, private communication, July 1961.

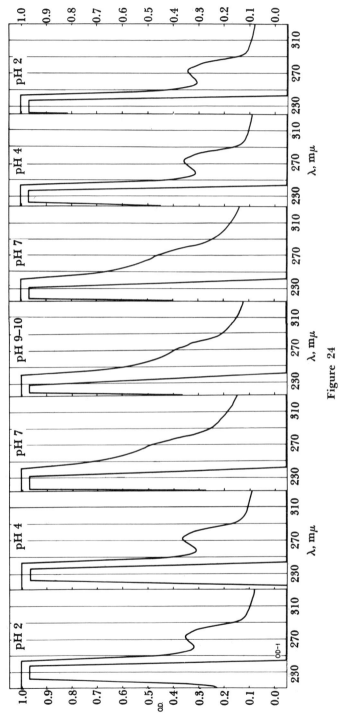

Figure 24

Ultraviolet absorption spectra of extract of meteorite Murray.

72

earth's, and Mars outside. Venus is warmer than the earth by about 10°C; Mars, being farther out, is cooler than the earth by about 10°C. We do not know the surface temperatures of these two planets. We cannot even see the surface of Venus; it is covered with a permanent cloud, and the only materials identified in that cloud are large amounts of carbon dioxide. There is presumably water there, perhaps other things, but these are the only compounds identified up to now (47, 48, 49).

The possibility that there might be living things on Venus, however, is a real one. Venus is almost the same size as the earth (only slightly smaller); its gravity is about the same; there is carbon in its atmosphere, and probably water, so that the conditions are sufficiently close to support living things on its surface. We have no evidence to deny this possibility since we cannot see the surface of Venus.

Mars presents quite another question and is a different kind of object. It is considerably smaller than the earth and, of course, it is cooler. Its atmosphere is only about half as dense as that of the earth. It contains a small amount of CO_2 (more than does the earth's, actually) but no large amounts of oxygen and only small amounts of water. However, there are polar caps, which are visible and which shift with the Martian seasons. Mars has been called the Red Planet because certain parts of it look red to observers' eyes. But photographs of Mars show no real colors, only shades of gray. There are light and dark areas, and the interesting fact is that when the polar cap (presumed to be an ice cap) seems to melt or sublime (because the pressures are so small), the dark area seems to travel toward the equator. When the polar cap returns, the dark area recedes again. This movement behaves very much as though the dark area were something alive (such as lichens) which grew and blossomed forth, one might say, with the availability of small amounts of moisture which came to it from the polar cap. This is one of the basic notions involved with the idea that there are living organisms on Mars.

Perhaps more important than this is a recent observation by the astronomer Sinton, who focussed the 200-inch Palomar telescope on the light and dark areas of Mars (50). He looked with a spectrograph at the 3.5-micron region, which corresponds to the absorption of light by carbon-hydrogen bonds. He was barely able to separate the light and the dark areas with the telescope to see if there was any difference between them in the 3.5-micron region. He says that the dark areas of Mars have much more of the 3.5-micron vibration (absorption) in them than do the light areas. If this is true and if this migration of the dark areas occurs with the seasons, it means that carbon-hydrogen bonds are forming and disappearing with the Martian seasons, which is exactly what a terrestrial living thing would do under the circumstances. This is perhaps the best evidence to date that anything is alive on the surface of Mars.

I think we will have answers to both the Venusian and the Martian questions certainly within a decade, probably much sooner than that.

Life in Other Galactic Systems

The last question is: What are the probabilities that living things exist elsewhere than our solar system? I have not speculated beyond Venus and Mars in our solar system because of the reasons mentioned earlier. Bodies such as Jupiter and Mercury might not support a terrestrial type of life but they might support some other kind, a matter beyond discussion at this point.

Let us then think about places other than our own solar system. Here we must resort entirely to two kinds of information: (1) a theory of the origin of the solar system, and (2) statistics. We begin with the generally accepted notion of the origin of our own solar system and galaxy—and of all the galaxies, for that matter—that it resulted from a gravitational accretion of dust particles and gases. When such accretion became large enough with very high gravitational temperatures, there was ultimate fusion of the hydrogen to give self-luminous bodies like the sun; when the accretion was smaller, and the space had been swept out so that not much material was left, planetary bodies formed around such self-luminous bodies, such as our own solar system. One can then make some deductions as to the probable existence of earthlike planets elsewhere in the universe, and how many.

First, we have to determine the number of self-luminous stars. With the biggest telescope, the 200-inch at Mt. Palomar, the number of self-luminous stars that can be seen has reached 10^{21} (one with 21 zeros after it). Then we have to make an assumption about the way these self-luminous bodies were formed, and I have just made that assumption. We can then estimate how many earthlike planets there will be in the visible universe.

In our solar system, which is one on the edge of one galaxy, the number of earthlike planets is one out of ten, so let us take one out of ten as the number of earthlike planets for each sunlike star, that is, those which are the right distance from their heat source, have the right size, have the right atmosphere of the proper chemical composition, and undergo all the changes outlined as a necessary sequence which might give rise to living substances. For a more conservative estimate, following Shapley (51), let us assume that only one star in one thousand has planets, and further assume that only one planet in one thousand is an earthlike one. We make several other assumptions which give four successive fractions of one thousand; this will produce a figure of 100,000,000 other earthlike planets in the visible universe. This is defining it very narrowly, for I was very conservative in every one of these cutoffs. I took one in a thousand instead of one in ten, in each case. We have reason to believe that there is more than one in a thousand in each case. There are, therefore, at least 100,000,000 planets in the visible universe which were, or are, very much like the earth. From what we have discussed so far, this would mean certainly that we are not alone in the universe. Since man's existence on the earth occupies but an instant in cosmic time, surely intelligent life has progressed far beyond our level on some of these 100,000,000 planets.

Interstellar Communication

The question arises as to whether or not we can communicate with these organisms, whose character we do not know, in these other places (52, 53). This presents a very difficult problem. First of all, relativity places a limitation on the speed with which we can communicate. Accepting that limitation, one of my astronomer colleagues, presently at the Goddard Space Flight Center, made a calculation as to which one of the stars within 10 light-years would have earthlike planets (54, 55, 56). He decided on two particular ones, τ Ceti and ϵ Eridani, and this has led to an attempt to listen to those two stars to see if anybody is talking to us. This is Project Ozma (57).

The course of biological evolution is long, and the course of human evolution within this biological evolution is very short—a million years or less (if you want to be particular about what you call a man!). This is really but an instant in time in terms of the age of the universe. It is therefore very likely that some of these earthlike planets have gone beyond us, some of them not as far, in their evolutionary sequences. So one might expect that in some of these places may be sentient beings developed far beyond our knowledge and sending messages to us for some reason. The big radiotelescopes have been focussed on these two stars in an attempt to hear some periodic signal. So far, none has come, but this work has been going on only for a year, a very short period in terms of evolutionary time.

Man's Place in the Universe

The fact that we have come to the conclusion that we are not alone makes us look back again on the place that life occupies on the earth, the solar system, the galaxy, and the universe. When life is measured in terms of the fraction of the total number of atoms involved in living processes, it is not very large. However, the effects of life are more far-reaching. The surface of the earth has been completely transformed by the evolution of living matter, and it is being changed even more by one of the more recent forms of this living matter—man. I believe that this places life in a somewhat different perspective than the view formerly held that the earth was a minor planet in the outer wing of an ordinary galaxy. A quite different attitude prevails now, when you think that life is present everywhere in the universe, not just on this minor planet in a minor galaxy. And life is changing those places where it occurs in very profound ways (58, 59).

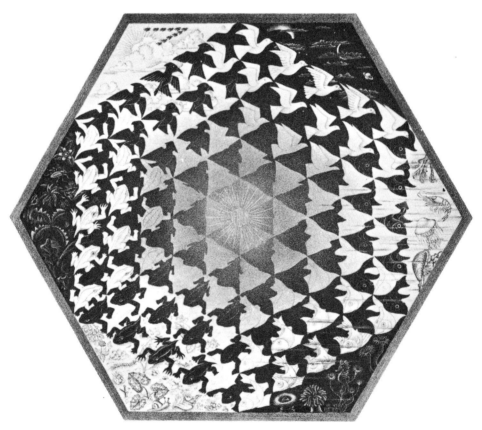

Figure 25

Photograph of "Verbum," by M. C. Escher (Baarn, Holland).

It is quite clear now that we have much to look forward to, both in the immediate future and in the more distant future. I have been thinking about these matters specifically for about a decade, and on a recent trip to Holland I encountered in the office of a chemistry professor a lithograph of a picture which struck me as representing, in an artistic form, the essence of what I had been thinking about the nature of evolution and living processes. A photograph of this picture is shown in Figure 25. In the middle is the word Verbum. Around the periphery is the sky, by day and by night; the sea, by day and by night; and the land, by day and by night. The gradual merging of the figures, one to another, and the transformations which eventually became apparent, seem to me to represent the essence not only of life but of the whole universe.

Acknowledgment

I want to express my thanks to Professor Luther S. Cressman, Dean Henry P. Hansen, and Dean Ralph Steetle, of the Condon Lectures Committee, for the privilege of visiting Oregon under such auspices. I have been acquainted with the work that goes on here from a distance, but this is my first opportunity to visit the state itself, and I am grateful for it and for its hospitality, which is in the true western tradition.

References

1   C. Darwin and A. R. Wallace, On the Tendency of the Species to Form Varieties and on the Perpetuation of the Species by Natural Means of Selection, *J. Proc. Linnaean Soc. London (Zoology)*, **3**, 45 (1858).

2   A. R. Wallace, On the Tendency of Varieties to Depart Indefinitely from Original Types; unpublished manuscript written in June 1858 and incorporated into the longer Darwin-Wallace paper (Ref. *1*).

3   Notes and Records of The Royal Society of London, **14**, No. 1 (1959).

4   A. Winchell, *Sketches of Creation,* Harper, New York, 1870.

5   J. B. S. Haldane, Collection of Essays on The Origin of Life, *New Biology,* No. 16, Penguin, London, 1954.

6   A. I. Oparin, *The Origin of Life,* 3rd English ed., Oliver and Boyd, London, 1957. See also earlier edition edited by S. Margulis, Macmillan, New York, 1935.

7   M. H. Briggs, Dating the Origin of Life on the Earth, *Evolution,* **13**, 416 (1959).

8   A. I. Oparin (ed.), *The Origin of Life on Earth,* Proc. Intern. Union Biochemistry Symposium, Moscow, August 1957. Pergamon, London, 1960. This book gives a review of the ideas about the origin of life through the date of the conference.

9   H. Gaffron, The Origin of Life, *Perspectives Biol. Med.,* **3**, 163 (1960).

10 M. H. Briggs, The Origins of Life on the Earth: A Review of the Experimental Evidence, *Sci. Cult.* (*Calcutta*), **26**, 160 (1960).

11 W. M. Garrison, J. G. Hamilton, D. C. Morrison, A. A. Benson, and M. Calvin, The Reduction of Carbon Dioxide in Aqueous Solutions by Ionizing Radiation, *Science*, **114**, 416 (1961).

12 S. L. Miller, Production of Some Organic Compounds under Possible Primitive Earth Conditions, *J. Am. Chem. Soc.*, **77**, 2351 (1955).

13 S. L. Miller and H. C. Urey, Organic Compound Synthesis on the Primitive Earth, *Science*, **130**, 245 (1959).

14 M. Calvin, Chemical Evolution and the Origin of Life, *Am. Scientist*, **44**, 248 (1956).

15 M. Calvin, Evolution of Enzymes and the Photosynthetic Apparatus, *Science*, **130**, 1170 (1959).

16 D. Shemin, Biosynthesis of Porphyrins, *Harvey Lectures*, **50**, 258 (1954).

17 S. W. Fox, K. Harada, and A. Vegotsky, Thermal Polymerization of Amino Acids and a Theory of Biochemical Origin, *Experientia*, **15**, 81 (1959).

18 J. D. Watson and F. H. C. Crick, General Implications of the Structure of DNA, *Nature*, **171**, 964 (1953).

19 G. Scheibe, Wechselseitige Bindung und Energieübertragung in Molekülen in flüssiger Phase, *Z. Elektrochem.*, **52**, 283 (1948).

20 M. Calvin, From Microstructure to Macrostructure and Function in the Photosynthetic Apparatus, *Brookhaven Natl. Lab. Symp.*, **11**, 160 (1958).

21 R. W. G. Wyckoff and L. W. Labaw, On the Structure of Macromolecular Crystals, *Exptl. Cell Res. Suppl.*, **3**, 395 (1955).

22 R. J. Goldacre, Surface Films, Their Collapse on Compression, the Shapes and Sizes of Cells, and the Origin of Life, in *Surface Phenomena in Chemistry and Biology*, Pergamon, London, 1958, pp. 278-298.

23 F. Millich and M. Calvin, Coacervation of Salts of Polyvinylsulfonic Acid Induced by Heavy Metal Ions, *Univ. Calif. Rad. Lab. Rep. UCRL-9519*, Jan. 31, 1961, p. 4.

24 The idea of the appearance of amino acids before nucleic acids on the primitive earth is expressed by S. W. Fox, How Did Life Begin? *Science*, **132**, 200 (1960).

25 The theory of the appearance of nucleic acids before amino acids on the primitive earth is given by N. H. Horowitz, On Defining Life, *in* The Origin of Life on the Earth, *Intern. Union Biochem. Biochemical Symp. Ser.*, **1**, 106 (1960).

26 A. J. Swallow, *Radiation Chemistry of Organic Compounds*, Pergamon, London, 1960, p. 244.

27 W. E. Groth and H. v. Weyssenhoff, Photochemical Formation of Organic Compounds from Mixtures of Simple Gases, *Planetary Space Sci.*, **2**, 79 (1960).

28 C. Palm and M. Calvin, Irradiation of Methane, Ammonia, Hydrogen, and Water, *Univ. Calif. Rad. Lab. Rep. UCRL-9519*, Jan. 31, 1961, p. 30.

28a C. Palm and M. Calvin, Primordial Organic Chemistry, I. Compounds Resulting from Electron Irradiation of $^{14}CH_4$; submitted to *J. Am. Chem. Soc.*

29   J. Oro and A. P. Kimball, Synthesis of Imidazoles and Purines under Primitive Earth Conditions, Abstracts of paper presented at the American Chemical Society Meeting, New York, September 1960, Division of Biological Chemistry, Abstract 68, p. 25C.

29a   J. Oro and A. P. Kimball, Synthesis of Purines under Possible Primitive Earth Conditions, I. Adenine from Hydrogen Cyanide, *Arch. Biochem. Biophys.*, **94**, 217 (1961).

29b   J. Oro and S. S. Kamat, Amino Acid Synthesis from Hydrogen Cyanide under Possible Primitive Earth Conditions, *Nature,* **190**, 442 (1961).

30   J. Oro, Synthesis of Adenine from Ammonium Cyanide, *Biochem. Biophys. Res. Comm.*, **2**, 407 (1960).

31   J. Oro and G. Guidry, A Novel Synthesis of Polypeptides, *Nature,* **186**, 156 (1960).

32   J. Oro, A. P. Kimball, and F. Moser, Amino Acid Synthesis from Formaldehyde and Hydroxylamine, *Arch. Biochem. Biophys.*, **85**, 115 (1959).

32a   J. Oro and A. P. Kimball, Synthesis of Purines under Possible Primitive Earth Conditions, I. Adenine from Hydrogen Cyanide, *Arch. Biochem. Biophys.*, **94**, 217 (1961).

33   H. Pettersson, Cosmic Spherules and Meteoritic Dust, *Sci. Am.*, **202** (1960).

34   B. Mason, Origin of Chondrules and Chondritic Meteorites, *Nature,* **186**, 230 (1960).

35   B. Mason, The Origin of Meteorites, *J. Geophys. Res.*, **65**, 2965 (1960).

36   E. Anders and G. G. Goles, Theories on the Origin of Meteorites, *J. Chem. Educ.*, **38**, 58 (1961).

37   H. H. Nininger, *Out of the Sky: Story of Meteoritics,* Dover, New York, 1959.

38   E. L. Krinov, *Meteorites* (English trans.), Pergamon, London, 1960.

38a   E. L. Krinov, *Principles of Meteoritics* (English trans.), Pergamon, London, 1960.

39   G. Mueller, Properties and Theory of Genesis of Carbonaceous Complex in the Cold Bokkeveld Meteorite, *Geochim. Cosmochim. Acta,* **4**, 1 (1953).

40   For a description of the Murray meteorite see J. R. Horan, The Murray, Calloway County, Kentucky, Aerolite, *Meteoritics,* **1**, 114 (1953).

40a   S. K. Vaughn and M. Calvin, Extraterrestrial Life: Some Organic Constituents of Meteorites and Their Significance for Possible Extraterrestrial Biological Evolution. *Proc. 1st Intern. Space Sci. Symp.,* Nice, France, 1960.

41   B. Nagy, W. G. Meinschein, and D. J. Hennessy, Mass Spectroscopic Analyses of the Orgueil Meteorite: Evidence for Biogenic Hydrocarbons, *Ann. N. Y. Acad. Sci.*, **93**, 25 (1961).

42   M. Calvin, Origin of Life on Earth and Elsewhere: II. *Univ. Calif. Rad. Lab. Rep. UCRL-9440,* Oct. 19, 1960; *Ann. Internal Med.*, **54**, 954 (1961).

43   J. Lederberg and D. Cowie, Moondust, *Science,* **127**, 1473 (1958).

44   C. Sagan, Indigenous Organic Matter on the Moon, *Proc. Natl. Acad. Sci.*, **46**, 393 (1960).

45   C. Sagan, Organic Matter and the Moon, *Natl. Acad. Sci. Rept. 757,* in press.

46 E. Anders, The Moon as a Collector of Biological Material, *Science*, **133**, 1115 (1961).

47 C. Sagan, Origin and Planetary Distribution of Life, *Radiation Res.*, **15**, 174 (1961).

48 C. Sagan, Production of Organic Molecules in Planetary Atmospheres, *Astron. J.*, **65**, 499 (1960).

49 C. Sagan, The Radiation Balance of Venus, *Jet Propulsion Lab. Rept. JRP-TR-32-34*, Sept. 15, 1960.

50 W. M. Sinton, Further Evidence of Vegetation on Mars, *Science*, **130**, 1234 (1959).

51 H. Shapley, *Of Stars and Men*, Beacon Press, Boston, 1958.

52 H. Freudenthal, *Lincos: Design of a Language for Cosmic Intercourse*, North-Holland, Amsterdam, 1960.

53 See G. A. W. Boehm, *Fortune*, **63**, 144 (1961).

54 Su-Shu Huang, The Problem of Life in the Universe and the Mode of Star Formation, *Astron. Soc. Pacific*, **71**, 421 (1959); **72**, 106 (1960).

55 Su-Shu Huang, Occurrence of Life in the Universe, *Am. Scientist*, **47**, 397 (1959).

56 Su-Shu Huang, The Limiting Sizes of the Habitable Planets, *Natl. Aeronautics and Space Administration Rept. NASA TN-D-499*, Sept. 1960.

57 F. D. Drake, Project Ozma, *Sky and Telescope*, **19** (1960).

58 M. Calvin, Round Trip from Space, *Evolution*, **13**, 362 (1959).

59 For a more complete discussion of the idea of man's place in evolution and in the universe, see Ref. *58*. See also M. Calvin, *Univ. Calif. Rad. Lab. Rept. UCRL-9005*, Dec. 1959, The Origin of Life on Earth and Elsewhere: I. Also, M. Calvin in *Logic and Personal Knowledge*, Routledge and Kegan Paul, London, 1960, p. 207.

Suggested Readings

I. From Molecule to Microbe

1 J. B. S. Haldane, Origin of Life, *New Biology*, No. 16, Penguin, London, 1954.

2 A. I. Oparin, The Origin of Life, 3rd English ed., Oliver and Boyd, London, 1957.

3 A. I. Oparin (ed.), *The Origin of Life on the Earth*, Pergamon, London, 1960.

4 M. Florkin (ed.), *Some Aspects of the Origin of Life*, Pergamon, London, 1961.

5 *Evolution: Symposium VIII of the Society for Experimental Biology (Great Britain)*, Cambridge University Press, New York, 1953; particularly the article entitled "The Origin of Life" by J. W. S. Pringle.

6 J. Huxley, *Evolution in Action*, Harper, New York, 1953; New American Library (paperback), 1957.

7 H. F. Blum, *Time's Arrow and Evolution*, 2nd ed., Princeton University Press, 1955; Princeton (paperback), 1959.

8 G. G. Simpson, *Meaning of Evolution*, Yale University Press, New Haven, 1949; rev. paperback ed., Yale, 1960.

9 J. D. Bernal, *The Physical Basis of Life,* 1951.

10 J. Alexander, *Life, Its Nature and Origin,* Reinhold, New York, 1948.

11 E. Schrodinger, *What Is Life?* Cambridge University Press, New York, 1945.

12 J. Pfeiffer, *Physics and Chemistry of Life,* Simon and Schuster, New York, 1955.

II. Origin of Life on Earth and Elsewhere

1 H. Shapley, *Of Stars and Men,* Beacon Press, Boston, 1958; Washington Square Press (paperback), 1960.

2 F. Hoyle, *Nature of the Universe,* 2nd ed., Harper, New York, 1960.

3 H. S. Jones, *Life on Other Worlds,* rev. ed., Hodder and Stoughton, London, 1960.

4 H. C. Urey, *The Planets,* Yale University Press, New Haven, 1952.

5 E. L. Krinov, *Principles of Meteoritics* (English trans.), Pergamon, London, 1960.

6 H. H. Nininger, *Out of the Sky: Story of Meteoritics,* Dover, New York, 1959.

7 H. Kallman (ed.), *Space Research,* Proc. 1st International Space Sciences Symposium, Nice, France, North-Holland, Amsterdam, 1960.

8 G. P. Kuiper (ed.), *Atmospheres of the Earth and Planets,* University of Chicago Press, Chicago, 1952.

9 F. G. Watson, *Between the Planets,* Harvard University Press, Cambridge, 1956.

Su-Shu Huang

6 ❋ OCCURRENCE OF LIFE
IN THE UNIVERSE

The necessary requirements for the occurrence of life, especially in an advanced form, are here discussed in the light of our present knowledge of the stars and their evolution.

Man has overcome the confines of the earth's gravitational field. In a few years he will learn with certainty about the existence or non-existence of life on the other planets in the solar system. However, because of the vast distances between the stars, he is still a long way from being able to detect empirically the occurrence of life outside the solar system. This does not prevent him from attacking the problem in a "theoretical" way with our present knowledge of astrophysics, biology, and chemistry as a guide.

In order to study the problem of life in the astronomical universe, we have to consider two independent questions: (1) the possibility of formation of planets around stars, and (2) the possibility of occurrence of life on such planets. The first question is connected with the mode of star formation and will not be discussed here. Suffice it to say that, according to current understanding, planet formation around a star is by no means rare (*1*). The second problem is of "astrobiological" interest and is the main concern of this note.

Granted that all kinds of stars have an equal chance of possessing planets, we ask: Is there any way of knowing which kinds of stars favor the existence of life on their planets? This question can be reasonably answered, we find, with our present knowledge.

It is well known that most atoms do not possess the property of coagulating into large molecules which are the building blocks of living matter. It is principally carbon atoms that have this property. So, if life exists on other worlds, it must depend upon this remarkable property of carbon atoms. In other words, the chemistry of organic substances should be universal, although actual morphological forms of life may be different in different places. Therefore, we can only expect life to exist on planets where the temperature lies within certain limits. It is from this fact that we draw the following conclusions.

Time Scales of Biological and Stellar Evolution

Let us first define t_b as the time of biological evolution which brings the chaotic inanimate atoms into an orderly form of intelligent life. In the case of biological evolution on the earth, t_b is of the order of a few billion years.

Next, we consider the evolution of stars which are but a large mass of gaseous particles held together by their mutual gravitational attraction. The luminosity of a star (i.e., its rate of energy output in the form of radiation) is maintained either by thermonuclear reactions of its constituent particles or by gravitational contraction. In the very beginning, when the star is not hot enough to start thermonuclear reactions, its luminosity is derived from gravitational contraction. This is the first phase of stellar evolution. When the temperature of the star rises as a result of gravitational contraction, thermonuclear reactions, converting hydrogen into helium, take place in the core of the star. From then on the energy output of the star is exactly balanced by the energy liberated in these reactions. Therefore, the star maintains for a long time its constant energy output and constant radius until the hydrogen in the core is exhausted. We call this a main-sequence star. The luminosity and effective temperature of the star on the main sequence depends upon its mass. A star remains in the main-sequence stage for a much longer time than in the early contracting stage. After the exhaustion of hydrogen in the core, the star moves away from the main sequence and again evolves rapidly with changing luminosity forming the third stage of evolution. Now, in order to have life on one of its planets, the central star must be on the main sequence; otherwise, the rapidly evolving stars of changing luminosity will destroy life. Thus, if we define the time of stellar evolution, t_s, as the time that a star remains on the main sequence, the first condition for expecting life in an advanced form on any planet of a star is

$$t_s \geqslant t_b$$

Otherwise, life will be destroyed (by evolution of the star) before it reaches a climax. Now, t_s can be computed for main-sequence stars of different masses. It varies from 10^7 years for early O-type stars to more than 10^{11} years for M-type stars (1).

We now ask what is the value of t_b. The earth is about 4.5×10^9 years old, while paleontological evidence shows the existence of life on the earth over an interval of 1×10^9 years. We may tentatively take $t_b = 3 \times 10^9$ years. If so, the time scales, t_s, of all the early-type stars (O, B, A) are less than t_b. Hence, we would not expect life on an advanced order to develop on planets associated with these kinds of stars.

One may question the wisdom of using 3×10^9 years for t_b in general, because this value is only based on a single case—that of the earth. However, we can argue that the time scale, t_b, cannot be greatly shortened because, according to current ideas in biology, the natural selection and evolution of organisms is a result of mutations which are of a random nature and are therefore slow. Here one may ask: Because of intense ultraviolet radiation, and possibly also of high-energy corpuscles from early-type stars, should one expect a higher mutation rate for the living organisms on their planets than on the earth and, thereby, an accelerated evolution of organisms? In order to answer this question we must point out that most mutations are harmful. It follows that, in order to work for natural selection, mutations must be rare. If mutations were too frequent, there would be a considerable chance of different mutations occurring in one and the same individual. The injurious ones would dominate the advantageous ones because the former occur more frequently. Thus, the species would perish instead of being improved by an overactivity of the mutation process (2). Consequently, the value of t_b cannot be greatly shortened. In this way we exclude O, B, A, and maybe early F stars as the energy sources which could make life in its advanced forms flourish on their planets. For O and B stars, t_s is of the order of 10^7 to 10^8 years; we therefore wonder whether life even in its most primitive forms is possible on their planets.

The Habitable Zone of a Star

Let the luminosity of a star be L. This energy supplies necessary heat to the living organism. The heat received by the living beings on a planet must be neither too large nor too small. Otherwise they will perish. In consequence, we can define a habitable zone around each star such that the rate of energy received per unit area facing the star, i.e., $L/(4\pi R^2)$ where R, the distance from the star, lies between an upper limit

$$\epsilon_1 = \frac{L}{4\pi R_1^2}$$

and a lower limit

$$\epsilon_2 = \frac{L}{4\pi R_2{}^2}$$

where ϵ_1 and ϵ_2 are constants independent of the nature of the star itself, while R_1 and R_2 are defined by these two equations. A planet is habitable if its distance R from the star satisfies the condition that

$$R_1 < R < R_2$$

If all planets of a star are formed nearly in one fundamental plane (like those in the solar system) the habitable zone is a concentric circular ring having an area A equal to

$$A = \pi(R_2{}^2 - R_1{}^2) = \frac{L}{4}\left(\frac{1}{\epsilon_2} - \frac{1}{\epsilon_1}\right)$$

which is proportional to the luminosity L of the star. If the planets could be formed throughout the entire space surrounding the star, the habitable zone would consist of a concentric spherical shell having a volume V, equal to

$$V = \frac{4}{3}\pi(R_2{}^3 - R_1{}^3) = \frac{L^{3/2}}{6\pi^{1/2}}\left(\frac{1}{\epsilon_2{}^{3/2}} - \frac{1}{\epsilon_1{}^{3/2}}\right)$$

which is proportional to $L^{3/2}$. In any case, the habitable zone increases with the luminosity of the star. The more luminous the star, the greater is the probability that a planet falls into its habitable zone and can thereby support life. Therefore, stars on the lower part of the main sequence (like late-K- and M-type dwarfs) have a small chance of possessing planets within their habitable zones. For example, a K5 main-sequence star is only 1/10 as luminous as the sun. Thus, its habitable zone is only 1/10 as large as the sun's if all planets of the star are confined to a plane. The habitable zone is only $1/10^{3/2}$ as large if its planets are not confined to a plane. Since the luminosity decreases rapidly when we move from K5 down the main sequence, the habitable zones of late-K and M stars become very small indeed.

The chance of finding life on planets associated with intrinsically faint stars will be even smaller if we consider the fact that planetary orbits are usually not circular but are elliptical. For, if only a small part of its eccentric orbit falls outside the habitable zone, the planet will become uninhabitable.

Of course, we cannot rule out completely the possibility of finding life on planets revolving around faint main-sequence stars. But, the probability of finding life there is extremely small. Since there are a great number of faint dwarf stars in our galaxy and perhaps also in other galaxies, chances are that a few may possess planets with living beings. If the latter do exist they have a long time for their biological evolution because the faint dwarfs remain for an extremely long time on the main sequence. Consequently, living organisms there can evolve to a very high form.

From the arguments given here and in the preceding section we conclude that, if we want to look for life of a high order outside the solar system, the likely places to look are in the main-sequence F (preferably late-F), G, and K (preferably early-K) stars. If they should possess planets, there is a good chance that life flourishes on some of them. It is interesting to note that our sun, which is a main-sequence G2 star, does support life abundantly on at least one of its planets, fully in agreement with the present conclusion.

Dynamical and Other Considerations

Since we know that about one-half of the stars in the solar neighborhood are binary and multiple systems, it would be of interest to examine whether such combinations of stars favor the occurrence of life on their planets. The answer is clear-cut. They have damaging effect on the development of life for two reasons, one dynamical, the other physical.

Dynamically, a planet around one component of a binary or multiple system is always perturbed by its companions. Its chance of remaining within the habitable zone of its central star in a time scale greater than t_b, and therefore of supporting life on it, is greatly reduced. For binary systems of large separations (visual binaries), quasi-stable orbits in the immediate neighborhood of each component are possible. This can be seen, for example, from the fact that the orbit of the moon around the earth is reasonably stable in spite of the perturbation by the sun. However, the actual time scale during which a planet remains within the habitable zone of its central star is a problem involving three bodies and is difficult to estimate. For close binaries (eclipsing and spectroscopic), the habitable zone which must surround both components most likely does not contain dynamically stable orbits unless the mass of one component is very much greater than that of the other or their separation is very small.

Physically if either one of the components in a close binary system is of early type (O, B, A), no life is expected for the same reason as given in the earlier discussion, no matter what kind of star the other component is. For binaries of large separation, this restriction does not apply and we can consider both components separately. However, even in binaries of large separation, the presence of a white dwarf as a component may make the system an unlikely abode for living beings. If, as astronomers nowadays suspect, a star has to undergo some catastrophic change in luminosity (like in a nova explosion, etc.) before it finally degenerates into a white dwarf, such changes in luminosity, with possibly accompanying high-energy corpuscles, would destroy all life that is nearby. Then another time interval of t_b has to elapse before life may appear again on the planets of the system where the catastrophic change took place.

Finally, one may ask whether the orbit of a star around the galactic center has any bearing on the life-supporting property of its planets. The sun moves with most of its neighbors approximately in a circular orbit around the galactic center, so that there is very little change in its immediate surroundings in each revolution (of about 2×10^8 years). If a star (like a high-velocity star) moves in an eccentric orbit in the galaxy, has the change in its environment any harmful effect on the maintenance of life? To attempt to answer this question would be speculative and is therefore outside the scope of the present note.

Examination of Nearby Stars

The conclusions already reached are valid wherever the chemical principle, or more fundamentally the quantum mechanics, applies. That the latter applies everywhere in the universe can be seen from the spectral lines the distant galaxies emit, for the spectral lines are predicted by quantum mechanics. In fact, both the spectral lines emitted by atoms and the formation of molecules are quantum mechanical phenomena of the same valency electrons. Thus, the previous discussions can give us an upper limit to the percentage of stars with which living beings may be associated. Because most stars in space are M-dwarfs, many are close binaries, and a large number are not main-sequence stars, we set the upper limit at 5 per cent for stars near the solar neighborhood. The exact percentage of stars that actually support life depends upon the mode of star and planet formation and cannot be estimated objectively.

Before concluding this note let us examine the life-supporting ability of the nearby stars. Within 5 parsecs (about 16.7 light-years) of the solar system, there are 42 stars (including the sun) (3) of which most are faint M-dwarfs and late-K stars. Many are binary and multiple systems, some with white dwarf companions. If we further exclude from consideration the high velocity stars which are only tem-

Table 1

*Nearby Stars on Whose Planets (If Any) Living Beings Have a
Better-Than-Average Chance to Develop*

Star	Distance, light-years	Spectral type	Luminosity, L
Sun		G2	1.00
ε Eridani	10.8	K2	0.34
τ Ceti	11.8	G4	0.38

porary visitors in the solar neighborhood, there are left only three stars (listed in Table 1) on whose planets life may be found. Among these three, the sun has the highest luminosity and therefore has the best chance for supporting life on its planets. If both ε Eridani and τ Ceti are truly single stars, there is also a good chance of finding their planets (if any) abundant with life. That τ Ceti is one of the stars in the immediate neighborhood of the solar system that may possess planets inhabited by living beings because of its close resemblance to the sun, has been mentioned on several occasions before by Struve.

Finally, we inquire into the problem of life on planets (if any) of our nearest neighbor, α Centauri. This is a triple system, the two more massive components (G4, K1) of which revolve around each other in an orbit with a semi-major axis of only about 20 astronomical units. The eccentricity of this binary orbit is quite large. Thus, it is difficult to imagine that its planets can remain in the habitable zone for a long time. Consequently we do not expect any well-evolved life on any planet of our nearest neighbor in space.

Acknowledgment

I thank Professor O. Struve for valuable discussions on this interesting subject of life in the astronomical universe.

References

1 O. Struve, *Stellar Evolution*, Princeton University Press, Princeton, N.J., 1950.
2 E. Schrödinger, *What Is Life?*, Macmillan, New York, 1941.
3 P. van de Kamp, *Sky and Telescope*, 14, 498 (1955).

Su-Shu Huang

7 ❋ THE PROBLEM OF LIFE
IN THE UNIVERSE
AND THE MODE
OF STAR FORMATION*

General Conclusions Concerning the Occurrence
of Life in the Universe

In a recent paper we have discussed the problem of life, especially in its advanced form, in the universe, and derived some general conclusions concerning its occurrence (*1*). We first compare the time scales of biological and stellar evolution. Since the development of life requires a near constancy of temperature, we should expect that only those planets associated with main sequence stars would be able to support life. For only the main sequence stars keep their luminosities constant for considerable lengths of time. Now biological evolution results from mutation—a random process—and is therefore slow. In the case of our experience on the earth, its time scale is of the order of 10^9 years. If we accept this as an average value for biological evolution in general, we find that the time scale of evolution for main-sequence stars of early spectral types (O, B, A, and perhaps early F) is too short for developing an advanced form of life on their planets even if the latter do exist.

Next we consider the size of the habitable zone around a star. One can determine this zone by computing the amount of energy received per unit time per unit area facing the star. All points at which the computed values lie between two given limits (which can be assigned

* Presented in part at the San Francisco meeting of the Astronomical Society of the Pacific, June 1959.

numerically from biological and other considerations, but which are independent of the nature of the star itself) form the habitable zone of the star. A simple calculation shows that the habitable zone of a star increases with its luminosity. Thus the habitable zone of a star becomes smaller and smaller as we go down the main sequence. Because of this, we regard the main-sequence stars of M type or even of late K type as an unlikely source of energy and negative entropy for supporting life.

From the previous considerations we conclude that if we wish to look for life of a higher order outside the solar system, the best candidates are the hypothetical planets of main sequence F (preferably late F), G, and K (preferably early K) stars. Combined with the consideration that the orbit of a planet within the habitable zone of a binary or multiple system is likely to be unstable, the previous results lead us to predict that out of the 42 known stars (including the sun) within 5 parsecs from us, only three stars (the sun, ϵ Eridani, and τ Ceti) have a good chance for supporting advanced living beings on their planets, if such planets exist.

Detecting Planets Belonging to Stars Other Than the Sun

The previous considerations are, however, of limited usefulness because we have assumed an equal probability for the existence of planets around any star. The actual frequency of occurrence of life in the universe depends much upon the mode of star formation. If the formation of planetary systems around stars is a rare event as compared to the formation of the stars themselves, the occurrence of life will be correspondingly rare. If planet formation is favored only in connection with very massive stars, with stars of very small masses, or with binary or multiple systems, the chance of the existence of life on these planets will still be small. Only if planet formation is a common phenomenon in connection with single F, G, and K stars would the chance of abundant life in the universe be great. Therefore the problem of the occurrence of life in the universe reduces to the problem of discovering whether single main sequence F, G, and K stars possess planets.

The search for a planet belonging to a star other than the sun has been discussed previously by Struve (2) and is unpromising at present. This can be illustrated by a hypothetical system (frequently mentioned by Struve in private discussions) of the sun and Jupiter. At a distance of 10 parsecs and in the orbital plane of the system, how accurate must our measurements be in order to detect the existence of Jupiter by observing the sun? Table 1 shows the necessary accuracy that is re-

Table 1

Precision of Measurements for Detecting the Existence of Jupiter in a
Hypothetical Sun-Jupiter System at a Distance of Ten Parsecs

Means of detection	Requirement
Astrometric	To measure an angular deviation of $0''.0005$
Spectroscopic	To measure a radial velocity correct to 0.01 km/sec
Photometric	To measure a change in luminosity of $0^m.01$

quired in different ways of detection. The present accuracy in both astrometric and spectroscopic observation falls far below that required. The photometric means of detection appears to be within the feasibility of present techniques. On the other hand, the eclipse lasts only about a day in about every 12 years, even if observed in the orbital plane. A few minutes of arc away from the orbital plane no eclipse would be observed. Therefore a systematic search by photometric means is not practicable. However, planets of Jupiter's size could be *accidentally* discovered by photometric observations. Of course, a planet of Jupiter's size falling within the orbit of Mercury has a much better chance of detection spectroscopically.

The Problem of the Existence of Planets

If we cannot detect directly any planets outside of our solar system, can we find some indirect evidence that would suggest their existence? The answer is yes. We have three indirect arguments for believing that formation of planets around stars is a common phenomenon.

First, we know that there is no sharp distinction between binary or multiple stars and planetary systems. According to Kuiper, the mean value of the separation of the components in all binaries that have been investigated is about 20 A.U. and is thus of the same order as the distance of the major planets from the sun (3). Also, from the astrometric study of small perturbations of the binary 61 Cygni, Strand found $0.01m_\odot$ for the mass of the unseen faint companion (4). This value lies between stellar masses and the mass of Jupiter. Therefore it is reasonable to believe that from the masses of the fainter components of binary stars to those of planets there exists a continuous range without any sharp demarcation. Since binaries are so numerous in the galaxy, comprising more than half of the stellar population, we would naturally expect that planetary systems are not rare.

Next we have Urey's results, derived from studies of the structure and composition of meteorites (5). According to him, a certain type of meteorite must have undergone in its past history a stage of high pressure that can only have existed in a body the size of the moon. He has, moreover, developed from this result a model for the origin of the solar system. We have called these moon-like objects "pre-stellar nuclei" and regarded them as an important stage in the formation of both stars and planets (6). If so, the formation of planets will usually accompany the emergence of a star from a medium that has in it a great number of pre-stellar nuclei.

Finally let us consider the angular momentum of stars. It was first pointed out by Struve that rapid axial rotation of the main sequence stars stops rather abruptly near spectral type F5 (7). In other words, the average angular momentum per unit mass of the main sequence stars suffers a conspicuous discontinuity at this point. Naturally one asks what has happened to the angular momentum of those single stars below F5 on the main sequence. A reasonable answer (or supposition) is that it is accounted for by the orbital motion of the unobservable planets that are revolving around the stars (6). In other words, planetary systems emerge as the axial rotation declines. According to this view, planets are formed around the main-sequence stars of spectral types later than F5. Thus, planets are formed just where life has the highest chance to flourish. Based on this view we can predict that nearly all single stars of the main sequence below F5 and perhaps above K5 have a fair chance of supporting life on their planets. Since they compose a few per cent of all stars, life should indeed be a common phenomenon in the universe.

Acknowledgment

I wish to express my thanks to Dr. Otto Struve for valuable discussions.

References

1   S.-S. Huang, *Am. Scientist*, **47**, 397 (1959).
2   O. Struve, *Observatory*, **72**, 199 (1952).
3   G. P. Kuiper, *Publ. Astron. Soc. Pacific*, **47**, 15, 121 (1935).
4   K. A. Strand, *Astron. J.*, **61**, 319 (1956).
5   H. C. Urey, *Astrophys. J.*, **124**, 623 (1956).
6   S.-S. Huang, *Publ. Astron. Soc. Pacific*, **69**, 427 (1957).
7   O. Struve, *Astrophys. J.*, **72**, 1 (1930); *Stellar Evolution*, Princeton University Press, Princeton, N.J., 1950, Chap. 2.

Su-Shu Huang

8 ✻ LIFE-SUPPORTING REGIONS IN THE VICINITY OF BINARY SYSTEMS

In two previous papers we have discussed the requirements that a star should fulfill in order to be able to support life of a high form in its neighborhood (*1*). We have concluded that in general there should be a smaller chance of finding a life-supporting* planet in binary systems than near single stars. We have further stated, although qualitatively, that if a life-supporting planet does exist in a binary system at all, it must be an interior planet in the case of a distant binary and an exterior planet in the case of a close binary. In this paper we shall make a quantitative study of the previous statement.

Habitable Zone of a Binary System

Let us consider a point at distances r_1 and r_2 from the primary and secondary, respectively, of a binary system. The total energy received per unit area at this point from both stars depends of course upon the orientation of the receiving surface. As an approximation, however, we can neglect the effect of orientation and write the energy received per unit area per second as

$$\epsilon = \frac{l_1}{4\pi r_1{}^2} + \frac{l_2}{4\pi r_2{}^2} \tag{1}$$

where l_1 and l_2 are the luminosities of the primary and secondary stars, respectively. If we express ϵ in terms of the amount of energy received

* By the term "life-supporting" we merely mean capable of supporting life, not necessarily having it at the present time.

per unit time per unit area by a surface facing the sun and located at the mean distance of the earth from the sun, Eq. (1) can be written as $\epsilon = l_1/r_1^2 - l_2/r_2^2$, or

$$\frac{1}{(r_1/a)^2} + \frac{l_2}{l_1}\frac{1}{(r_2/a)^2} = C \tag{2}$$

where

$$C = \frac{a^2\epsilon}{l_1} \tag{3}$$

The luminosities are now expressed in solar units, and the distances and the separation of the two components (a) in astronomical units. The quantity ϵ is obviously a factor controlling the feasibility of biological evolution. With the unit we have chosen, life cannot develop at any place where ϵ is several orders of magnitude different from unity. A more definite estimate of the range of ϵ over which life is tolerated can be obtained from a study of its values in the solar system as given in Table 1, from which we estimate that the upper limit ϵ_1 is of the order of 5.0, and that the lower limit ϵ_2 is of the order of 0.1. Thus, in order to find life we must have

$$\epsilon_1 > \epsilon > \epsilon_2 \tag{4}$$

Once we have the two limits of ϵ, the thermally habitable zone of a binary system can be derived from (2) which, for a definite value of l_2/l_1, defines a series of surfaces of constant C (called the iso-C surfaces). These surfaces have cylindrical symmetry. Therefore any section in a plane through the axis suffices to show the shape of the surfaces. Fig-

Table 1

Values of ϵ for Different Planets

Planet	ϵ
Mercury	6.68
Venus	1.913
Earth	1.000
Mars	0.433
Jupiter	0.037
Saturn	0.011

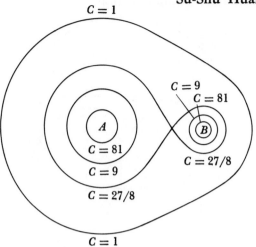

Figure 1

The iso-C surfaces for $l_2/l_1 = 0.125$. A unit area anywhere on each of these surfaces will receive roughly the same amount of energy per unit time from the two stars represented by A and B.

ure 1 illustrates sections of several of these surfaces for $l_2/l_1 = 0.125$. When the separation a and luminosity l are given, the thermally habitable zone of the system is the space bounded by the two surfaces defined by

$$C = C_1 = \frac{a^2 \epsilon_1}{l_1} \quad \text{and} \quad C = C_2 = \frac{a^2 \epsilon_2}{l_1}$$

Dynamical Stability of the Orbit of a Third Body in a Binary System

The problem of finding periodic orbits of a small body moving in the gravitational field of two large bodies and studying their stability has taxed the energy of several great mathematicians. The most important result derived lies in the so-called restricted three-body problem, in which the two large masses revolve around their center of mass in circular orbits (2). In the framework of the restricted three-body problem, we can find two critical surfaces for each binary system—the inner contact surface and the outermost contact surface (3). For simplicity, we

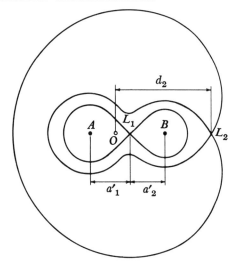

Figure 2

The critical surfaces in the restricted three-body problem. In the diagram A and B represent two large bodies and O is their center of mass. The inner contact surface which passes through L_1 limits the periodic orbits of the interior planets, while the exterior periodic orbits of physical interest are expected to lie outside the outermost contact surface, which passes through L_2. The points $A, O, L_1, B,$ and L_2 all lie on the same line.

consider only the intersection of these two critical surfaces with the equatorial plane of the two large masses (shown in Figure 2) and study the orbits of the third body, assumed to have infinitesimal mass, only in this plane. We may then expect stable orbits of the third body to lie either inside the inner contact surface (for interior planets) or outside the outermost contact surface (for exterior planets). This does not mean that there is no other stable periodic orbit. In fact, several orbits have already been found that do not fall into the two previous categories. For example, there are the famous triangular solutions of Lagrange. However, these require some special initial conditions or some limited values for the mass ratio of the two large bodies. Hence they are probably not of interest for our present problem. Indeed, when a binary system is formed from a whirling mass of gas and dust, we can easily visualize the formation of planets moving in nearly circular orbits either closely around each component or around both components at large distances. That planets may be formed around each component in spite of perturbations by the other component can be seen from the fact that gaseous rings are frequently observed to be revolving around the more massive component of even close binaries (4).

We know that stable orbits inside the inner contact surface are easy to obtain from the existence of satellites in the solar system. Also, it is obvious that the nearer to either one of the two components an interior planet lies, the more stable is its orbit. However, the critical size of the largest stable orbits within the inner contact surface over a time of, say, 3×10^9 years, is difficult to compute. But we can study this problem in a semi-empirical manner. Consider the motion of a satellite in any sun-planet system as a restricted three-body problem. The corresponding inner and outermost contact surfaces can be computed from the mass ratio of the sun and the planet (2, 3). Thus, we list in Table 2 the radius of the orbit of the outermost satellite in each system and the distance a_2' between the Lagrangian point L_1 (see Figure 2) and the planet, in terms of the separation between the sun and the respective planet. Since a_2' measures the size of the secondary lobe of the inner contact surface, we can see immediately how far a satellite can be away from the planet inside the inner contact surface and still remain in a stable orbit. It appears from Table 2 that $a_2'/2$ is the limit, because no satellite has been found whose orbit has a semi-major axis greater than this value. Returning to the problem of planets in a binary system, we would therefore expect that the radii of

Table 2

The Radius R of the Orbit of the Outermost Satellite and the Size a_2' of the Inner Contact Surface, Expressed in Terms of the Separation of the Parent Planet from the Sun

Satellite system	R	a_2'
Earth	2.565×10^{-3}	9.97×10^{-3}
Mars	1.031×10^{-4}	4.75×10^{-3}
Jupiter	3.043×10^{-2}	6.67×10^{-2}
Saturn	9.07×10^{-3}	4.50×10^{-2}
Uranus	2.04×10^{-4}	2.42×10^{-2}
Neptune	7.86×10^{-5}	2.56×10^{-2}

stable orbits of interior planets around the primary and secondary components would be smaller than $a_1'/2$ and $a_2'/2$, respectively.

If the distance of the point L_2 from the center of mass of the system is d_2 (see Figure 2), an exterior planet must have an orbit of radius greater than d_2 in order to be outside of the outermost contact surface. Here it is interesting to note that d_2 varies only slightly—and moreover not monotonically—with the mass ratio, ranging from 1.0 to 1.27 times the separation of the two components (3). Thus d_2 may not be as good a criterion for the size of stable exterior orbits as are a_1' and a_2' for interior orbits, because we would expect a monotonic dependence of the size of the smallest stable exterior orbit on the mass ratio. If we consider Saturn as the third body in the sun-Jupiter system, the orbit of Saturn, which is $1.8d_2$ away from the sun, is already stable. However, with a larger mass for the secondary component we may not expect to find stable periodic orbits at such a distance. Indeed, nearly all of the known triple systems are composed of one close pair and a third more distant companion. Moreover, the case of exterior orbits also applies to very close binaries in which each component is greatly distorted by the gravitational attraction of the other. Under these conditions the perturbations on the third body are much more complicated than those produced by two point masses. Consequently we will take $10d_2$ as the minimum size of an exterior orbit for a third body in a close binary system. This value is of course subject to further investigation.

Life-Supporting Ability of a Binary System in Terms of the Separation between the Components

Let us consider first an interior planet. According to the previous considerations, a life-supporting planet must have an orbit within $a_1'/2$ of the primary and $a_2'/2$ of the secondary. On the other hand it cannot be too near the star because it would then be too hot to lie within the thermally habitable zone. These two conditions impose a lower limit for the separation of binaries that can support life on their interior planets. From (3) and (4) this condition can be written as

$$a > \left(\frac{C_i l_1}{\epsilon_1}\right)^{1/2} \quad \text{A.U.} \tag{5}$$

where C_i is the maximum value of C for the largest stable orbit inside the inner contact surface. Physically this inequality gives the condition for the overlapping of the thermally habitable zone and the dy-

Table 3

Values of C_i and C_e

m_1/m_2	C_i		C_e
1	P:	17.78	0.01669
	S:	17.78	
1.25	P:	15.34	0.00933
	S:	8.54	
2.5	P:	11.42	0.00783
	S:	2.19	

namically stable zone in a binary system. Actually, a should be much larger than this value before the overlapping space reaches an appreciable size. Only when a reaches the value

$$\left(\frac{C_i l_1}{\epsilon_2}\right)^{1/2} \quad \text{A.U.} \tag{6}$$

has the binary component a life-supporting space as large as if it were a single star.

Adopting a mass-luminosity relation $l \propto m^4$, we have computed the values of C_i for three mass ratios, on the assumption that the largest stable orbit for an interior planet is at most as far away from its central star as $a_j'/2$ ($j = 1, 2$ for the two components). The results are given in Table 3, where the values of C_i are listed both for orbits around the primary (P) and around the secondary (S).

Next let us consider exterior planets. Dynamically these must always be more than a certain distance from the center of mass of the system. But from considerations of the thermally habitable zone they cannot be too far away. Hence from (3) and (4) we obtain the necessary condition

$$a < \left(\frac{C_e l_1}{\epsilon_2}\right)^{1/2} \quad \text{A.U.} \tag{7}$$

where C_e is the minimum value of C that the smallest stable orbit of an exterior planet assumes. When a decreases from this limit, the overlapping space of the thermally habitable zone and the dynamically stable zone increases until a reaches the limit

$$\left(\frac{C_e d_1}{\epsilon_1}\right)^{1/2} \quad \text{A.U.} \tag{8}$$

after which the overlapping space remains at its maximum value. Assuming the smallest orbit to be at elast $10d_2$ away from the center of mass at any time, we give in Table 3 the values of C_e, for three mass ratios.

As a numerical example we find from (5) and Table 3 that for $m_1 = m_2$ a life-supporting space begins to exist inside the inner contact surface when a is equal to $2l_1^{1/2}$ A.U. It increases until a reaches $13l_1^{1/2}$ A.U., after which, according to (6), the binary nature of the stars does not affect the size of the life-supporting space around them. This condition is not stringent: Many visual and several spectroscopic binaries have separations greater than this limit. In other words, many binaries have as good a chance to support life as do single stars. However, we should emphasize that this is true only for distant binaries having nearly circular orbits. The situation is not so favorable if the binary has a highly eccentric orbit.

In the case of close binaries, we apply the criterion given by (7). For the case $m_1 = m_2$, life-supporting planets could begin to exist when a is less than $0.4l_1^{1/2}$ A.U. The overlapping space reaches its maximum value when $a < 0.06l_1^{1/2}$ A.U. Consequently very close binaries like W Ursae Majoris systems could have habitable planets revolving around the entire system. But any binary of $m_1 = m_2$ with a separation between $0.4l_1^{1/2}$ A.U. and $2l_1^{1/2}$ A.U. has no chance of possessing habitable planets. Also, the chance is smaller than for a corresponding single star if the separation is between $0.06l_1^{1/2}$ A.U. and $13l_1^{1/2}$ A.U. For other mass ratios, the forbidden range is different but can be computed in a similar manner.

The probable number of habitable planets in binary systems depends to a large extent on the mode of formation of binary systems. Are the formation of binary systems and the formation of planetary systems mutually exclusive processes, or can they occur simultaneously? Unfortunately we cannot answer this question at the present time.

Finally let us consider our nearest neighbor in space—the α Centuri triple system. The relative orbit of the two more massive components has a semi-major axis of 23.4 A.U. and an eccentricity of 0.52. Therefore the separation is large enough to allow habitable planets inside the inner contact surface. But the orbit is too eccentric to justify the direct application of the previous analysis. In a recent investigation we have suspected that the system may be in an evolutionary stage before the main sequence (5). If so, it would be too young to develop life of a high form on its planets even if the system possesses life-supporting planets.

References

1 S.-S. Huang, *Am. Scientist,* 47, 397 (1959); *Publ. Astron. Soc. Pacific,* 71, 421 (1959).

2 F. R. Moulton, *An Introduction to Celestial Mechanics,* Macmillan, New York, 1914, Chap. 8; for recent references see P. J. Message, *Astron.* 64, 226 (1959). For an elementary discussion see O. Struve and S.-S. Huang, *Occasional Notes Roy. Astron. Soc.,* 3, 161 (1957).

3 G. P. Kuiper, *Astrophys. J.,* 93, 133 (1941); Z. Kopal, *Jodrell Bank Ann.,* 1, 37 (1954); G. P. Kuiper and J. R. Johnson, *Astrophys. J.,* 123, 90 (1956).

4 A. H. Joy, *Publ. Astron. Soc. Pacific,* 54, 35 (1947); O. Struve, *Stellar Evolution,* Princeton University Press, Princeton, N.J., 1950.

5 S.-S. Huang, to be published.

Su-Shu Huang

9 ✳ THE SIZES
OF HABITABLE PLANETS

In order to obtain some idea of the sizes of habitable planets, it is necessary first to examine the conditions under which life may emerge. Authorities generally agree that coacervates in the aqueous solution represent the earliest stage of evolution of organic substances into living organisms (1). Therefore a habitable planet must have a solid crust and be able to hold water gravitationally. Indeed, the existence of living organisms without the support of some substances in the liquid form is quite inconceivable.

Since stars and planets are formed out of the interstellar medium, it is likely that in the early stages of evolution a planet (or more properly a proto-planet) will have a high percentage of hydrogen, especially in its outer envelope (2). Life may first appear under reducing conditions (1), but an atmosphere composed mainly of hydrogen does not favor the development of a high form of life. Thus, the hydrogen atmosphere must first be at least partially dissipated (3). The present atmosphere of the earth is actually a secondary one, formed as a result of chemical processes that took place subsequent to the formation of the planet (4). We therefore impose the condition that for a planet to be habitable, the hydrogen atmosphere must be lost completely or partially in a time short compared with that of stellar evolution. For the stars most likely to support life in their vicinity, the evolution time is of the order of 10^9 to 10^{11} years (5). With this range of values we can derive an upper limit for the total mass of a habitable planet because a very massive planet (Jupiter, for example) will retain its hydrogen atmosphere too long (3). On the other hand, for life of an advanced form to arise, the secondary atmosphere must not be lost before living organisms have evolved. The time scale of biological

102

evolution on the earth is of the order of 3×10^9 years. This condition gives us a lower limit to the mass of a habitable planet.

We would like to emphasize that in discussing the dissipation of a hydrogen atmosphere we do not mean such a large loss of mass by a planet (or proto-planet) as to change drastically its relative chemical composition. Indeed, Shklovskiy has demonstrated conclusively that such a change is not possible (6). On the other hand, hydrogen must be a dominant ingredient in the upper layers of a planet in its early stages because of its high cosmic abundance and lightness.

Jeans has derived the rate of mass loss of planetary atmospheres by computing the number of molecules that cross a unit area of a sphere in an outward direction per unit time and that have a speed greater than the escape velocity (7). He gives also the time t_1 for the complete dissipation of the atmosphere. Since he assumes a constant rate of dissipation, the time for the loss of one-half of the atmosphere is simply $t_1/2$. Several more-refined calculations for the escape rate have since been made, but these do not lead to any significant difference from Jeans' original formula (8).

If we denote the radius and mean density of a planet by a and ρ, and the rms molecular velocity by c, we have

$$t_1 = \frac{4.35}{4\pi G\rho} \frac{c^3}{a(c^2 + 4\pi G\rho a^2)} \exp\left(\frac{4\pi G\rho a^2}{c^2}\right) \qquad (1)$$

In order to see clearly the physical implication of this formula we introduce the two parameters

$$\tau_0 = (4\pi G\rho)^{-1/2} \qquad \text{and} \qquad \tau_1 = a/c \qquad (2)$$

By writing

$$x = \tau_1/\tau_0 \qquad (3)$$

Eq. (1) is reduced to the following dimensionless form:

$$\frac{t_1}{\tau_0} = \frac{4.35}{x(1 + x^2)} e^{x^2} \qquad (4)$$

Assuming t_1 to be 3×10^9 and 6×10^9 years, respectively, we have determined x for the values of τ_0 corresponding to three values of ρ. The results are given in Table 1. It is significant that the value of x derived from Eq. (4) does not change greatly with either t_1 or ρ. The time that a star of spectral type F, G, or K stays on the main sequence varies from 10^9 to 10^{11} years. In order to have life on any planet associated with these stars, t_1 must be within this range. The corresponding values of x range only between 5.8 and 6.4. Consequently, for all

Table 1

Values of x

ρ, g/cm^3	τ_0, sec	x, $t_1 = 3 \times 10^9$ yr	x, $t_1 = 6 \times 10^9$ yr
3.5	5.838 × 10^2	6.056	6.116
4.5	5.149 × 10^2	6.067	6.126
5.5	4.658 × 10^2	6.076	6.135

practical purposes x may be regarded as constant. Physically, this means that whether a planet retains an atmosphere or not depends not so much on its age as on its radius and mean density.

The upper limit of the radius of a habitable planet is therefore

$$a = c\tau_0 x \qquad (5)$$

where c represents the velocity of molecular or atomic hydrogen. As just stated, x can be regarded as constant. Also τ_0 varies rather little since it is inversely proportional to the square root of the mean density, and the mean density does not vary greatly from one solid celestial body to another. For example, in the case of the planets in the solar system the mean density lies between 0.7 and 5.5. Actually we have reason to believe that hydrogen may be dissipated during the early stage of evolution of a planet when the mean density is lower than its final value. Even so, we would not expect this to cause a change in the order of magnitude of τ_0. Consequently the upper limit of a is determined mainly by c, which is the thermal velocity in the outermost layer of the atmosphere (the "exosphere" as it is sometimes called), and which is difficult to estimate, especially in the early stages of planetary evolution. However, we can assume a range of reasonable temperatures in order to compute the upper limit of a. The results are given in Table 2, where the velocity of molecular hydrogen has been used. If atomic hydrogen dominates, the limits of a in Table 2 should be increased by a factor of 1.4.

We can calculate the lower limits of the radii in a similar way. If we impose the condition that oxygen must not be completely lost in 3×10^9 or 6×10^9 years, the lower limit of a is given again by Eq. (5) except that c is now the velocity of oxygen, either molecules or atoms, depending on the physical conditions in the exosphere. Since the thermal velocity of oxygen molecules is only one-fourth that of hy-

Table 2

Greatest Radii of Habitable Planets

T, °K	c, km/sec	Radii, 10³ km		
		$\rho = 3.5$	$\rho = 4.5$	$\rho = 5.5$
173	1.47	5.2	4.6	4.2
273	1.84	6.5	5.8	5.2
373	2.15	7.6	6.7	6.1
573	2.66	9.4	8.3	7.5
1000	3.51	12.4	11.0	9.9
2000	4.96	17.5	15.5	14.0

drogen molecules, the lower limits of *a* are one-fourth of the values previously derived.

We may also write Eq. (5) in the following form:

$$a = \left(\frac{3kT}{4\pi G \rho m}\right)^{1/2} x \qquad (6)$$

where *m* is the mass of the molecules concerned. Since *x* is nearly constant, both the upper and lower limits of *a* are directly proportional to $(T/\rho)^{1/2}$.

We may conclude tentatively that a habitable planet most likely will have a radius lying between 1000 and 20,000 km. This is a generous estimate as this range includes the moon and Mercury, both of which are known to be uninhabitable. Dr. A. Poveda has recently suggested that the rate of biological evolution on a planet may increase with its surface area if other conditions are equal. If so, our earth has not only a favorable position in the solar system but also a favorable size for developing living organisms.

Finally we should emphasize that the escape of a planetary atmosphere is a very complicated process. One should not think that the principles just discussed can be applied to the escape of hydrogen from the earth at the present time, because hydrogen is no longer free in the earth's atmosphere. The rate of escape of hydrogen at present is actually determined by the rate of diffusion of hydrogen-containing molecules (such as H_2O) from the lower to the upper atmosphere, and the efficiency of dissociation of these molecules in the upper atmosphere (*3*). Fortunately for our present purpose we do not have to consider this kind of problem because we regard any atmosphere like that on the earth as already exhausted of free hydrogen.

Acknowledgments

I am indebted to Drs. J. E. Kupperian, Jr., and B. Donn for valuable discussions and to Dr. A. Poveda for permitting me to quote his idea concerning the rate of biological evolution.

References

1 A. I. Oparin, *The Origin of Life on the Earth,* Academic, New York, 1957.
2 H. C. Urey, *The Planets,* Yale University Press, New Haven, Conn., 1952.
3 H. C. Urey, in S. Flugge (ed.), *Handbuch der Physik,* Springer, Berlin, 1959, Vol. 52, p. 363.
4 H. Brown, in G. P. Kuiper (ed.), *The Atmospheres of the Earth and Planets,* University of Chicago Press, Chicago, 1952, Chap. 9.
5 S.-S. Huang, *Am. Scientist,* **47,** 397 (1959); *Publ. Astron. Soc. Pacific,* **71,** 421 (1959).
6 I. S. Shklovskiy, *Dokl. Akad. Nauk USSR,* **76,** 193 (1951); *Astron. J. USSR,* **29,** 225 (1952).
7 J. H. Jeans, *The Dynamical Theory of Gases,* Cambridge University Press, New York, 1925, Chap. 15.
8 L. Spitzer, Jr., in G. P. Kuiper (ed.), *The Atmospheres of the Earth and Planets,* University of Chicago Press, Chicago, 1952, Chap. 7.

A. G. W. *Cameron*

I0 ✳ STELLAR LIFE ZONES

In his article "Occurrence of Life in the Universe" (Chapter 6), Su-Shu Huang has opened discussion on the very interesting question of determining the probability that planets can be found within a suitable distance interval that their temperatures can support life. We shall call such a distance interval the life zone of a star. In his article, Huang makes the basic assumption that the probability of finding a planet in any position near a star is proportional either to the element of area on the orbital plane, or to the element of volume in space. These assumptions are consistent with what we might term "the principle of least knowledge."

It is the purpose of this note to point out that Huang's assumptions are not valid for the solar system. Hence we should seek another assumption that is consistent with what we know about the solar system, since that is the only system available from which observations can be generalized.

Table 1 contains the relevant data with which we must work. In the table are given the distances of the planets from the sun and of the satellites from certain of the planets with large satellite systems. Satellites with very irregular orbits have not been included. The final column of the table contains a rough calculation of the fractional distance within which any one planet or satellite can be said to be dominant. This has been computed by defining the boundary of a planet's or satellite's influence as the geometric mean of the distances of the planet or satellite and of its closest neighbors, both inwards and outwards. If Δr is the distance between these boundaries, and r is the distance of the planet or satellite, then $\Delta r/r$ is the fractional distance of dominance.

It may be seen from Table 1 that $\Delta r/r$ is subject to some variation. This must depend in a complicated way upon the masses of the primary, of the secondary under consideration, and of the neighbors

Table 1

The Intervals of Radial Distance Associated with Planets and Satellites

Primary	Secondary	Distance[a]	$\Delta r/r$
Sun	Venus	0.723	0.443
Sun	Earth	1.000	0.390
Sun	Mars	1.524	0.538
Sun	Ceres	2.767	0.628
Sun	Jupiter	5.203	0.625
Sun	Saturn	9.539	0.915
Sun	Uranus	19.19	0.778
Jupiter	Io	5.905	0.606
Jupiter	Europa	9.401	0.470
Jupiter	Ganymede	14.995	0.534
Saturn	Enceladus	3.99	0.231
Saturn	Tethys	4.94	0.235
Saturn	Dione	6.33	0.300
Saturn	Rhea	8.84	0.672
Saturn	Titan	20.48	0.445
Saturn	Hyperion	24.82	0.643
Uranus	Umbriel	10.2	0.440
Uranus	Titania	16.8	0.375

[a] Measured in astronomical units for the planets and in radii of the primary planet for the satellites.

of the secondary. Nevertheless the variations are not very large. For the purposes of the present discussion it is sufficient to say that $\Delta r/r$ is approximately 0.5 for the planets in the solar system and also for three of the regular satellite systems. The implication is that the fractional distances of domination represent the regions from which material could be gathered together to form planets or satellites, or from which it would in general be ejected by perturbations in 4.5 billion years (with the obvious exception of Ceres).

The above statement can be made more definite and also generalized by stating as a hypothesis that about any star with planets the number of planets between radial distances r_1 and r_2 is

$$N = 2 \ln (r_2/r_1) \tag{1}$$

We now wish to find how many planets exist in stellar life zones. In the case of a life zone, r_1 is the distance from a star at which a planet is just cool enough to support life, and r_2 is the distance at which it is just hot enough to support life. These distances probably have some dependence on the size of the planet (if the planet can support life under any circumstances), but we shall not try to allow for such second-order effects.

The temperature of a rapidly rotating black body in space is

$$T = \left(\frac{L}{16\pi\sigma r^2}\right)^{1/4} \tag{2}$$

where σ is the radiation constant, L is the stellar luminosity, and r is the orbital radius of the body. Hence from Eqs. (1) and (2) we note that the number of planets between black-body temperatures T_1 and T_2 is

$$N = 4 \ln (T_1/T_2) \tag{3}$$

The great importance of Eq. (3) lies in the fact that T_1 and T_2 are fixed temperatures defining the limits between which life can be supported. The stellar luminosity does not appear in this equation. Hence we find that every stellar life zone contains on the average the same number of planets, independent of the class of star involved (but excluding binary stars). We have not said that the planets have masses suitable for the support of life. I suspect that the planetary masses are quite variable, even for a given class of star.

Let us now attempt to determine the number of planets in a stellar life zone. Again we shall argue on the basis of relations within the solar system.

The planet Venus has been found from studies of its radio emission to have a surface temperature of about 600°K, more than 200°K above its expected black-body temperature. The high surface temperature may be due to a greenhouse effect in the atmosphere and depend on the rather large mass of the atmosphere of the planet. The details are not understood. If there were no greenhouse effect it is probable that the temperature would be suitable for the support of life, at least on some parts of the planet. However, owing to the high surface temperature actually existing, let us exclude Venus from the solar life zone and estimate $r_1 = 0.8$ astronomical units.

One of the greatest challenges to space exploration is to determine whether Mars has developed and supports life. The conditions there appear to be somewhat severe but not extremely so. They might be less severe if Mars had a greater mass. But Mars must be near the outer boundary of the solar life zone, and hence let us estimate $r_2 = 1.6$ astronomical units. Hence, from Eq. (1), $N = 1.4$.

There is one restrictive condition that must be investigated before the above conclusion can be fully generalized. We must check to find out whether the region containing the stellar life zone was ever inside the parent star during the contraction phase of that star. Such a condition would presumably have prevented planets from forming in the life zone.

According to the discussion in Chapter 3, the largest radius ever possessed by a star is that at which the ionization of hydrogen and helium has just been completed throughout most of its volume. Dilhan Ezer and I have recently found this radius to be 57 times the present radius for the sun, or 0.266 astronomical units. It may be seen that this has probably prevented the formation of another planet inside the orbit of Mercury (0.387 astronomical units).

This maximum stellar radius varies in direct proportion to the mass of a star. We see from Eq. (2) that the radius r_1 of the inner boundary of the life zone varies as the square root of the stellar luminosity. Hence this boundary must approach the maximum stellar radius as the mass and associated luminosity of a star decrease (the luminosity varies about as the fourth power of the mass for stars near the sun).

However, the inner boundary of the life zone is still about 1.4 times the maximum stellar radius for faint red dwarf stars of class M5. Mass and luminosity data are very unreliable for still smaller stars, but it appears likely that stellar life zones will not start disappearing until the very late M dwarf stars with mass around 10 per cent of that of the sun.

Hence we reach the final conclusion that all single stars in space (except those with very low heavy-element contents) have a life zone containing an average of about 1.4 planets of undetermined size.

Huang suggested that the best probability for finding life in a stellar system within 5 parsecs would be in the ϵ Eridani and τ Ceti systems. But there are about 26 other single stars of smaller mass within this distance, each of which should have a comparable probability of having a life-supporting planet according to the present analysis.

Freeman J. Dyson

I I ❊ SEARCH FOR ARTIFICIAL STELLAR SOURCES OF INFRARED RADIATION

Cocconi and Morrison (*1*) have called attention to the importance and feasibility of listening for radio signals transmitted by extraterrestrial intelligent beings. They propose that listening aerials be directed toward nearby stars which might be accompanied by planets carrying such beings. Their proposal is now being implemented (*2*).

The purpose of this report is to point out other possibilities which ought to be considered in planning any serious search for evidence of extraterrestrial intelligent beings. We start from the notion that the time scale for industrial and technical development of these beings is likely to be very short in comparison with the time scale of stellar evolution. It is therefore overwhelmingly probable that any such beings observed by us will have been in existence for millions of years, and will have already reached a technological level surpassing ours by many orders of magnitude. It is then a reasonable working hypothesis that their habitat will have been expanded to the limits set by Malthusian principles.

We have no direct knowledge of the material conditions which these beings would encounter in their search for lebensraum. We therefore consider what would be the likely course of events if these beings had originated in a solar system identical with ours. Taking our own solar system as the model, we shall reach at least a possible picture of what may be expected to happen elsewhere. I do not argue that this is what *will* happen in our system; I only say that this is what *may have* happened in other systems.

The material factors which ultimately limit the expansion of a technically advanced species are the supply of matter and the supply of energy. At present the material resources being exploited by the human species are roughly limited to the biosphere of the earth, a mass of the order of 5×10^{19} grams. Our present energy supply may be generously estimated at 10^{20} ergs/sec. The quantities of matter and energy which might conceivably become accessible to us within the solar system are 2×10^{30} g (the mass of Jupiter) and 4×10^{33} ergs/sec (the total energy output of the sun).

The reader may well ask in what sense can anyone speak of the mass of Jupiter or the total radiation from the sun as being accessible to exploitation. The following argument is intended to show that an exploitation of this magnitude is not absurd. First of all, the time required for an expansion of population and industry by a factor of 10^{12} is quite short, say 3000 years if an average growth rate of 1 per cent per year is maintained. Second, the energy required to disassemble and rearrange a planet of the size of Jupiter is about 10^{44} ergs, equal to the energy radiated by the sun in 800 years. Third, the mass of Jupiter, if distributed in a spherical shell revolving around the sun at twice the earth's distance from it, would have a thickness such that the mass is 200 g/cm² of surface area (2 to 3 m, depending on the density). A shell of this thickness could be made comfortably habitable, and could contain all the machinery required for exploiting the solar radiation falling onto it from the inside.

It is remarkable that the time scale of industrial expansion, the mass of Jupiter, the energy output of the sun, and the thickness of a habitable biosphere all have consistent orders of magnitude. It seems, then, a reasonable expectation that, barring accidents, Malthusian pressures will ultimately drive an intelligent species to adopt some such efficient exploitation of its available resources. One should expect that, within a few thousand years of its entering the stage of industrial development, any intelligent species should be found occupying an artificial biosphere which completely surrounds its parent star.

If the foregoing argument is accepted, then the search for extraterrestrial intelligent beings should not be confined to the neighborhood of visible stars. The most likely habitat for such beings would be a dark object, having a size comparable with the earth's orbit, and a surface temperature of 200° to 300°K. Such a dark object would be radiating as copiously as the star which is hidden inside it, but the radiation would be in the far infrared, around 10 microns wavelength.

It happens that the earth's atmosphere is transparent to radiation with wavelength in the range from 8 to 12 microns. It is therefore feasible to search for "infrared stars" in this range of wavelengths, using existing telescopes on the earth's surface. Radiation in this range from Mars and Venus has not only been detected but has been spectroscopically analyzed in some detail (3).

I propose, then, that a search for point sources of infrared radiation be attempted, either independently or in conjunction with the search for artificial radio emissions. A scan of the entire sky for objects down to the 5th or 6th magnitude would be desirable, but is probably beyond the capability of existing techniques of detection. If an undirected scan is impossible, it would be worthwhile as a preliminary measure to look for anomalously intense radiation in the 10-μ range associated with visible stars. Such radiation might be seen in the neighborhood of a visible star under either of two conditions. A race of intelligent beings might be unable to exploit fully the energy radiated by their star because of an insufficiency of accessible matter, or they might live in an artificial biosphere surrounding one star of a multiple system, in which one or more component stars are unsuitable for exploitation and would still be visible to us. It is impossible to guess the probability that either of these circumstances would arise for a particular race of extraterrestrial intelligent beings. But it is reasonable to begin the search for infrared radiation of artificial origin by looking in the direction of nearby visible stars, and especially in the direction of stars which are known to be binaries with invisible companions.

References

1   G. Cocconi and P. Morrison, *Nature,* **184,** 844 (1959).
2   *Science,* **131,** 1303 (1960).
3   W. M. Sinton and J. Strong, *Astrophys. J.,* **131,** 459, 470 (1960).

Addendum

In *Science,* **132,** 250 (1960) appeared three letters commenting on the above article. John Maddox, Washington, D.C., pointed out that the shell surrounding Dyson's biosphere could not be rigid and self-supporting against shear and other forces acting on it. Poul Anderson, Orinda, California, suggested that an advanced society would either approach its Malthusian limit too rapidly to permit the energy resources to be spent on a major scheme of cosmic engineering, or else an enforced scheme of population control would be likely to limit the population at a level far short of that envisioned by Dyson. Finally, Eugene A. Sloane, Detroit, Michigan, suggested that if an advanced civilization of the capability assumed by Dyson existed, it would be scarcely conceivable that they should not have detected us. F. J. Dyson responded as follows:

In reply to Maddox, Anderson, and Sloane, I would like only to add the following points which were omitted from my earlier communication.

1. A solid shell or ring surrounding a star is mechanically impossible. The form of "biosphere" which I envisaged consists of a loose collection or swarm of objects traveling on independent orbits around the star. The size and shape of the individual objects would be chosen to suit the convenience of the inhabitants. I did not indulge in speculations concerning the constructional details of the biosphere, since the expected emission of infrared radiation is independent of such details.

2. It is a question of taste whether one believes that a stabilization of population and industry is more likely to occur close to the Malthusian limit or far below that limit. My personal belief is that only a rigid "police state" would be likely to stabilize itself far below the Malthusian limit. I consider that an open society would be likely to expand by a proliferation of "city-states" each pursuing an independent orbit in space. Such an expansion need not be planned or dictatorially imposed; unless it were forcibly stopped it would result in the gradual emergence of an artificial biosphere of the kind I have suggested. This argument is admittedly anthropomorphic, and I present it in full knowledge that the concepts of "police state" and "open society" are probably meaningless outside our own species.

3. The discovery of an intense point source of infrared radiation would not by itself imply that extraterrestrial intelligence had been found. On the contrary, one of the strongest reasons for conducting a search for such sources is that many new types of natural astronomical objects might be discovered.

Freeman J. Dyson

I2 ❋ GRAVITATIONAL MACHINES

The difficulty in building machines to harness the energy of the gravitational field is entirely one of scale. Gravitational forces between objects of a size that we can manipulate are so absurdly weak that they can scarcely be measured, let alone exploited. To yield a useful output of energy, any gravitational machine must be built on a scale that is literally astronomical. It is nevertheless worthwhile to think about gravitational machines, for two reasons. First, if our species continues to expand its population and its technology at an exponential rate, there may come a time in the remote future when engineering on an astronomical scale will be both feasible and necessary. Second, if we are searching for signs of technologically advanced life already existing elsewhere in the universe, it is useful to consider what kinds of observable phenomena a really advanced technology might be capable of producing.

The following simple device illustrates the principle that would make possible a useful gravitational machine (see Figure 1). A double star has two components A and B, each of mass M, revolving around each other in a circular orbit of radius R. The velocity of each star is

$$V = (GM/4R)^{1/2} \tag{1}$$

where

$$G = 6.7 \times 10^{-8}\, \text{cm}^3/\text{sec}^2\text{g} \tag{2}$$

is the gravitational constant. The exploiters of the device are living on a planet or vehicle P which circles around the double star at a distance much greater than R. They propel a small mass C into an orbit which falls toward the double star, starting from P with a small velocity. The orbit of C is computed in such a way that it makes a close approach to B at a time when B is moving in a direction opposite to the direction of arrival of C. The mass C then swings around B and escapes with greatly increased velocity. The effect is almost as

115

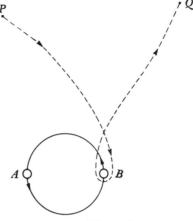

Figure 1

The solid line indicates the orbit of A and B; the dashed line indicates the orbit of C.

if the light mass C had made an elastic collision with the moving heavy mass B. The mass C will arrive at a distant point Q with velocity somewhat greater than $2V$. At Q the mass C may be intercepted and its kinetic energy converted into useful form. Alternatively the device may be used as a propulsion system, in which case C merely proceeds with velocity $2V$ to its destination. The destination might be a similar device situated very far away, which brings C to rest by the same mechanism working in reverse.

It is easy to imagine this device converted into a continuously operating machine by arranging a whole ring of starting points P and end points Q around the double star, masses C being dropped inward and emerging outward with increased velocity in a continuous stream. The energy source of the machine is the gravitational potential between the stars A and B. As the machine continues to operate, the stars A and B will gradually be drawn closer together, their negative potential energy will increase, and their orbital velocity V will also increase. The machine will continue to extract energy from their mutual attraction until they come so close together that orbits passing between them are impossible. For a rough estimate one may suppose that the machine can operate until the distance between the centers of the two stars is equal to $4a$, where a is the radius of each star. The total energy extracted by the machine from the gravitational field is then

$$E = GM^2/8a \tag{3}$$

If A and B are ordinary stars like the sun, the radius a is of the order of 10^{11} cm. The energy E is then equal to the luminous energy radiated by the stars in a few million years. Under these conditions the available gravitational energy may be exploited, but it is of minor importance compared with the luminous energy of the system. A technically advanced species would presumably put its main efforts into harnessing the luminous energy.

If the stars A and B are typical white dwarfs, the situation is entirely reversed. In that case the optical luminosity is less than that of the sun by a factor of about a thousand, while the available gravitational energy is increased by a factor of a hundred. It is therefore logical to expect that around a white-dwarf binary star a technology based on gravitational energy might flourish. For purposes of illustration, let us assume

$$M = 1 \text{ solar mass} = 2 \times 10^{33} \text{ g} \tag{4}$$

$$a = 10^9 \text{ cm} \tag{5}$$

$$R = 2a = 2 \times 10^9 \text{ cm} \tag{6}$$

Then we find

$$V = 1.3 \times 10^8 \text{ cm/sec} \tag{7}$$

$$E = \quad 3 \times 10^{49} \text{ ergs} \tag{8}$$

The orbital period of the binary star is

$$P = 100 \text{ sec} \tag{9}$$

A search for eclipsing binaries of such short period among the known white dwarfs was suggested many years ago by H. N. Russell (1). The search was subsequently made by F. Lenouvel (2), with negative results. The negative result is not surprising, since the total number of identified white dwarfs is very small.

A white-dwarf binary star with the parameters (4) to (9) would have the interesting property that it could accelerate delicate and fragile objects to a velocity of 2000 km/sec at an acceleration of 10,-000g, without doing any damage to the objects and without expending any rocket propellant. The only internal forces acting on the accelerated objects would be tidal stresses produced by the gradients of the gravitational fields. If the over-all diameter of the object is d, the maximum tidal acceleration will be of the order of

$$A = GMd/a^3 = \tfrac{1}{8}d \qquad (10)$$

For example, if A is taken to be 1 earth gravity, then $d = 80$ m. So a large space ship with human passengers and normal mechanical construction could easily survive the 10,000g acceleration. It may be imagined that a highly developed technological species might use white-dwarf binaries scattered around the galaxy as relay stations for heavy long-distance freight transportation.

An important side effect of a short-period white-dwarf binary would be its enormous output of gravitational radiation. According to the standard theory of gravitational radiation (3), which is not universally accepted, a pair of stars of equal mass moving in a circular orbit radiates gravitational energy at a rate

$$W = 128V^{10}/5Gc^5 \qquad (11)$$

where c is the velocity of light. It would be extremely valuable if we could observe this radiation, both to verify the validity of the theoretical formula (11) and to detect the existence of white-dwarf binaries. Inserting the value of V from (7) into (11), we find

$$W = 2 \times 10^{37} \text{ ergs/sec} \qquad (12)$$

which is 5000 times the sun's optical luminosity. Comparing (12) with (8), we see that the gravitational radiation itself will limit the lifetime of this white-dwarf binary to about 40,000 years. However, since the dependence of W on V is so extreme, a binary with $V = 5 \times 10^7$ cm/sec could live for many millions of years. A technologically advanced species might then choose the value of V to suit its particular purposes.

Assuming the value (12) for the intensity of a source of gravitational waves at a distance of 100 parsecs, we find that the signal to be detected on earth has the intensity

$$I = 2 \times 10^{-5} \text{ erg/cm}^2/\text{sec} \qquad (13)$$

Unfortunately the period of the radiation is 100 sec, which is not short enough to be observed with the existing apparatus of J. Weber (4). However, it is quite likely that a detector could be built which would be sensitive to the incident flux (13) at a period of 100 sec. This would then allow us to detect by its gravitational radiation any white-dwarf binary of period 100 sec within a volume of space containing over half a million stars (5).

According to astrophysical theory (6), a white dwarf is not the most condensed type of star that is possible. A still more condensed form of matter could exist in "neutron stars," which would have masses of the same order as the sun compressed into radii of the order of 10 km. Whether neutron stars actually exist is uncertain; they would be very faint objects, and the fact that none has yet been observed does not argue strongly against their existence.

If a close binary system should ever be formed from a pair of neutron stars, the consequences would be very interesting indeed. Consider for example a pair of stars of solar mass, each having radius

$$a = 10^6 \text{ cm} \tag{14}$$

and with their centers separated by a distance $2R = 4a$. According to (1) and (11), each star moves with velocity

$$V = 4 \times 10^9 \text{ cm/sec} \tag{15}$$

in an orbit with period 5 msec, and the output of gravitational radiation is

$$W = 2 \times 10^{52} \text{ ergs/sec} \tag{16}$$

But by (3), the gravitational energy of the pair is at this moment

$$E = 3 \times 10^{52} \text{ ergs} \tag{17}$$

Thus the whole of the gravitational energy is radiated away in a violent pulse of radiation lasting less than 2 sec. A neutron-star binary beginning at a greater separation R will have a longer lifetime, but the final end will be the same. According to (11), the loss of energy by gravitational radiation will bring the two stars closer with ever-increasing speed, until in the last second of their lives they plunge together and release a gravitational flash at a frequency of about 200 cycles and of unimaginable intensity.

A pulse of gravitational radiation of magnitude (17) at a frequency around 200 cycles should be detectable with Weber's existing equipment (4) at a distance of the order of 100 Mparsecs. So the death cry of a binary neutron star could be heard on earth, if it happened once in 10 million galaxies. It would seem worthwhile to maintain a watch for events of this kind, using Weber's equipment or some suitable modification of it.

Clearly the immense loss of energy by gravitational radiation is an obstacle to the efficient use of neutron stars as gravitational machines. It may be that this sets a natural limit of about 10^8 cm/sec to the velocities that can be handled conveniently in a gravitational technology. However, it would be surprising if a technologically advanced species could not find a way to design a nonradiating gravitational machine, and so to exploit the much higher velocities which neutron stars in principle make possible.

In conclusion, it may be said that the dynamics of stellar systems, under conditions in which gravitational radiation is important, is a greatly neglected field of study. In any search for evidences of technologically advanced societies in the universe, an investigation of anomalously intense sources of gravitational radiation ought to be included.

References

1 H. N. Russell, Centennial Symposia, *Harvard Monographs,* **7,** 187 (1948).

2 F. Lenouvel, *J. Observateurs,* **40,** 15 (1957).

3 L. Landau and E. Lifshitz, *Classical Theory of Fields,* trans. by M. Hamermesh, Addison-Wesley, Reading, Mass., 1951, p. 332.

4 J. Weber, *Phys. Rev.,* **117,** 306 (1960).

5 R. P. Kraft, J. Matthews, and J. L. Greenstein have discussed the extremely interesting object Nova WZ Sagittae, a binary star with one white-dwarf component and an observed orbital velocity of about 7×10^7 cm/sec. They point out that gravitational radiation from this object is certainly important and may be detectable. The author is indebted to Dr. Kraft for a preprint of this work.

6 J. R. Oppenheimer and G. M. Volkoff, *Phys. Rev.,* **55,** 374 (1939); A. G. W. Cameron, *Astrophys. J.,* **130,** 884 (1959).

Edward Purcell

I3 ✳ RADIOASTRONOMY
AND COMMUNICATION
THROUGH SPACE

It is a great privilege for me to open the series of Brookhaven Lectures. The principles on which these are conceived I heartily endorse, but I am just about to violate them by giving a talk which is really not, for the most part, a description of my own work. Indeed some of it will not be a description of any one's work, but instead some speculations about the future. In a way, you might regard this talk as a logical sequel to Dr. DuBridge's Pegram Lectures (*1*) of a year ago. It has three parts whose relation to one another will not be obvious until the end. The first part, at least, has to do with solid scientific matter, radioastronomy. Without revealing now the nature or motive of the last two parts, I would like to describe one branch of radioastronomy and what has come out of it in the last several years. I have not been active in this field myself in recent years, but I have been watching it develop.

Radioastronomy

Until 15 or 20 years ago, all man's information about the external world beyond the earth came to him in a small band of wavelengths of visible light. Everything the astronomers saw, all the images on their photographic plates, were collected by absorbing light within a range of wavelengths varying by no more than a factor of two from the shortest to the longest waves. It was the discovery, about two decades ago, that there were also radio waves coming through which started off radioastronomy.

These two great apertures, or windows, as they are often called,

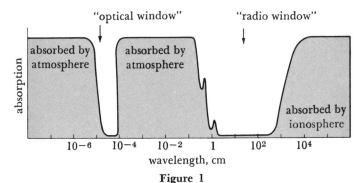

Figure 1

Absorption spectrum of the earth's atmosphere versus wavelength.

may be seen in Figure 1, which shows the absorption spectrum of the atmosphere of the earth on a scale of wavelengths, running from very short wavelengths in the ultraviolet region, through the visible, up into the range of radio wavelengths. Over nearly all of that range with two exceptions either the atmosphere, or the ionosphere just beyond it, absorbs 100 per cent of incoming radiation. It is only in these two regions of the spectrum that our atmosphere will let anything come through. The radio "window" extends from a few centimeters to several meters wavelength. Electromagnetic waves in this band from any celestial source can reach our antennas on the earth. The branches of radioastronomy are many because radiation comes to us from all sorts of objects. A great deal of radio energy comes from the sun; radio waves come from stars and various odd astronomical objects. I shall discuss only one branch of radioastronomy, the study of the structure of the galaxy, that is, our Milky Way, by means of radio waves. My purpose in talking about it is to show how much information one can derive, from enormous distances, with little energy.

To begin with, let us place ourselves in the universe in the usual way by taking a look at a galaxy (Figure 2). No talk like this is complete without a picture of a spiral nebula. This is one of the most beautiful and, furthermore, is one which is probably rather like the galaxy in which we live. Of course it is not the one in which we live, or we could not have taken this picture. This is a large flat cluster of about 100 billion stars seen more or less on a slant. Observe its irregular shape with rather ill-defined arms spiraling off; it is a spiral nebula. There are hundreds and thousands of galaxies of this type.

Figure 2

Spiral nebula.

We happen to inhabit one of them. The one we inhabit is perhaps an ordinary one, but of course it is of special interest to us, and we would like to know what it looks like. It is very hard to find out because we cannot see it from the outside. Let me describe our galaxy by showing what it might look like in cross section, if we could examine a slice taken right down through the disk (Figure 3).

There are about 10^{11} stars in an object of this sort; the sun is one of these and happens to be out rather near the edge, about 25,000 light-years from the center. The thickness of this disk is only some 700 light-years on this scale. In addition to the stars, the galaxy has in it dust (small grains of matter) and hydrogen atoms. It has hydrogen atoms to the tune of about one per cubic centimeter through most of the spaces where there are no stars. In saying this I am getting ahead of my story, but it will make the story easier to follow. The stars make up most of the mass, but the hydrogen atoms are a nonnegligible part; they make up perhaps $\frac{1}{3}$ or $\frac{1}{4}$ of the mass of this whole assembly. The

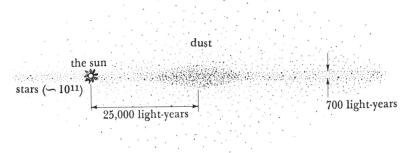

Figure 3

The galaxy, seen edge on.

dust in itself doesn't amount to much—except as a nuisance; the dust makes this large collection of stars almost opaque to visible light. A telescope situated at the position of the sun or the earth can see only a little way into the galaxy, in most directions, because before long the path of vision is interrupted by a cloud of dust. One cannot see anything like the *whole* structure looking out with a telescope, or with the eye. Indeed if one could, the Milky Way, which is what we do see of the galaxy, from our vantage point, would present a very different spectacle. It would be a very narrow, very bright band, absolutely straight, going across the sky like a great circle. We are buried within this pancake, out near the edge, able to see with a telescope only part of the pancake in our vicinity. For this reason, until a tool became available to explore the greater depths of the system, one had rather little idea of the details of its structure. The dust grains, being very small, do not hinder the passage of radio waves at all. A 1-m-wavelength radio wave oozes around a tiny dust grain without the slightest trouble and goes on as if nothing were there. Thus the pancake is, by and large, completely transparent to radio waves, and, if there is a source of them, one can see that source no matter how far away it may be in the disk of stars and gas.

There is a radio wave that is emitted by the gas itself, and I will briefly describe this source before telling what it leads to (Figure 4). The hydrogen atom, which consists of an electron and a proton, happens to have in its structure a natural frequency which is in the precession frequency: 1,420,405,750 cycles/sec

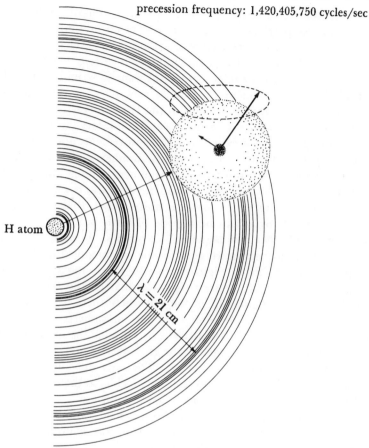

H atom

$\lambda = 21$ cm

Figure 4

The hydrogen atom emits radio waves.

radio range. The frequency is 1420 Mc/sec, corresponding to a wave-length of 21 cm. This frequency arises from the magnetic interaction between the electron and the proton. The cloud in Figure 4 represents the electron, and the arrow represents the axis about which the electron spins. The proton spins around an axis, too. Because of the spin each particle acts like a bar magnet. The two little magnets try to set them-selves parallel, but because they are spinning they don't achieve it. Instead, they precess around like gyroscopes. When the hydrogen atom is all by itself out in free space, with no perturbations or anything, and is in its lowest possible energy state, the electron spin axis quietly precesses around with a frequency of 1,420,405,750 cycles/sec.

I confess that the fact that this number is so long has no bearing whatever on the present subject, but I did want to write it out to show what kind of measurements are made nowadays in the branch of physics which measures these atoms in the laboratory. It is the branch carried on in Dr. Cohen's atomic beam laboratory at Brookhaven. This number is an actual experimental measurement, not a theoretical number like π, and not a social security number, which it rather resembles. There is, at present, some argument among the fraternity about the last one or two digits. But there is also a recent development in atomic beams which makes it quite certain that within a year or two even more digits will be known. This is probably one of the most accurately known numbers in all of physics. As we shall see, that doesn't really do us very much good in the astronomical problem, but it does some good. From Figure 1, which shows the radio window in the spectrum, it may be seen that, fortunately, the wavelength of 21 cm falls right in the middle of the gap where there is practically no absorption in either the atmosphere or the ionosphere. Furthermore, the atom which emits this frequency is by all odds the most abundant atom in the universe. Hydrogen in the ground state makes up probably 65 per cent of the gas in the galaxy. The only difficulty is that the emission from any one atom is exceedingly feeble, so that we just about need that much hydrogen in order to get a result.

Nowadays, there is wide activity in this field. Many observatories are studying the emission that comes in from the hydrogen atoms in the galaxy. This is done with a standard kind of radio telescope. Figure 5 shows a radio telescope at the National Radio Astronomy Observatory in Green Bank, West Virginia, which is a small sister institution to Brookhaven, being run by AUI. This is the 85 ft radio telescope which is used for both hydrogen studies and other observations and is doing very beautiful work in the hands of the group there. In the old days we did this type of work more on a shoestring basis, and, for old times' sake, I have a photograph (Figure 6) showing the first antenna at Harvard for the 21-cm radiation, with Harold Ewen, who did the work. This antenna, a simple horn, was fashioned by our carpenter and installed on the roof at a total cost of about $400.00. The electronics was all scrounged and no price was ever computed for it. The principle of this kind of astronomy is really very simple; Figure 7 shows it stripped of all irrelevant details. One has a radio receiver and a large antenna. The antenna is large simply so that one can

Figure 5
Radio telescope.

collect more energy or look at a particular spot in the sky. It feeds into a rather conventional receiver, where the radio energy is amplified and, finally, recorded on something to show its intensity. Of course, it isn't music; it's just noise. One records the average energy coming in

Figure 6

First radio telescope antenna at Harvard.

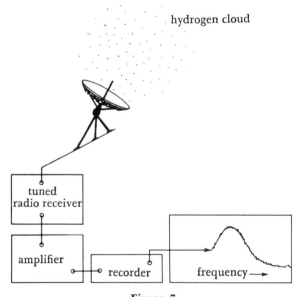

Figure 7

21-cm astronomy.

on a given wavelength band. The recorder cranks out some paper and the pen traces a graph showing that at a particular frequency there was reception of energy. That is really all there is to it, except for the electronics, which calls for some elegance of design if one is to make the most of the very feeble signal. We needn't go into that at all.

If we look at the radiation that does come in from a hydrogen cloud or a cencentration of hydrogen that was in the Milky Way, this is what we might see (Figure 8). Indeed this is what we do see in one particular direction. If one were looking at hydrogen in the laboratory, a frequency scan would give a single narrow line, the dotted peak in the figure, at the precise frequency I wrote down earlier. Instead of that, looking out into the galaxy, one sees quite a broad affair which often has a structure such as the three-humped curve I have drawn. The reason is very simple. It is the old business of the Doppler effect. The hydrogen which is emitting this "light" is not at rest with respect to us. It may, as a whole, be moving and streaming. We know that astronomical objects are commonly in motion. If the hydrogen cloud is coming toward us, the line will come in at a somewhat higher frequency, and if it is going away, at lower frequency, than if it were stationary with respect to our antenna. In this case we know, and I will try to explain in a minute how we know, that the three humps are emissions from hydrogen located at three different places; at these different places the hydrogen is moving with different speeds. And that is about all one can say; something can be inferred about the temperature and density of the hydrogen, but we needn't go into that.

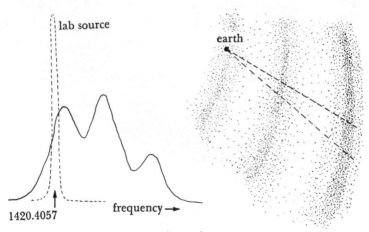

Figure 8
A hydrogen line from the galaxy.

Despite its limitations, the astronomers, notably the Dutch astronomers Oort and Van de Hulst at Leiden, found how to exploit this kind of information. Van de Hulst, incidentally, was the first one to recognize the possibility of detecting the galactic hydrogen emission. Oort and Van de Hulst discovered a way to extract, from records like Figure 8, by a kind of indirect argument, the actual *location* of the hydrogen along the line of sight. Remember, this is not like radar. We are not sending out a wave and getting it back; there is no "echo time" to tell us how far away the stuff is. We are just sitting here receiving, and the only thing we can tell directly is how fast the source is moving toward or away from us. To deduce the location of the source we need to know something else about the galaxy.

Imagine this disk is the galaxy (Figure 9). This is just a cloud of stars, and we know that it is not stationary; it is rotating. Astronomers knew that from their observations of the motion of stars. But it is not rotating like a phonograph record, all as one piece, because the stars are not rigidly connected to one another. Rather, it is rotating

Figure 9

Model of the galaxy showing locations of concentrations of hydrogen gas.

much more the way the planets revolve around the sun: The outer planets are moving relatively slowly, the inner planets, closer to the central mass, are moving with higher velocity. In fact, one can think of the galaxy as a sort of planetary system. It has no single, dominant body at its center, but it does have a general concentration of mass in the central portion of the disk. The rotational velocity must vary with distance from the center in a way that we can easily predict once we know how the mass is distributed. We begin by adopting a radial mass distribution—a galactic model—that is reasonable in the light of other astronomical evidence. For this distribution we work out the required speed of revolution for material at any given distance from the galactic center—the modified "Kepler's law" for the system.

If one looks out now in a certain direction and sees a source with a certain velocity, one can pin it to a certain position on the line of sight. Of course this involves the assumption about the radial distribution of mass. But one can work backward, and continue until the whole picture is consistent with itself. This is what has been done by the radioastronomers in both Holland and Australia, who have gradually built up a map of the hydrogen gas in the galaxy.

Figure 9 is a model * of the galaxy which shows the locations of the concentrations of hydrogen gas. The chart (Figure 10) is one that was made and published by Westerhout in Leiden, who has been one of the leaders in this exploration. Westerhout, for reasons that we needn't go into here, left out the central part. There is a tremendous amount of hydrogen in the middle but not much is known about it. In making the model we fudged it back in, adding the patches in the center. Of course these bear no relation, in detail, to what is really there. The arms, however, are real. The left half of this picture is the product of the radioastronomers in Sydney, Australia. They have a view of that half of the galaxy from the southern hemisphere. The right half is the product of the group in Leiden under Oort, Van de Hulst, and Westerhout. There is no doubt whatever that this is a spiral nebula. In fact, we can even locate ourselves in one of the arms. It is also evident that this is still a self-centered view of the galaxy; there is no reason for the near half to look so different from the far half except that we happen to have a better view of the former.

There are other things to be learned which I will point out now on the model. This is a scale model. It is probably the biggest scale that anybody has used around here: 1 inch = 300 light-years. It is to scale also in thickness. The $\frac{1}{4}$-inch thickness of the Plexiglas truly

* Made with the help of John Garfield and his staff in the Technical Photography and Graphic Arts Division.

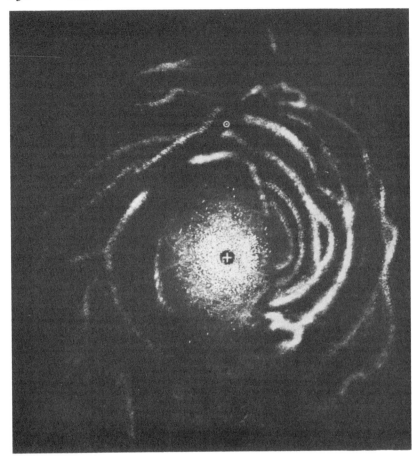

Figure 10
Westerhout's map of the galaxy.

represents the relative thickness of the pancake of stars. And the flatness is also true. In fact, it hardly does justice to the galaxy. On this
scale, the median surface of the hydrogen distribution is flat, over most
of the galactic disk, to 1/32 inch, a fact which came as a surprise to
astronomers. No one knows how a distribution of matter which is so
irregular in plan view can contrive to be so precisely flat. The fact
must have some deep significance for galactic dynamics. Actually, there
are interesting systematic departures from flatness near the edge. We
went to some trouble to bend the edges of our model to represent the

"snap brim" effect, as it has been called. The median surface, as observed by hydrogen emission, appears to turn up a little at one place, and down at the opposite part of the rim.

It is a pity that one cannot say for sure which way the spiral arms go. It is surprising to learn from astronomers that this question was not settled long ago. The naive assumption that because spiral nebulae look like pinwheels they must be moving like pinwheels is hard to defend without a convincing theory of galactic evolution. As for direct observation of another spiral nebula, Doppler shift of spectral lines reveals which side is approaching us, but there is no easy way to tell which edge is *nearer* to us, so the tantalizing ambiguity remains. I believe majority opinion favors the pinwheel sense. Further refinement of the hydrogen map of our own galaxy—where we *know* the absolute sense of rotation—may eventually settle the question beyond doubt.

This is what has been learned from this one branch of radioastronomy, and the point that I would like to make before I turn to the second part of my talk is that this has been learned by receiving a rather astonishingly small amount of energy, energy which has traveled a very long way to us. The total amount of power that comes to the earth in hydrogen radiation from everywhere in the universe, that is, the power falling on the entire earth, is about *1 watt*. The radioastronomers at Leiden, Harvard, Sidney, Greenbank, and elsewhere have been picking up a tiny fraction of that with their antennas. A more astonishing figure is one that I had to compute three times before I was sure of my arithmetic: The total *energy* received by *all* 21-cm observatories over the past nine years, is less that 1 erg! From less than 1 erg of energy we have built this picture of our galaxy. Most of you know what an erg is—you can't knock the ash off your cigarette with an erg. That point I want you to remember. It is germane to the thesis which I shall try to establish in the last two parts of this talk, which depart from sober science and go in other directions.

Space Travel

In the second part I shall talk briefly about space travel, and I want to say very distinctly that I am not going to argue the case, pro or con, for travel around the solar system—visiting the moon and Mars and so on. We shall look at wider horizons, as all the astronautical types do, and talk about travel *beyond* the solar system. A lot has been written about this. You are probably as tired of hearing about it as I am, but I hope that if we look at it in one particular way, it may present a fresh aspect. Of course, everything is very far away. The stars are very far away. The nearest star, Alpha Centauri, is 4 light-years distant. People have worried about this but they blandly say, "That's all right because we will travel at nearly the speed of light. Even without relativity we will get there fast and with relativity we will get there and be young anyway." That is perfectly correct, in my view, so far as it goes. Special relativity is reliable. The trouble is not, as we say, with the *kinematics* but with the *energetics*. I would like to develop that briefly, with a particular example. Figure 11 defines my example. Let us consider taking a trip to a place 12 light-years away, and back. Because we don't want to take many generations to do it, let us arbitrarily say we will go and come back in 28 years earth time. We will reach a top speed of 99 per cent speed of light in the middle, and slow down and come back. The relativistic transformations show that we will come back in 28 years, only 10 years older. This I really believe. It would take 24 years for light to go out and come back; it takes the traveler 28 years as seen by the man on earth but the traveler is only 10 years older when he gets back. I don't want to stop and argue the "twin paradox" here because if one *does not* accept its implications then the conclusion that I am going to draw becomes even *stronger*. Personally,

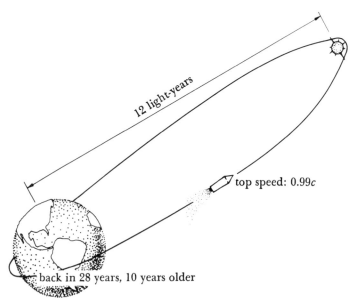

Figure 11
Trip to a place 12 light-years away.

I believe in special relativity. If it were not reliable, some expensive machines around here would be in very deep trouble.

Now let us look at the problem of designing a rocket to perform this mission. Let us begin with a reminder of what a rocket is (Figure 12). It is a device that has some propellant which it burns and throws out the back. The mechanical reaction accelerates the rocket. When the propellant is all gone, the rocket has reached its final speed and only the payload remains. That is the *best* one can do—carrying along extra hardware only makes it worse. Staging of rockets, i.e., the use of four or five successively smaller stages, is merely a way of trying to *approach* this ideal. The performance of a rocket depends almost entirely on the velocity with which the propellant is exhausted, V_{ex}, as I have called it, ex for exhaust. The rocket people talk about specific impulse, but the impulse they talk about really has the dimensions of a velocity. Let us look at the role this velocity plays in rocket propulsion (Figure 12). Here is the rocket with its V_{ex} and we want to get it up to some final speed V_{max}. Then the elementary laws of mechanics— in this case relativistic mechanics, but still the elementary laws of mechanics—inexorably impose a certain relation between the initial mass and final mass of the rocket in the *ideal* case. This relation, shown in Figure 13, is relativistically exact. It follows very simply from conservation of momentum and energy, the mass-energy relation, and *nothing else*. In other words, the only thing that could possibly be wrong with this equation is that I made a mistake in deriving it. That is always possible, but I don't think I did. It checks all right at the limits.

Figure 12
Rocket.

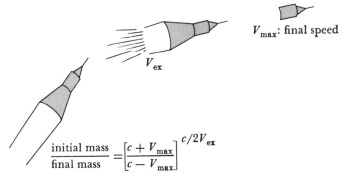

V_{max}: final speed

V_{ex}

$$\frac{\text{initial mass}}{\text{final mass}} = \left[\frac{c + V_{max}}{c - V_{max}}\right]^{c/2V_{ex}}$$

Figure 13

Relation between the initial mass and the final mass of a rocket in the ideal case.

You can plainly see the disadvantage of low exhaust velocity. If we demand a final speed V_{max} very near the velocity of light, this denominator is going to get awfully small, and the exponent will get large. This is not peculiar to the relativistic domain but occurs in ordinary rocketry, too, wherever the final speed required greatly exceeds the exhaust velocity—as it unfortunately does in the case of earth satellites launched with chemically fueled rockets.

For our vehicle we shall clearly want a propellant with a *very* high exhaust velocity. Putting all practical questions aside, I propose, in my first design, to use the *ideal nuclear fusion* propellant (Figure 14). I am going to burn hydrogen to helium with 100 per cent efficiency; by means unspecified I shall throw the helium out the back with kinetic energy, as seen from the rocket, equivalent to the entire

With perfect *nuclear fusion* propellant:

$$4H \rightarrow He \qquad V_{ex} \approx \tfrac{1}{8}c$$

If V_{max} is to be 0.99 c,

$$\frac{\text{initial mass}}{\text{final mass}} = 1.6 \times 10^9$$

Figure 14

With perfect *antimatter* propellant:

$$V_{ex} \approx c$$

For $V_{max} = 0.99\ c$,

$$\frac{\text{initial mass}}{\text{final mass}} = 14$$

But to stop, return home, and stop,

$$\frac{\text{initial mass}}{\text{final mass}} = (14)^4 = 40{,}000$$

Figure 15

mass change. You can't beat that, with fusion. One can easily work out the exhaust velocity: it is about $\frac{1}{8}$ the velocity of light. The equation of Figure 13 tells us that to attain a speed $0.99c$ we need an initial mass which is a little over a *billion* times the final mass. To put up a ton we have to start off with a million tons; there is no way to beat this if we can't find a better reaction.

There simply *are* no better fusion reactions in nature, except one. This is no place for timidity, so let us take the ultimate step and switch to the perfect matter-antimatter propellant (Figure 15). Matter and anti-matter annihilate; the resulting energy leaves our rocket with an exhaust velocity of c or thereabouts. This makes the situation very much better. To go up to 99 per cent the velocity of light only a ratio of 14 is needed between the initial mass and the final mass. But remember, that isn't enough; we have only reached V_{max} and our mission is only one-quarter accomplished, so to speak. We have to slow down to a stop, turn around, get up to speed again, come home, and stop. That does not make the ratio 4×14, that makes it 14^4, which is 40,000. So to take a 10-ton payload over the trip described in Figure 11 I see no way whatever to escape from the fact that at take-off we must have a 400,000-ton rocket, half matter and half antimatter.

Incidentally, there is one difficulty which I should have mentioned earlier, but at this stage it is comparatively trivial. If you are moving with 99 per cent the velocity of light through our galaxy, which contains one hydrogen atom per cubic centimeter even in the "empty spaces," each of these hydrogen atoms looks *to you* like a 6-billion-volt

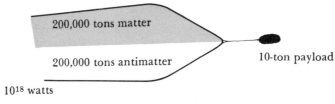

200,000 tons matter

200,000 tons antimatter

10-ton payload

10^{18} watts

Figure 16

proton, and they are coming at you with a current which is roughly equivalent to 300 cosmotrons per square meter. So you have a minor shielding problem to get over before you start working on the shielding problem connected with the rocket engine. That problem is quite formidable as you will see from Figure 16, which shows our final design. We have 200,000 tons of matter, 200,000 tons of antimatter, and a 10-ton payload, preferably pretty far out. The accelerations required are of the order of 1g over the whole trip, and not merely in leaving the earth. It just happens that g times 1 year is about equal to the speed of light, so if we want to reach the speed of light in times of the order of years, we are going to be involved in accelerations of the order of 1g. (This is the *one* respect in which relativistic astronautics is simple. No space-medical research is needed to assure us that we can stand 1g. We have been doing it all our lives.) In order to achieve the required acceleration our rocket, near the beginning of its journey, will have to radiate about 10^{18} watts. That is only a little more than the total power the earth receives from the sun. But this isn't sunshine, it's gamma rays. So the problem is not to shield the *payload,* the problem is to shield the *earth.*

Well, this is preposterous, you are saying. That is exactly my point. It *is* preposterous. And remember, our conclusions are forced on us by the elementary laws of mechanics. All those people who have been seriously talking about *lebensraum* in space, and so on, simply haven't stopped to make this calculation and until they do, what they say is nonsense—no matter how highly placed they may be or how big a budget they may control.

Communication through Space

Now I would like to turn to a quite different subject, one which is also speculative, but which involves an entirely different scale of magnitudes, the problem of communication through space. We have already

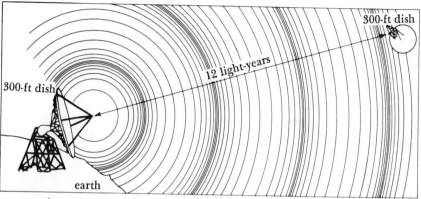

to transmit a 10-word telegram we have to radiate about $1 worth of electrical energy

Figure 17

seen how little energy was involved in the amount of information which revealed the structure of our galaxy. An example, in terms of practical communication of messages, is given in Figure 17. If I can transmit a message by point-to-point operation with a reasonably large antenna at each end, a 10-word telegram can be transmitted over the 12-light-year path discussed above with a dollar's worth of electrical energy. This is possible because we can detect, amplify, and identify in a radio circuit an amount of energy exceedingly small, and because the energy travels to us suffering no loss whatever except the "inverse square" diminution of intensity as it spreads.

Of course, the trouble is that there isn't anybody at the other end to communicate to. Or is there? What I would like to talk about now is not a new subject and I may not say anything new about it, but I have thought about it a good bit. It is the question of communicating with other people out there, if there are any.

Let us look at the galaxy again. There are some 10^{11} stars in the galaxy. *Double* stars are by no means uncommon, in fact there appear to be almost as many double stars as single stars. Astronomers take this as a hint that invisible companions in the form of planets may not be very uncommon either. Moreover, a large number of stars have lost their angular momentum and are not spinning. One good way for a star to lose its angular spin is by making planets; that is what probably happened in our own solar system. So the chance that there are hundreds of millions of planetary systems among these hundred billion stars seems pretty good. One can elaborate on this, but I am not going to try here to estimate the probability that a planet occurs at a suitable distance from a star, that it has an atmosphere in which life is possible, that life developed, and so on. Very soon in such a speculation the word probability loses operational meaning. On the other hand, one can scarcely escape the impression that it would be rather remarkable if only one planet in a billion, say, to speak only of our own galaxy, had become the home of intelligent life.

Since we can communicate so easily over such vast distances, it ought to be easy to establish communication with a society (let us use that word) in a remote spot. It would be even easier for them to initiate communication, if they were ahead of us. Shall we try to listen for such communications, or shall we broadcast a message and hope someone hears it? If you think about it a little, I think you will agree that we want to listen *before* we transmit. The time scale of the galaxy is very long. Wireless telegraphy is only 50 years old, and really sensitive receivers are much more recent. If we look for people who are able to receive our signals but have not surpassed us technologically, i.e., people who are not more than 20 years behind us but still not ahead, we are exploring a very thin slice of history. On the other hand, if we listen, we are looking for people who are *anywhere* ahead providing they happen to have the urge to send out signals. Also, being technologically advanced, they can transmit much better than we can. (For rather fundamental reasons, transmitting is harder than receiving in this game.)

So it would be silly to transmit before listening for a long time. This is an amusing game to play. I won't dwell on it long because you will have more fun trying it yourself, but let me suggest its nature. In the first place, it is essentially cryptography in reverse. Let me assume —this may not be true, but let me assume it—that there is somebody out there who is technologically ahead of us. He can transmit 10 Mw as easily as we can transmit a kilowatt, and he wants us to receive his signal. He surely knows more about us than we know about him, and moreover, he is a relatively close neighbor of ours in the galaxy. We share the same environment; he knows all about the hydrogen line— he learned it centuries ago. He knows that that line is the only prominent line in that window of the spectrum.

If you want to transmit to a fellow and you can't agree on a frequency, it's nearly hopeless. To search the entire radio spectrum for a feeble signal entails a vast, and calculable, waste of time. It is like trying to meet someone in New York when you have been unable to communicate and agree on a meeting place. Still, you know you want to meet him and he wants to meet you. Where do you end up? There are only two or three places: Grand Central Station, etc. Here, there is only one Grand Central Station, namely, the 1420-Mc line which is, by a factor of 1000 at least and probably more, the most prominent radio frequency in the whole galaxy. There is no question about where you transmit if you want the other fellow to hear, you pick out the frequency that he knows. Conversely, he will pick the frequency he knows we know, and that is the frequency to listen on. If you play this game carefully you will find the conclusion inescapable. We know what to do; we know where to listen. We don't know quite what his code will be but we know how to set up a computer program to search for various codes. Let us make some reasonable assumptions, for example, about power. Let us give the transmitter the capability of radiating a megawatt within a 1-cycle/sec band. This is something we could do next year if we had to; it is just a modest stretch of the present state of the art. Indeed, my information may be obsolete, there may be contracts out now calling for such performance. Suppose we receive with a 300-ft disk and he transmits with one as large. How we process the signals will affect the ultimate range, but, making very simple and conservative assumptions about that part of the problem, I find that we should be able to recognize his signal even if it comes from several hundred light-years away. With the new MASER receivers which have just begun to be used in radioastronomy, 500 light-years ought to be easy. A sphere only 100 light-years in radius contains about 400 stars of roughly the same brightness (± 1 stellar magnitude) as the sun. And remember, the volume accessible by communication goes up as the cube of the range. I have argued that it is ridiculously difficult to travel even a few light-years, and ridiculously easy to communicate over a few hundred. I think these numbers actually underestimate the disparity. But even so, the ratio of the volumes is 1 million (Figure 18).

There are other interesting questions. When we get a signal, how do we know it is real and not just some accident of cosmic static? This I like to call the problem of the axe head. An archeologist finds a lump of stone that looks vaguely like an axe head, down in about the right layer. How does he know it is an axe head and not an oddly shaped lump of stone? Actually, they are usually *very* sure. An arrowhead can look rather like an elliptical pebble, and still there is no doubt that it is an arrowhead. Our axe-head problem can be solved in many ways. The neatest suggestion I know of originated with Cocconi and Morrison (2), who have published a discussion of this whole subject. Morrison would have the sender transmit a few prime numbers. That's all you need: 1, 3, 5, 7, 11, 13, 17—by then you *know*. There

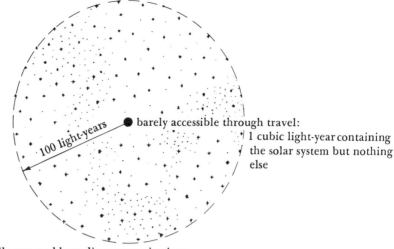

barely accessible through travel:
1 cubic light-year containing
the solar system but nothing
else

easily spanned by radio communication:
3 million cubic light-years containing 500 stars like the sun

Figure 18

are no magnetic storms or anything on Venus making prime numbers.

What can we talk about with our remote friends? We have a lot in common. We have mathematics in common, and physics, and astronomy. We have the galaxy in which we are near neighbors. The Milky Way looks about the same to them; 400 light-years is only $\frac{1}{8}$ inch on our model here. We have chemistry in common, inorganic chemistry, that is. Whether their organic chemistry has developed along the lines of ours is another question. So we can open our discourse from common ground before we move into the more exciting exploration of what is not common experience. Of course, the exchange, the conversation, has the peculiar feature of built-in delay. You get your answer back decades later. But you are sure to get it. It gives your children something to live for and look forward to. It is a conversation which is, in the deepest sense, utterly benign. No one can threaten anyone else with objects. We have seen what it takes to send *objects* around, but one can send information for practically nothing. Here one has the ultimate in philosophical discourse—all you can do is exchange ideas, but you do that to your heart's content.

I am not sure we are in a position to go about this yet. I am not advocating spending a lot of money setting up listening posts, although, as a matter of fact, a listening program on a very modest scale is going on at Green Bank under Frank Drake, who has some very imaginative and, I think, sound ideas on how it should be done. They haven't heard anything yet.

But in my view, this is too adult an activity for our society to engage in, on a large scale, at the present time. We haven't grown up to it. It is a project which has to be funded by the *century*, not by the fiscal year. Furthermore, it is a project which is very likely to fail *completely*. If you spend a lot of money and go around every 10 years and say, "We haven't heard anything yet," you can imagine how you make out before a congressional committee. But I think it is not too soon to have the fun of thinking about it, and I think it is a much less childish subject to think about than astronautical space travel. In my view, most of the projects of the space cadets are not really imaginative. And the notion that you have to *go* there seems to me childish. Suppose you took a child into an art museum and he wanted to *feel* the pictures —you would say, "That isn't what we do, we stand back and look at the pictures and try to understand them. We can learn more about them that way." All this stuff about traveling around the universe in space suits—except for *local* exploration, which I have not discussed— belongs back where it came from, on the cereal box.

References

1 A. DuBridge, *Introduction to Space,* Columbia University Press, New York, 1960.
2 G. Cocconi and P. Morrison, *Nature,* **184,** 844 (1959).

Sebastian von Hoerner

I4 ✳ THE GENERAL LIMITS
OF SPACE TRAVEL

The goal of this discussion is to find out whether interstellar space travel (travel from star to star) might become possible for us in the far future, and might therefore already be possible for other, more advanced beings. Is there any hope of making direct interstellar visits, or will all communication between civilizations be confined to electromagnetic signals? Certainly, from present estimates we cannot give a direct and conclusive answer of the yes-no type, but we can point out the significant basic facts and get as close to an answer as is possible at our present state of knowledge, leaving the final conclusion to the reader.

I shall begin by summarizing the present limitations and problems of space flight, trying to pin down the few basic points, and trying to separate the general difficulties from the merely temporary ones. From this starting point we may then proceed to estimate the possibilities of future space flight.

The prime postulate in these estimates is a technology much more highly advanced than our present one. Thus, we completely neglect all technical problems, however serious they actually might be. Only such fundamental properties as time, acceleration, power, mass, and energy are considered.

The results are given in terms of the minimum travel times deriving from various assumptions. Furthermore, we calculate some basic requirements for reaching these travel times.

Chemical Binding Energy

The only propelling mechanism actually used at present is acceleration of exhaust material by combustion, where the relatively low binding energy between atoms sets a limit in two ways: in the energy content of fuels, and in the heat resistance of combustion-chamber and nozzle materials.

In order to remove 1 kg of matter from the earth against gravity, we need an energy of 17.4 kwhr. But the best fuel burning hydrogen with oxygen yields only 3.2 kwhr/kg of fuel (explosives yield still less— for example, TNT yields 1.1 kwhr/kg). Thus we need 5.4 kg of fuel to remove 1 kg of matter, but the supply of fuel has to be accelerated, too, and this again requires much more fuel, and so on. Despite this difficulty of low-fuel-energy content, small payloads can still be removed, but with an extremely low efficiency.

The availability of more energetic fuels would not be of too much help. No nozzle material can stand temperatures above about 4000°C at the utmost limit. If a combustion gas of that temperature escapes through a nozzle, it will do so with an exhaust velocity of 4.0 km/sec if it is water vapor, and of less than that if substances other than hydrogen are burnt. But the rocket itself needs a velocity of 11.2 km/sec to leave the gravitational field of the earth, and far greater velocities if interstellar distances are to be covered within a reasonable time.

The velocity of a rocket after burnout of all its fuel, V, the exhaust velocity generated by the propellant, S, and the so-called mass ratio, $\mathfrak{M} = M_i/M_0$, are connected by the well-known rocket formula

$$\frac{V}{S} = \ln \mathfrak{M} \tag{1}$$

where M_i is the total initial mass of the rocket (including fuel) and M_0 is the mass after burnout—that is, M_i minus the mass of fuel. Now, the logarithm is a function which increases very slowly with its argument; even if fuel constitutes 90 per cent of the initial mass, the rocket velocity will be only 2.3 times the exhaust velocity. And if a one-stage rocket with fuel constituting 99.9 per cent of its initial mass could be built, even then we would achieve a velocity of only $V = 6.9S$. We cannot at present build such a rocket, but we do imitate it through multistage rockets. With these the difficulty remains the same, because the mass ratios of all stages accumulate in a multiplicative way (a tiny payload in the last stage, as compared to a huge fuel mass in the first stage), but the stage velocities accumulate only additively. Thus, with combustion-powered rockets, even of many stages, we are just able to leave the earth, but we cannot reach very high velocities.

In order to see this more precisely, we define the efficiency of a rocket, Q, as the useful energy- (the energy contained in the final velocity of the empty rocket) divided by the energy content of all fuel burnt. We then have

$$Q = \frac{(V/S)^2}{e^{V/S} - 1} \qquad (2)$$

This efficiency has its maximum value, $Q = 0.647$, at $V/S = 1.59$, but it drops off very fast and is only 1 per cent at $V/S = 9$. And in the case of many stages the efficiency gets still smaller by a large factor. The efficiency of an ideal multistage rocket is only 0.1 per cent for $V/S = 6$.

These difficulties connected with low binding energy are only temporary ones, because they are confined to combustion processes. In increasing the energy content of fuels we can make a huge step if we use atomic energy; the fission of uranium, for example, yields 20 million kwh/kg. And nozzles as well as high temperatures can be avoided completely when we learn to use ion thrust as a propelling mechanism (charged particles—ions—are accelerated by electrical fields to a high velocity, with which they leave the rocket). A 5000-volt acceleration, for example, could give S of the order of 100 km/sec. With this mechanism, S increases with the square root of the acceleration voltage.

In dealing with these difficulties we have discovered one fundamental principle:

> In order to avoid unreasonably low efficiencies, the exhaust velocity S should be about as large as the required final velocity of the rocket, V, or at least of the same order of magnitude. $\qquad (3)$

Power-Mass Ratio

As soon as these two difficulties have been overcome, by obtaining a high energy content in fuel and a high exhaust velocity, one will immediately encounter the next fundamental difficulty. The acceleration of a rocket, b, is of course given by

$$b = \frac{\text{thrust of engine}}{\text{total mass of rocket}} \qquad (4)$$

Now, the thrust equals the exhaust mass-flow (mass/sec) times the exhaust velocity S; and the needed power of the engine equals the mass-flow times one-half the square of the exhaust velocity. We thus can write [instead of Eq. (4)]:

$$b = 2P/S \qquad (5)$$

where P is the ratio of power of engine to total mass of rocket.

This means that, if we are working with a high exhaust velocity S, we need a high power-mass ratio P, as otherwise we would get only a small acceleration b.

But nuclear reactors and all the equipment needed to give a strong ion thrust are so complicated and massive, as compared with the relatively simple combustion equipment, that there is no hope at present of reaching, with reactors, the value of P already attained with combustion rockets. The acceleration thus will be extremely small until we can find a way to increase the power-mass ratio of a reactor by many orders of magnitude.

Distances for Interstellar Space Travel

The only goal which may be important enough to justify the immense effort needed for interstellar space travel appears to be the search for other intelligent beings. In a recent article (1) I tried to estimate the distances between neighboring technical civilizations in order to guide preparations and stimulate a search for possible electromagnetic signals. The points of interest for our present purpose may be summarized as follows:

1. It would be megalomania to think that we are the one intelligent civilization in the universe. On the contrary, we should assume from our present knowledge that life and intelligence will have developed, with about the same speed as on earth, wherever the proper surroundings and the needed time have been provided. From our present limited data, we judge that this might have been the case on planets of about 6 per cent of all stars. The nearest ten such stars are at an average distance from us of about 5.6 parsecs (1 parsec = 3.09×10^{13} km = 3.26 light-years).

2. It would be equally presumptuous to think that our present state of mind is the final goal of all evolution. On the contrary, we should assume that science and technology are just one link in a long chain and will be surpassed one day by completely new and unpredictable interests and activities (just as gods and demons unpredictably have been surpassed by science in offering explanations of many important phenomena). We should assume a finite longevity L of the

technical state of mind; if we call T the age of the oldest stars and D the average distance to the nearest ten technical civilizations, we get

$$D = 5.6 \text{ parsecs} \left(\frac{T}{L}\right)^{1/3} \qquad (6)$$

We may take about 10 billion years for T, but it is extremely difficult to estimate the value of L. It is my personal opinion that we should take some ten thousands of years for L, but since many scientists regard this as being too pessimistic, we will take 100,000 years for our present purpose—a value which gives about 250 parsecs for D. Fortunately, the uncertainty of L enters the value of D only with the power $\frac{1}{3}$, and if we change L even by a factor of 8, D will change by only a factor of 2.

With respect to interstellar space travel we must clearly separate two questions: (a) We may want to know what the possibilities are for *our* future interstellar travel. In this case we are interested in locating *any* kind of intelligent life, and the distance we are required to reach is

$$5.6 \text{ parsecs } (= 18.6 \text{ light-years}) \qquad (7)$$

(b) We may examine the possibility of other beings visiting us. In this case the other civilization must be a *technical* one, and for the calculations that follow we will use, for the above-mentioned distance to be covered by these other beings

$$250 \text{ parsecs } (= 820 \text{ light-years}) \qquad (8)$$

In order to help visualize these astronomical distances, I will describe them with a model of scale 1:180 billion. The earth, then, is a tiny grain of desert sand, just visible to the naked eye, orbiting around its sun, which now is a cherrystone a little less than 3 ft away. Within approximately the same distance, some few feet, lies the goal of our present space travel: the other planets of our solar system, such as Mars and Venus. But the nearest star, Proxima Centauri, is another cherrystone 140 miles away; and the next stars with habitable planets, where we might look for intelligent life, are to be expected at a distance of 610 miles. The next technical civilizations, however, will be at a distance as great as the circumference of the earth. Just for fun one may add the distance to the Andromeda nebula, the next stellar system comparable to our own galaxy: In our model it is as far away as, in reality, the sun is from the earth. The most distant galaxies seen by astronomers with their best telescopes are 2000 times as far away, and here even our model fails to help.

Relativistic Treatment

One thing is now clear: In order to cover interstellar distances within reasonable times we ought to fly as close as possible to the velocity of light, the utmost limit of any velocity, according to the theory of relativity (and in accordance with all experiments with high-energy particles). But as we approach the velocity of light, the formulas of normal physics must be replaced by those of relativity theory.

This might be of some help, because one of the most striking statements of relativity theory is that time itself is not an absolute property but is shortened for systems approaching the velocity of light. If, for example, we are to move out and back a distance of 800 light-years, then people remaining on earth will have to wait at least 1600 years for the return of the rocket. But if the speed of the rocket closely approaches the velocity of light, then the flow of time for this rocket and its crew becomes different from that on earth, and one may expect that the crew members will have to spend only a few years, perhaps, of their own lifetimes between start and return.

The equations that follow are derived under the assumption that the formulas of the special theory of relativity still hold under conditions of permanent acceleration and deceleration—a view which is generally assumed but not yet accepted. I will keep this part of the discussion as short as possible, and any reader who abominates formulas, relativistic or not, may skip to the next section.

We use the following definitions: τ is rocket time and t is earth time (both equal zero at the start of the rocket flight); v is the velocity of the rocket (as seen from the earth); c is the velocity of light; b is the acceleration of the rocket (as measured *within* the rocket by the pressure of a unit mass against a spring), assumed to be constant; and x is the distance between the rocket and the earth.

The differentials of τ and t are connected by

$$d\tau = dt(1 - [v/c]^2)^{1/2} \tag{9}$$

and the differential equation for v reads

$$\frac{d}{dt}\left\{\frac{v}{(1 - [v/c]^2)^{1/2}}\right\} = b \tag{10}$$

which is easily integrated. Solving for v we get

$$v(t) = \frac{bt}{(1 + [bt/c]^2)^{1/2}} \tag{11}$$

With the help of Eq. (11) we can integrate Eq. (9):

$$\tau(t) = \int_0^t (1 - [v/c]^2)^{1/2} \, dt = \frac{c}{b} \text{arc sinh} \frac{bt}{c} \tag{12}$$

while the distance is integrated according to

$$x(t) = \int_0^t v \, dt = \frac{c^2}{b} \{(1 + [bt/c]^2)^{1/2} - 1\} \tag{13}$$

We realize that, in order to get an equivalent to our rocket formula [Eq. (1)], thrust and acceleration, if both are measured within the rocket, should be connected as usual:

$$-\frac{dM}{d\tau} S = Mb \tag{14}$$

where M is the total mass of the rocket at any time and $-dM/d\tau$ is the exhaust mass flow. But in order to reach $v \approx c$, we need also $S \approx c$ according to relationship (3), and S in Eq. (14) should be replaced by $S(1 - S^2/c^2)^{-1/2}$. Furthermore, $S \approx c$ demands so much energy that in integrating Eq. (14) the mass loss due to mass defect should be considered, too. In the calculations that follow, however, we shall find that, even with atomic energy, both S and v still are much less than c, so that no relativistic treatment is needed, and Eq. (1) may be used.

The only means of reaching $v \approx c$ turns out to be complete annihilation of matter. In this case one will use photon thrust, and Eq. (14) should be written

$$-\frac{dM}{d\tau} c = Mb \tag{15}$$

We derive the following formulas for annihilation of matter as the energy source and photon thrust as the propelling mechanism (ignoring all doubts about the practical realization of either). We integrate Eq. (15) from start ($M = M_i$) to burnout of all fuel ($M = M_0$). The durations of this period of acceleration for the crew, τ_0, and [from Eq. (12)] for people on earth, t_0, then are

$$\tau_0 = \frac{c}{b} \ln \mathfrak{M} \tag{16a}$$

and

$$t_0 = \frac{2c}{b} (\mathfrak{M} - \mathfrak{M}^{-1}) \tag{16b}$$

where, again, $\mathfrak{M} = M_i/M_0$, and the distance traveled between start and burnout, x_0, is

$$x_0 = \frac{c^2}{2b} \left(\mathfrak{M} + \mathfrak{M}^{-1} - 2 \right) \tag{17}$$

After burnout, the final velocity of the rocket, V, is given by

$$V = c \frac{1 - \mathfrak{M}^{-2}}{1 + \mathfrak{M}^{-2}} \tag{18}$$

—a velocity which causes a time dilatation, on the further (unaccelerated) portion of the journey, of

$$\left(\frac{dt}{d\tau}\right)_0 = \frac{\mathfrak{M} + \mathfrak{M}^{-1}}{2} \tag{19}$$

We notice that the final velocity and time dilatation do not depend on b or t_0; it does not matter how quickly we burn our fuel.

The mass ratio should be, of course, as large as possible, and for $\mathfrak{M} \gg 1$ the equations just given reduce to

$$t_0 \approx 2 \frac{c}{b} \mathfrak{M} \tag{20a}$$

$$x_0 \approx \frac{c^2}{2b} \left(\mathfrak{M} - 2 \right) \tag{20b}$$

$$V \approx c(1 - 2/\mathfrak{M}^2) \tag{20c}$$

and

$$\left(\frac{dt}{d\tau}\right)_0 \approx \frac{1}{2} \mathfrak{M} \tag{20d}$$

(see 2). Finally, Eq. (5) needs a slight modification, too; for photon thrust it reads simply:

$$b = P/c \tag{21}$$

Energy Content of Nuclear Fuels

Having seen, earlier in this article, that the energy per mass of fuel is one of the important considerations in space travel, we now ask for the most energetic fuels. The utmost possible limit is set by one of the fundamental laws of relativity:

$$E = mc^2 \tag{22}$$

which gives the energy E obtained by complete annihilation of matter of mass m. Or we might say it another way: Energy E has an inertial mass (its resistance against acceleration) of $m = E/c^2$. If we call ϵ the specific energy content (energy/mass), we have for complete annihilation, $\epsilon = c^2 = 9 \times 10^{20}$ ergs per gram.

Complete annihilation takes place only if matter and antimatter are brought together: when a proton combines with an antiproton, electron combines with positron, and so on. But the world we live in consists of matter only, and to store a large amount of antimatter with equipment consisting of matter seems quite impossible, from all we know. We thus have to look for some other source of energy.

If antimatter is omitted, then according to another fundamental rule of nuclear physics the combined number of heavy elementary particles (protons plus neutrons) must stay constant, and the only thing left is to unite several light nuclei into a heavy one (fusion) or to split up a heavy nucleus into several light ones (fission), leaving the sum of protons and neutrons constant. In doing this we may gain or lose energy, according to the different amounts of nuclear binding energy of the various elements. The total energy content per nucleon (proton or neutron), in case of annihilation, would be 931.13 million electron volts for hydrogen; it drops quickly to 924.88 for helium, and then slowly to a flat minimum of 922.55 for iron. From then on it increases again, but very slowly, to 922.65 for uranium. The differences in these figures represent the energy available for nuclear reactions, and the most energy is gained if we start at either end and stop at the lowest point, at about iron. Since hydrogen has a higher value than uranium, we can gain more energy by fusion than by fission; and furthermore, since the minimum is an extremely flat one, it is not important to stop exactly at iron.

At present we use fission in reactors; the fission products are a mixture of elements of all masses, and the gain in energy is about half that which would result if all fission products were iron. Fusion of hydrogen into helium is the source of energy of our sun and of most other stars; it is used in hydrogen bombs only. Scientists in many countries have worked hard to produce controlled fusion, but without success so far.

The only fuel used at present for space travel releases energy by chemical reactions, where the burning of hydrogen to water yields only an energy-mass ratio of 1.15×10^{11} ergs per gram. If we learn to use uranium reactors instead, the energy-mass ratio will be increased by a factor of 5.6 million. If it ever became possible to use the fusion

Table 1

Energy per Mass of Fuel for Nuclear Reactions

Fuel	Final product	Energy/mass 10^{18} ergs/g
	Annihilation	
Matter plus antimatter	Radiation	900
	Fusion	
Hydrogen	Helium	6.3
Hydrogen	Iron	8.3
	Fission	
Uranium	Mixture, as produced in reactors	0.65
Uranium	Iron	1.1

of hydrogen into helium as a power source for space travel, one would gain another factor of 10; and if complete annihilation were practicable, a further factor of 140 would be gained. Table 1 summarizes these facts.

Acceleration and Time

Thus equipped with an understanding of nuclear fuel, if not with the real thing, and with relativistic formulas, we proceed with estimating the general limits of future space travel.

As a first step we neglect even the requirements of energy and power. The only limitation then remaining will be the maximum amount of acceleration which a crew can stand. It has been estimated (3) that a terrestrial crew can stand, for a period of *years,* approximately $b = 1g$. It seems likely that, over a long trip, any crew will stand only about as much acceleration as its members are used to experiencing on their home planet. This might differ from our case by a factor of, say, 2 or 3 in either direction, but probably by less if the conditions for the development of life are carefully regarded. In the following discussion we will use a limit of $1g$.

If the acceleration is limited to this fixed value, the shortest travel time for a given distance will result if we accelerate with $1g$ half of

Table 2

Total Duration and Distance Reached, with Constant
Acceleration and Deceleration at 1g

Duration (out and back), years		Distance reached, parsec
For crew on board rocket	For people on earth	
1	1.0	0.018
2	2.1	0.075
5	6.5	0.52
10	24	3.0
15	80	11.4
20	270	42
25	910	140
30	3,100	480
40	36,000	5,400
50	420,000	64,000
60	5,000,000	760,000

the way and then decelerate with 1g over the second half of the trip, returning in the same way. On the basis of this assumption and of Eqs. (11) and (13), Table 2 has been calculated.

We see that the relativistic time dilatation yields an effective gain for the crew only if the crew members spend more than about 10 years of their lives on the voyage. The further increase, however, is a very

Table 3

Total Durations, for Rocket-Crew Members and for People on Earth,
of Round-Trip Voyages to Distances of 5.6 and 250 parsecs,
with Constant Acceleration and Deceleration at 1g

Distance reached, parsec	Duration, years	
	For crew	On earth
5.6	12.3	42
250	27.3	1550

steep one (exponential); if the crew members spent 30 years of their lives on the voyage they would be able to fly to the Orion nebula and back, and 3000 years would have elapsed on earth between their departure and their return. For our goals of travel to distances of 5.6 and 250 parsecs, we obtain the values in Table 3.

With these results, many readers may already have lost hope of future interstellar space travel; others still may be optimistic. But so far we have neglected the requirements of energy and power.

Energy and Time

Acceleration and deceleration require a lot of energy, which has to come from somewhere. One might perhaps think of providing the rocket with a large funnel in order to sweep up the interstellar matter for fuel. But the interstellar matter has only a very low density (about 10^{-24} g/cm³), and in order to collect 1000 tons of matter (10 times the fuel of one Atlas rocket) on a trip to a goal 5.6 parsecs away, one would need a funnel 100 km in diameter; we will rule out this possibility. We cannot refuel under way in this manner, or in any other way while traveling at high speed, and thus the rocket must be provided initially with all the energy it needs to reach its goal. But we might allow for refueling at the destination point, when the rocket will be at rest. For our estimate we will consider a three-stage rocket: Stages 1 and 2 are used for the trip to the destination, there stage 2 is refueled, and stages 2 and 3 are used for returning. There is thus one stage for each period of acceleration or deceleration.

The next thing to be fixed is the mass ratio $\mathfrak{M}$ of a single stage. Our present values for $\mathfrak{M}$ are around 10, but the values would become very low if any energy source other than combustion were to be used. Keeping in mind the extremely massive and complicated equipment needed for nuclear reactions, and for propelling mechanisms such as ion thrust, we think that a value of $\mathfrak{M} = 10$ could be used as an extreme upper limit, even for a much more advanced technology.

The only source of nuclear energy now in sight is the fission of heavy nuclei such as uranium, where 1 g yields 6.5×10^{17} ergs. The highest efficiency is achieved if the fission products themselves can be expelled for propulsion with their fission energy (although at present we have no idea how this can be accomplished). In this case, we will get an exhaust velocity of $S = 13,000$ km/sec $= c/23$—a value so small as compared to the velocity of light that Eq. (1) still may be used. With a mass ratio of 10 as a limit, the final velocity after burnout then is $V = 30,000$ km/sec $= c/10$. Relativistic effects, such as time dilatation, will not play a role of any importance. In order to reach greater distances we have to fly most of the time without acceleration (after burnout of the first stage) and decelerate shortly before reaching the goal with our second stage. The full travel time, out and back, is 380 years for 5.6 parsecs and 17,000 years for 250 parsecs. This certainly does not look very promising.

If one is optimistic enough to think that the fusion of hydrogen into helium might become usable for rocket propulsion, with a mass ratio of 10, even then only $V = c/5$ can be achieved, and time dilatation again will be unimportant. The full travel time is 180 years for 5.6 parsecs and 8000 years for 250 parsecs—not much better than before.

The utmost limit, which cannot be surpassed, is set by the mass equivalent of the needed energy itself (its resistance against acceleration), no matter how this energy is stored. Personally, I do not think that complete annihilation of matter, or some other means of storing "pure energy," ever will become practical for any purpose, let alone in rockets with a mass ratio of 10. But imagine that it does: Then 98 per cent of the velocity of light can be achieved, according to Eq. (20c), and as a result of the time dilatation, the time for the crew will get shorter than the time on earth (after burnout) by a factor of 5.0. For 5.6 parsecs, the full travel time will be 14 years for the crew and 42 years on earth, and for a distance of 250 parsecs we get 300 years for the crew and 1500 years on earth. We still must spend 14 years within a rocket in order to search for intelligent beings, and only after 300 years in a rocket will the inhabitants of some alien planet have a fair chance of meeting other beings, like ourselves, who are in just the same state of science and technology as they are.

I should mention again that the final velocity after burnout does not depend on the amount of acceleration b, either in the classical treatment [Eq. (1)] or in the relativistic one [Eq. (18)]. Only the energy content of the fuel and the mass of the rocket are important, not the rate at which fuel is consumed. The latter rate will influence the duration of the acceleration period, of course, but not the final velocity. This means that if we should prepare the crew to resist very high acceleration (by freezing them in a solid block of ice, or the like), we could shorten the acceleration periods but not the duration of the unaccelerated flight in between.

In the case of fission or fusion, almost all of the travel time is spent in unaccelerated flight after burnout, and high acceleration will not help at all. In the case of annihilation, however, 9.5 years of the crew's time is spent in accelerated or decelerated flight, and this period could be shortened through greater acceleration, but we are still neglecting the power requirements. For a distance of 5.6 parsecs, 4.2 years of the crew's time is spent in unaccelerated flight, and this period cannot be shortened in any way; again, for a distance of 250 parsecs, almost all of the time is spent in unaccelerated flight.

Power-Mass Ratio and Acceleration

For the interstellar distances discussed earlier we need a travel velocity close to the velocity of light, and according to principle (3) we must have $V \approx S$ for reasonable efficiency. These criteria taken together then demand that $S \approx c$. Furthermore, we have seen that complete annihilation of matter is the only hope as a power source in interstellar space travel, and since we must not waste any matter by using it for propulsion, only photon thrust is left us. In that case Eq. (21) applies, and $b = P/c$.

From Eq. (16) we see that the acceleration must be as large as possible in order to hold τ_0 small, but we have argued that b must be limited to about $1g$. The two considerations then demand that $b \approx 1g$.

Now, if Eq. (21) holds and $b \approx 1g$, then the power-mass ratio must have the extremely high value of

$$P = 3 \times 10^{13} \text{ cm}^2/\text{sec}^3 \tag{23}$$

or, in the power units of watt or horsepower,

$$P = 3 \times 10^6 \text{ watts/g} = 4 \times 10^3 \text{ hp/g} \tag{24}$$

In order to understand the full meaning of Eq. (24) we might consider our present fission reactors—those with the highest power-mass ratios. Reactors for ship propulsion, with power output of 15 Mw and weight of 800 tons give $P = 0.02$ watt/gram—a value too low by a factor of 1.5×10^8 to fulfill Eq. (24). If no shielding and no safety measures were needed, then the highest value theoretically possible would be $P = 100$ watts/gram, still too low, by a factor of 30,000. In fact, according to Eq. (24), the whole power plant of 15-Mw output (enough for a small town) should weigh not more than 5 g (the weight of 10 paper clips). Or to express it another way, to fulfill Eq. (24), the engine of a good car, producing 200 horsepower, could not weigh more than 50 mg—one-tenth the weight of a paper clip.

But that is not all. Not only do we need power, we have to get rid of it, too. Photons might be emitted in the optical or the radio range, and propulsion will result if all emission is in one direction. A large transmitting station of 100-kw power output can then give the tiny thrust of 30 milligrams, and so can an aggregate of searchlights with combined power of 100 kw. And all this should weigh not more than $\frac{1}{15}$ the weight of a paper clip. The power source and transmitter requirements must be combined, and the mass entering Eq. (24) must contain reactor as well as emitting stations.

So far we have neglected payloads and fuel, and the mass of these must be included in Eq. (24), too. As an example we start with a "small" space ship of 10-ton payload, and we add another 10 tons for power plant plus emitters. If we want to reach a velocity within 2 per cent of that of light (with a dilatation factor of 5), we need a mass ratio $\mathfrak{M} = 10$, according to Eq. (20d), and the total mass of the rocket will be 200 tons. We find, from Eq. (24), that in order to get an acceleration of $b = 1g$, we would need a power output of 600 million Mw. Thus,

> We would need 40 million annihilation power plants of 15 megawatts each, plus 6 billion transmitting stations of 100 kw each, altogether having no more mass than 10 tons, in order to approach the velocity of light to within 2 per cent within 2.3 years of the crew's time (25)

If requirement (25) is not fulfilled, we get equations for the periods of acceleration and deceleration as follows. From Eq. (16a) we have

$$\tau_0 = \frac{c^2}{P} \ln \mathfrak{M} \tag{26}$$

and from Eqs. (20a) and (20b) we get

$$t_0 = 2 \frac{c^2}{P} \mathfrak{M} \tag{27a}$$

and

$$x_0 = \frac{c^3}{2P} (\mathfrak{M} - 2) \tag{27b}$$

If, for example, we fail to fulfill requirement (25) by a factor of 10^6 (if we have 40 power plants plus 6000 transmitters, weighing, in all, 10 tons—still a fantastic value), then $b = 10^{-6}g$, and it would take 2.3 millions of years for the crew to approach the velocity of light to within 2 per cent.

Or, to put it the other way round, if one wants to get an acceleration of, say, $b = 100g$, in order to take full advantage of having a deep-frozen crew, then 100 times the weight of the equipment mentioned in requirement (25) must not total more than 10 tons; this means that power plants plus transmitters should have an output of 6000 Mw/g. Purcell (4) has arrived at similar conclusions from a study of the requirements of relativistic rockets. There is no way of avoiding these demands, and definitely no hope of fulfilling them.

Conclusion

The various questions dealt with in this article have not led to the definitive answer that interstellar space travel is absolutely impossible. We have found simply the minimum travel times given by different assumptions, and we have found the requirements needed for reaching these limits. This is, at present, all we can do, and the final conclusion as to the feasibility of such ventures is up to the reader. The requirements, however, have turned out to be such extreme ones that I, personally, draw this conclusion: space travel, even in the most distant future, will be confined completely to our own planetary system, and a similar conclusion will hold for any other civilization, no matter how advanced it may be. The only means of communication between different civilizations thus seems to be electro-magnetic signals.

Acknowledgment

I wish to thank F. D. Drake for reading the manuscript.

References and Notes

1 S. von Hoerner, *Science*, **134**, 1839 (1961).
2 A different derivation of Eq. (20), connecting V and M, has been given by J. R. Pierce [*Proc. Inst. Radio Engrs.*, **47**, 1053 (1959)] together with a good explanation of the so-called clock paradox. Pierce also investigates interstellar matter as fuel, with the same negative result as that given in this article.
3 *Space Handbook: Astronautics and Its Applications*, U.S. Government Printing Office, Washington, 1959, p. 113.
4 E. M. Purcell, *Brookhaven National Laboratory Lectures No. 1.*

Giuseppe Cocconi and Philip Morrison

15 ✳ SEARCHING FOR INTERSTELLAR COMMUNICATIONS

No theories yet exist which enable a reliable estimate of the probabilities of (1) planet formation; (2) origin of life; (3) evolution of societies possessing advanced scientific capabilities. In the absence of such theories, our environment suggests that stars of the main sequence with a lifetime of many billions of years can possess planets, that of a small set of such planets, two (earth and very probably Mars) support life, that life on one such planet includes a society recently capable of considerable scientific investigation. The lifetime of such societies is not known; but it seems unwarranted to deny that among such societies some might maintain themselves for times very long compared to the time of human history, perhaps for times comparable with geological time. It follows, then, that near some star rather like the sun there are civilizations with scientific interests and with technical possibilities much greater than those now available to us.

To the beings of such a society, our sun must appear as a likely site for the evolution of a new society. It is highly probable that for a long time they will have been expecting the development of science near the sun. We shall assume that long ago they established a channel of communication that would one day become known to us, and that they look forward patiently to the answering signals from the sun which would make known to them that a new society has entered the community of intelligence. What sort of a channel would it be?

The Optimum Channel

Interstellar communication across the galactic plasma without dispersion in direction and flight time is practical, so far as we know, only with electromagnetic waves.

Since the object of those who operate the source is to find a newly evolved society, we may presume that the channel used will be one that places a minimum burden of frequency and angular discrimination on the detector. Moreover, the channel must not be highly attenuated in space or in the earth's atmosphere. Radio frequencies below ~1 Mc/sec, and all frequencies higher than molecular absorption lines near 30,000 Mc, up to cosmic-ray gamma energies, are suspect of absorption in planetary atmospheres. The bandwidths which seem physically possible in the near-visible or gamma-ray domains demand either very great source power or very complicated techniques. The wide radio band from, say, 1 Mc to 10^4 Mc, remains as the rational choice.

In the radio region, the source must compete with two backgrounds: (1) the emission of its own local star (we assume that the detector's angular resolution is unable to separate source from star since the source is likely to lie within a second of arc of its nearby star); (2) the galactic emission along the line of sight.

Let us examine the frequency dependence of these backgrounds. A star similar to the quiet sun would emit a power which produces at a distance R (in meters) a flux of

$$10^{-15} f^2 / R^2 \qquad \text{watts/m}^2 \text{ cps}$$

If the flux is detected by a mirror of diameter l_d, the received power is the above flux multiplied by l_d^2.

The more or less isotropic part of the galactic background yields a received power equal to

$$\left(\frac{10^{-12.5}}{f} \right) \left(\frac{\lambda}{l_d} \right)^2 (l_d)^2 \qquad \text{watts/cps}$$

where the first factor arises from the spectrum of the galactic continuum, the second from the angular resolution, and the third from the area of the detector. Thus a minimum in spurious background is defined by equating these two terms. The minimum lies at

$$f_{\min} \approx 10^4 \left(\frac{R}{l_d} \right)^{0.4} \qquad \text{cps}$$

With $R = 10$ light-years $= 10^{17}$ m and $l_d = 10^2$ m, $f_{\min} \approx 10^{10}$ cps. The source is likely to emit in the region of this broad minimum.

At what frequency shall we look? A long spectrum search for a weak signal of unknown frequency is difficult. But, just in the most favored radio region there lies a unique, objective standard of frequency, which must be known to every observer in the universe: the outstanding radio emission line at 1420 Mc/sec ($\lambda = 21$ cm) of neutral hydrogen. It is reasonable to expect that sensitive receivers for this frequency will be made at an early stage of the development of radio-astronomy. That would be the expectation of the operators of the assumed source, and the present state of terrestrial instruments indeed justifies the expectation. Therefore we think it most promising to search in the neighborhood of 1420 Mc/sec.

Power Demands of the Source

The galactic background around the 21-cm line amounts to

$$\frac{dW_b}{dS\,d\Omega\,df} \approx 10^{-21.5} \qquad \text{watts/m}^2 \text{ steradian cps}$$

for about two-thirds of the directions in the sky. In the directions near the plane of the galaxy there is a background up to 40 times higher. It is thus economical to examine first those nearby stars which are in directions far from the galactic plane.

If at the source a mirror is used l_s meters in diameter, then the power required for it to generate in our detector a signal as large as the galactic background is

$$\frac{dW_s}{df} = \frac{dW_b}{dS\,d\Omega\,df}\left(\frac{\lambda}{l_s}\right)^2\left(\frac{\lambda}{l_d}\right)R^2 = 10^{-24.2}\,R^2/l_s{}^2l_d{}^2 \qquad \text{watts/cps}$$

For source and receiver with mirrors like those at Jodrell Bank ($l = 80$ m), and for a distance $R \simeq 10$ light-years, the power at the source required is $10^{2.2}$ watts/cps, which would tax our present technical possibilities. However, if the size of the two mirrors is that of the telescope already planned by the U.S. Naval Research Laboratory ($l = 200$ m), the power needed is a factor of 40 lower, which would fall within even our limited capabilities.

We have assumed that the source is beaming toward all the sun-like stars in its galactic neighborhood. The support of, say, 100 different beams of the kind we have described does not seem an impossible burden on a society more advanced than our own. (Upon detecting one signal, even we would quickly establish many search beams.) We can then hope to see a beam toward us from any suitable star within some tens of light-years.

Signal Location and Bandwidth

In all directions outside the plane of the galaxy the 21-cm emission line does not emerge from the general background. For stars in directions far from the galactic plane search should then be made around that wavelength. However, the unknown Doppler shifts which arise from the motion of unseen planets suggest that the observed emission might be shifted up or down from the natural co-moving atomic frequency by $\pm\sim300$ kc/sec (±100 km/sec). Closer to the galactic plane, where the 21-cm line is strong, the source frequency would presumably move off to the wing of the natural line background as observed from the direction of the sun.

So far as the duration of the scanning is concerned, the receiver bandwidth appears to be unimportant. The usual radiometer relation for fluctuations in the background applies here, that is:

$$\frac{\Delta B}{B} \propto \sqrt{\frac{1}{\Delta f_d \cdot \tau}}$$

where Δf_d is the bandwidth of the detector and τ the time constant of the post-detection recording equipment. On the other hand, the background accepted by the receiver is:

$$B = \frac{dW_b}{df}\Delta f_d \qquad \text{and} \qquad \tau \propto \frac{\Delta f_d}{(\Delta B)^2}$$

If we set ΔB equal to some fixed value, then the search time T required to examine the band F within which we postulated the signal to lie is given by

$$T = \frac{F\tau}{\Delta f_d} \propto \frac{F}{(\Delta B)^2}$$

independent of receiver bandwidth Δf_d.

Of course, the smaller the bandwidth chosen, the weaker the signal which can be detected, provided $\Delta f_d \geqslant \Delta f_s$. It looks reasonable for a first effort to choose a bandwidth Δf_d normal in 21-cm practice, but an integration time τ longer than usual. A few settings should cover the frequency range F using an integration time of minutes or hours.

Nature of the Signal and Possible Sources

No guesswork here is as good as finding the signal. We expect that the signal will be pulse-modulated with a speed not very fast or very slow compared to a second, on grounds of bandwidth and of rotations. A message is likely to continue for a time measured in years, since no answer can return in any event for some 10 years. It will then repeat, from the beginning. Possibly it will contain different types of signals alternating throughout the years. For indisputable identification as an artificial signal, one signal might contain, for example, a sequence of small prime numbers of pulses, or simple arithmetical sums.

The first effort should be devoted to examining the closest likely stars. Among the stars within 15 light-years, seven have luminosity and lifetime similar to those of our sun. Four of these lie in the directions of low background. They are τ Ceti, 0_2 Eridani, ϵ Eridani, and ϵ Indi. All these happen to have southern declinations. Three others, α Centauri, 70 Ophiucus, and 61 Cygni, lie near the galactic plane and therefore stand against higher backgrounds. There are about a hundred stars of the appropriate luminosity among the stars of known spectral type within some 50 light-years. All main-sequence dwarfs between perhaps G0 and K2 with visual magnitudes less than about +6 are candidates.

The reader may seek to consign these speculations wholly to the domain of science fiction. We submit, rather, that the foregoing line of argument demonstrates that the presence of interstellar signals is entirely consistent with all we now know, and that if signals are present the means of detecting them is now at hand. Few will deny the profound importance, practical and philosophical, which the detection of interstellar communications would have. We therefore feel that a discriminating search for signals deserves a considerable effort. The probability of success is difficult to estimate; but if we never search, the chance of success is zero.

Frank D. Drake

16 ✳ HOW CAN WE DETECT RADIO TRANSMISSIONS FROM DISTANT PLANETARY SYSTEMS?

The question of whether there is intelligent life elsewhere in the universe, outside the bounds of the solar system, has long been fascinating, but apparently unanswerable. Optical telescopes offer no help with the problem. It would require a very large telescope outside the earth's atmosphere, say on the moon, merely to detect the existence of planets accompanying the closest stars. The presence of intelligent life would still be unrecognizable.

Could a radio telescope detect intelligent radio transmissions over interstellar distances? It is easy to show that the distance R over which a signal can be observed is given under most conditions by the accompanying formula. To see what ranges are obtainable with available equipment, let us consider an attempt by the 85-ft radio telescope of the National Radio Astronomy Observatory to detect a high-power radar signal.

Such a signal might be like that radiated by the Millstone Hill radar antenna at Westford, Massachusetts, when it achieved radar echoes from Venus (*Sky and Telescope,* May 1959, p. 384). At such times, the Millstone radar has roughly an effective radiating power P_e of 10^{10} watts and a bandwidth B of 10 cycles/sec. The 85-ft has an effective receiving area A of 370 m² and, if we are using a maser, T might be only 10°K and t about 100 sec.

Using these values in the formula, we find that the radar transmission would be detectable even if it originated 8.7 light-years away! This is as far as Sirius, and about twice as far as α Centauri (see Figure

1). Because of our large antennas and new sensitive receivers, we are already capable of detecting the radio transmissions of intelligent beings over interstellar distances.

When the receiving antenna is a parabolic reflector, this rule-of-thumb formula may be applied: The distance in light-years at which strong present-day transmitters can be detected is about equal to the diameter of the antenna in feet divided by 10. Thus the U.S. Navy's 600-ft antenna, now under construction at Sugar Grove, West Virginia, could detect intelligent life transmissions from as far away as 60 light-years, while the Cornell University 1,000-ft bowl in Puerto Rico and NRAO's proposed 1,000-ft antenna will be able to see about 100 light-years. Within that distance of the earth, there are something like 10,000 stars.

It is very difficult to estimate how many of those stars may be supporting civilizations as advanced as ours. For many years, it was felt that the formation of the solar system was the result of a chance collision between two stars, or some other unlikely event. Furthermore, the development of life on planets was thought to be a very rare occurrence. This led to a pessimistic picture of the abundance of life in the galaxy.

In recent times, however, it has become clear that the formation of a second body or bodies is an essential part of the formation of a star. It is possible that most stars, not members of binary or multiple systems, are accompanied by families of planets or meteorites. As ex-

---

Distance of Detection of Cosmic Radio Signals

$$R = 8 \times 10^{-6} (P_e A/T)^{1/2} (t/B)^{1/4} \text{ light-years}$$

R is the distance over which the signal can be observed

P_e is the effective radiated power of the transmitter, in the direction of the earth, expressed in watts

A is the effective area of the receiving antenna, in square meters

T is the excess receiver noise temperature of the receiver used, in degrees Kelvin

t is the receiver averaging time, in seconds

B is the accepted bandwidth of the signal (that is, the bandwidth of the receiver used) in cycles per second

For detailed explanations of the terms used in this formula and other information about radio receivers useful in the present discussion, refer to Dr. Drake's article in the November and December, 1959, issues of *Sky and Telescope*, pp. 26 and 87, respectively.

Figure 1

In this three-dimensional model by Sarah Lippincott, all known stars within 16 light-years of the sun (center) are shown as if they were being viewed from the direction of the vernal equinox. The triple star Alpha Centauri appears below and to the left of the sun; Altair is the large object at the extreme left; Sirius is the largest in the right half of the model. (Photograph courtesy of Sproul Observatory, Swarthmore College.)

plained by Otto Struve (*Sky and Telescope*, January 1960, p. 154), probably at least a few per cent of all stars are accompanied by planets.

How many of these planets might have intelligent life? The pioneering experiments of Stanley Miller at the University of Chicago, as well as later studies, have shown that complicated organic molecules could well have been formed in great quantities during the early history of the earth or any similar planet. These molecules, which are the basic building blocks of life, should provide for its emergence on other planets just as they apparently did on earth.

We might expect life to be quite common on planets, then. However, recent papers by K. Kordylewski in Poland and Su-Shu Huang in the United States consider anew the fact that life will thrive only on planets that are at such distances from their star that the temperature is appropriate. This factor limits intelligent life to just a few planets in each planetary system, including our own. And the star must be long-lived, not changing its brightness appreciably during the billions of years that are required for the evolution of intelligent beings from a collection of organic molecules. The over-all result is to limit such life to planets of main-sequence stars of spectral types F, G, K, and possibly M. However, this still includes about half of all the stars.

The stars have quite varied ages. This, plus the good probability that biological evolution occurs at unequal rates on different planets, means that the present level of evolutionary development may be quite different from planet to planet. The age of the sun appears to be average. Thus, it is likely that throughout the galaxy there are scattered civilizations more advanced, at the same level, and less developed than ours.

From all the considerations above, it appears that strong intelligent radio transmissions may emanate from the vicinities of, at best, 25 per cent of the stars and, at worst, perhaps one star in a million, which is the extremely conservative estimate recently suggested by Harlow Shapley in his book, *Of Stars and Men*. Obviously, these estimates are not very helpful, except in one respect: They make the possibility good that at least one of the 10,000 stars soon to be within our reach has a civilization using radio techniques. It is, then, worthwhile to apply our newly found technical prowess in an effort to detect interstellar radio transmission (see Figure 2).

What search frequency would be best? Consider what might be called the principle of technical perfection. It is only about 50 years since radio communication was invented, yet we have already very nearly achieved technically perfect instruments, and within 50 more years we should have them. By *technical perfection* we mean that the limits on communication-system sensitivities are not set by deficiencies in the apparatus, such as receiver noise, but by natural phenomena over which man has no control. This is a state in which further improvements in apparatus will not improve the operational results.

A century is only about a hundred-millionth of the age of our galaxy. Thus, on the galactic time scale, a civilization passes abruptly from a state of no radio ability to one of perfect radio ability. If we could examine a large number of life-bearing planets, we might expect to find in virtually every case either complete ignorance of radio techniques, or complete mastery. This is the principle of technical perfection. Our civilization may be one of an extremely small minority in transition between the two possible states—this, in fact, may be the only major feature in which man is unique.

Therefore, it may be logical to assume that the civilizations we might detect possess complete mastery of radio already. The transmissions we seek will obviously be very powerful ones, in which large information transfer over long distances is being attempted. Fre-

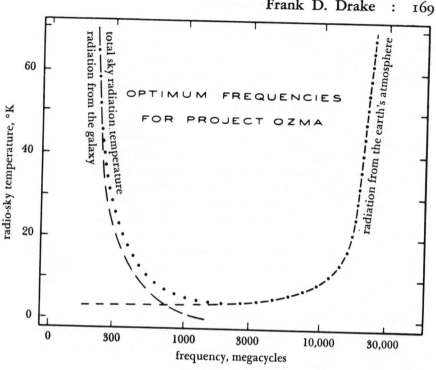

Figure 2

Only in a relatively narrow range of radio frequencies is there a reasonable chance of receiving transmissions from extraterrestrial beings. At low frequencies such signals would be smothered by radio noise of galactic origin; at high frequencies, radiation from the earth's atmosphere would overwhelm them. Both these types of interference are charted here, together with their resultant, the total sky radiation temperature. (NRAO graph.)

quencies will be chosen for which the natural limitations on performance are least. Two of these limitations are important: galactic radio noise emission, and noise from the planetary atmosphere, if reception from beneath the atmosphere is being attempted.

Both these emissions insert noise into the receiver, and have the same effect as though the receiver itself were noisy. The graph shows for the earth the radio-sky temperature produced by each of these sources of noise, and their combined effect. This last would be the excess receiver noise temperature of an otherwise perfect receiver. Obviously, the best frequencies to us for our search are those where this total sky temperature is least.

For instance, from beneath the atmosphere of a planet like the earth, the band from 1000 to 10,000 Mc/sec would be the optimum for reception of long-range transmissions. If, however, reception is being done from above the atmosphere, as the principle of technical perfection and our own success with satellites suggest, frequencies above 10,000 Mc are also good candidates.

Giuseppi Cocconi and Philip Morrison, of Cornell University, have gone one step further in a paper that appeared in the British journal *Nature* (Sept. 19, 1959, p. 844). They speculate that civilizations in space may have produced strong radio beams directed toward their nearby neighbors, in an effort to establish two-way radio communication at the earliest possible time. Such an attempt would use the frequency at which high-sensitivity, narrow-band radio telescopes would be first operated extensively during radio development of civilizations in the Milky Way. Throughout the galaxy it could very well be 1420 Mc, the frequency of the 21-cm interstellar hydrogen line.

All these considerations suggest confining our search to the band between 1000 and 10,000 Mc, and that possibly frequencies around 1420 Mc offer the best chance for success.

What will be the characteristics of the sought-after signals? Communication theory states that the narrower the bandwidth of a transmitted signal of fixed total power, the greater the range of successful transmission. Since we are attempting, in any case, to intercept transmissions of great power, where great range is presumably the goal, we can expect the signals to be of narrow bandwidth. This is advantageous, as it will allow us to distinguish the signals from naturally occurring cosmic noise, which is extremely broad in bandwidth.

We should expect an appreciable Doppler shift in the transmitted frequency over short periods, because of the likelihood that the transmitter will be in orbital motion around a star or planet. This shift will help us distinguish signals from cosmic noise and from terrestrial interference. The signal strength may vary with time, if coded information is being sent, and also possibly due to the changing orientation of the earth with respect to the transmitter. Finally, the transmission should come from the direction of a nearby star.

Summarizing this discussion, a receiver designed to detect interstellar radio signals at the surface of the earth should:

1. Operate at a frequency above 1000 Mc, with performance near 1420 desirable.

2. Operate over a considerable range of bandwidths, including 10 cycles/sec and less.

3. Have receiver frequency vary considerably less than the band-

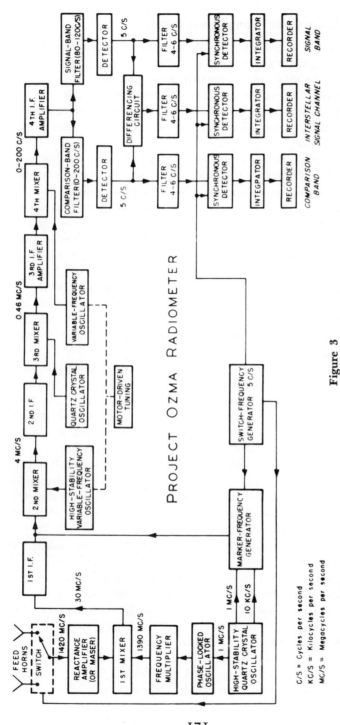

Figure 3

This block diagram indicates the operation of the radiometer now being completed for Project Ozma, to detect possible radio signals from the planets of other stars. Radio energy collected by the 85-ft antenna enters the feed horns shown at the upper left, and the desired signals, if any, are displayed by the recorder of the interstellar signal channel, lower right. In practice, the second mixer also functions as the second intermediate-frequency amplifier. (NRAO diagram.)

width during the averaging time of the receiver, specifically not more than about 1 cycle/sec in several minutes.

4. Have the most sensitive system now available.

5. Eliminate receiver noise effects as much as possible.

6. Discriminate against broad-band cosmic noise, if possible.

7. Preferably reject terrestrial interference that resembles the sought-after signal.

In an effort to detect interstellar radio transmissions, NRAO has established Project Ozma. It is named for the queen of the imaginary land of Oz—a place very far away, difficult to reach, and populated by exotic beings. A radiometer that fulfills the specifications above is now in the final stages of construction. Almost all of the assembly and testing to date have been carried on by W. Waltman, Purdue University, and R. W. Meadows, of the United Kingdom's Department of Scientific and Industrial Research.

Figure 3 is a block diagram of the Ozma radiometer, which operates near 1420 Mc. It is essentially a highly stable narrow-band superheterodyne receiver, which utilizes the principles of both the Dicke radiometer and the d.c.-comparison type (see *Sky and Telescope,* November 1959, pp. 26-28).

Two horns are placed together at the focus of the parabolic antenna, in order to eliminate terrestrial interference to some extent. These horns give the antenna two beams, one to point at the star under study, the other off into space near the star. As the electronic switch connects first one horn and then the other to the receiver, the telescope will look alternately at the star and at the sky beside it. Any radiation from the star will then enter in pulses whose duration is controlled by the switch. The synchronous detectors near the output end of the circuit will respond only to pulses synchronized with the switch, thus detecting only the desired signal. Receiver noise is eliminated, and also terrestrial disturbances.

Interference generally enters a radio telescope antenna through the horns directly, without a reflection from the paraboloid. In that case, both horns should receive the interfering signal with the same strength, and when the switch changes from one horn to the other there will be no change of level in the interference entering the receiver. As a result, the interference signal is not pulsed, and the synchronous detectors ignore it (see Figure 4).

In the present receiver, immediately after the switch there comes a reactance amplifier, to be replaced later with a maser. The amplifier, which gives the radiometer high sensitivity, was built by Ewen-

Figure 4

These cabinets contain those portions of the Ozma radiometer that are located in the control building of the radio telescope. Not shown are the feed horns, reactance amplifier, switch, first local oscillator system, and first intermediate-frequency oscillator.

Knight Corp., while the electronic switch was made by H. Hvatum of NRAO.

The signal then undergoes four frequency conversions, this many being necessary because the final intermediate frequencies are very low, owing to the narrow bandwidth requirements. The frequency received by the radiometer is directly dependent on the frequencies of the four oscillators, whose output signals beat with the true signal to produce the intermediate frequencies. In our specifications all four oscillators must hold their frequencies constant to better than 1 cycle/sec in 100 sec, if the over-all received frequency is also to be that constant.

This is a most difficult requirement for the first oscillator, because its final frequency is about 1390 Mc and it therefore must remain constant to one part in a billion. This accuracy is achieved by means of a special quartz crystal oscillator, the crystal being kept at a very constant temperature in an oven within an oven. The output of this oscillator is multiplied in frequency to give the desired final frequency.

A marker-frequency generator is used to provide weak signals from the output of the very stable oscillator at many fixed frequencies. These signals are inserted into the receiver for determining the exact frequency on which the receiver is operating, allowing the detection of Doppler effect.

After the fourth intermediate-frequency amplification, two filters pick out a broad band of noise, called the *comparison band,* and a narrow one designated the *signal band.* The gain of these filters is adjusted so that when very broad-band noise enters them their total outputs are equal. When these outputs are passed into the differencing circuit, its output is zero. However, a narrow-band signal fills only some of the frequencies of the filter for the comparison band, but all of those in the signal-band filter. The output of the narrow-band filter is then greater than that of the broad-band one, and there is a net output from the differencing circuit. This use of the d.c.-comparison circuit makes the radiometer respond only to narrow-band signals. As drawn here, the radiometer is set up for signals of about 40-cycle/sec bandwidth. In the actual receiver, the electronic filters have variable bandwidths that may be quickly adjusted to desired values.

The filters placed before the synchronous detectors pass only the frequencies to which the detectors will respond, and reject other frequencies that might cause them to operate improperly.

We see that an output from the final synchronous detector will occur only when receiving a narrow-band signal from a direction in which one of the antenna beams is pointing—the desired interstellar signal. The integrator only averages the signal strength over a chosen interval. The other two synchronous detectors and integrators connected directly to the comparison-band and signal-band channels monitor the performance of the radiometer.

Barring serious technical difficulties, our radiometer will go into operation on the 85-ft antenna early this year (see Figure 5). The first objects to be looked at are τ Ceti and ε Eridani, two solar-type stars about 11 light-years away. Unidentified radio sources whose celestial positions are close to those of nearby stars will also be studied at an early opportunity.

It appears probable that this project or a similar one will someday succeed in detecting an artificial signal. Needless to say, the scientific and philosophical implications of such a discovery will be extremely great.

Figure 5

Project Ozma's first experiments will be performed with the 85-ft Howard Tatel radio telescope, pending completion of the great 140-ft paraboloidal antenna at Green Bank. In this picture, the latter's concrete pier is almost finished, and cranes 186 feet high have been erected to lift parts of the telescope into place. When assembled, the polar axis, two pieces of which are in the foreground, will weigh about 800 tons. It is made of six- and eight-inch plate and of high-density concrete. The 140-ft aluminum dish is to have a surface accurate to within a quarter of an inch, in any position. All the receivers will be housed inside the pedestal, which has as much depth below ground as height above it. (Photograph from National Radio Astronomy Observatory.)

Frank D. Drake

17 ✳ PROJECT OZMA

Project Ozma organized the first systematic, high-sensitivity search for manifestations of extraterrestrial intelligent life. This program was carried on with the 85-ft radio telescope of the National Radio Astronomy Observatory during the months of May, June, and July, 1960. The object of the search was intelligent radio transmissions near the frequency at which atomic hydrogen radiates, 1420.4 Mc. A special receiver was used which provided high sensitivity, narrow radiofrequency bandwidth, good frequency stability, and the ability to discriminate strongly against terrestrial intelligent signals. It employed a semiconductor-diode parametric amplifier as the first amplifying stage in order to achieve high sensitivity, and the Dicke radiometer principle was used in order to allow the detection of signals much fainter than the receiver noise level.

Approximately 400 kc of bandwidth was explored while the telescope was pointed at each of two target stars, τ Ceti and ϵ Eridani. These stars were chosen as subjects because they are the nearest single sunlike stars observable from the telescope site. Throughout the search, a bandwidth of 100 cycles was used.

No signals of extraterrestrial origin were discovered during these preliminary observations. It is believed that signals would have been detected if they occupied less than 100 cycles of bandwidth and possessed an effective radiated power of 10^{13} watts or greater at the transmitter. This is about equivalent to a 1-Mw transmitter operating through a 600-ft antenna. The search was discontinued after these initial efforts because of the need for the telescope in other projects.

Since that time, theoretical studies of the means of detecting extraterrestrial life have been continued. These have led to the conclusion that improved information-handling procedures, such as cross-correlation of radiometer tracings and recording of phases as well as amplitude information, can lead to improved sensitivity to extraterrestrial intelligent signals. The invention of the optical maser has made possible a search on optical frequencies, but radio frequencies still appear to offer the greatest hope for success. It is also now clear that the large number of frequencies and stars which must be examined in the search for signal demands, for an efficient search, a receiver of very high information capacity. Thus multichannel receivers, or the equivalent, of great complexity are called for for future searches.

Bibliography

F. D. Drake, Project Ozma, *Phys. Today,* **14,** 40 (1961).

M. J. E. Golay, Note on the Probable Character of Intelligent Radio Signals from Other Planetary Systems, *Proc. Inst. Radio Engrs.,* **49,** 959 (1961).

J. A. Webb

18 ❋ DETECTION OF INTELLIGENT SIGNALS FROM SPACE

It is the purpose of this paper to discuss the possibility of interstellar radio contact, and to analyze detection techniques which might be used to further this venture.

It is highly unlikely that intelligent beings in other stellar systems are constantly broadcasting radio signals toward our sun in the hope that intelligent beings may some day evolve to the point of being able to answer the call. Although this possibility cannot be discounted entirely, it might be more rewarding to try a different approach to the problem.

A good place to start might be to analyze the present situation in the solar system. Here, earth is the only planet broadcasting intelligent signals, but earth is broadcasting on almost every frequency in the radiofrequency portion of the electromagnetic spectrum. None of these transmissions, however, are being beamed toward our stellar neighbors in an attempt to establish interstellar contact. In fact, even if such transmissions were considered likely to meet with success, it is not at all certain that this would be advisable.

It therefore appears most likely that radio listening stations might have greater chances for successful radio contact with other stellar systems by listening on frequencies which might be used by alien beings for defense, communications, or similar purposes. Although such transmissions might occur on any frequency from radiofrequency to the ultraviolet, there is good reason to believe that the microwave spectrum will be used by any advanced society. For one thing, the microwave and millimeter wavelengths offer the greatest receiver sensitivity available throughout the entire spectrum. Furthermore, geometric attenuation and antenna design tolerances are not excessive in this region.

At the lower end of the microwave spectrum, receiver sensitivity is generally limited by galactic noise. This noise varies greatly depending upon the area of the sky being viewed, but generally falls off with frequency according to the following relationship (1):

$$T_g = \frac{k_g}{f^{2.3}}$$ (1)

where T_g = equivalent receiver noise temperature due to galactic noise
K_g = constant of proportionality
f = frequency

The value of K_g will vary, but maximum and minimum mean values can be assigned for the galactic equator and the galactic pole.

The upper limit for communication is dependent upon whether the link is from earth-to-space, or space-to-space. For the earth-to-space link, atmospheric oxygen and water vapor absorption will limit the lowest receiver noise temperature to about 10°K. Practical considerations such as antenna sidelobe temperatures make it rather difficult to achieve even this figure at the present time. The frequency for minimum noise will be in the 1 to 7 kMc region, depending upon the area of the sky being viewed.

For a space-to-space communication link where atmospheric absorption can be ignored, quantum noise becomes the limiting factor in minimum receiver temperature. Quantum noise can be expressed as an equivalent receiver noise temperature T_q as follows:

$$T_q = \frac{h}{k}f$$ (2)

where h = Planck's constant
k = Boltzmann's constant

The minimum noise temperature for a space-to-space communication link is about 0.2 to 1.0°K. The frequency where this minimum occurs is between 3 and 10 kMc, depending upon the area of the sky being viewed.

Figure 1 shows a plot of galactic noise temperature for the galactic equator and the galactic pole, oxygen and water vapor absorption noise temperatures, and quantum noise temperature. Note that for a receiver operating at the surface of the earth, a minimum noise temperature of about 10°K occurs between 1 and 7 kMc. For a receiver operat-

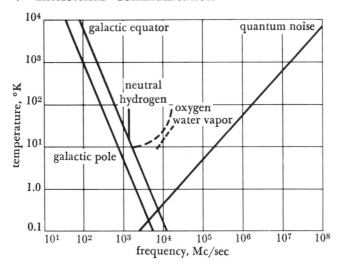

Figure 1

Natural noise sources.

ing entirely outside the atmosphere, a minimum receiver noise temperature of 0.2 to 1.0°K is attainable at frequencies of 3 to 10 kMc.

The total receiver noise power P_n can be expressed as follows:

$$P_n = KTB \tag{3}$$

where B = receiver bandwidth, and

$$T = \Sigma\ T_g + T_q + \cdots + T_x \tag{4}$$

Equation (4) includes apparent receiver noise temperatures due to losses, atmospheric noise, man-made noise, etc.

Recent developments in masers and parametric amplifiers have made it possible to obtain very low receiver thermal noise temperatures. Further developments will undoubtedly produce greater advances in this field. The temperatures shown in Figure 1, however, are theoretical lower noise limits that can be obtained regardless of the thermal temperature of the receiver. It is interesting to note that a receiver operating at light frequencies need not be cooled at all, since quantum noise already limits the lowest receiver noise temperature obtainable to room temperature or above. The same is true for radio-frequencies below a few hundred megacycles, owing in this case to the high galactic noise temperature.

Free space attenuation α in decibels can be expressed as follows (2):

$$\alpha = 91 + 20 \log d - 20 \log D \qquad (5)$$

where $d =$ propagation path length in nautical miles

$D =$ receiving antenna diameter in feet

Equation (5) assumes an omnidirectional antenna at the transmitter. Rather than consider transmitting antenna gain in Eq. (5) therefore, the transmitting power will be considered to be modified by antenna gain.

One light-year represents about 5.1×10^{12} nautical miles. Assuming a 100-ft-diameter receiving antenna and a propagation path length of 10 light-years, Eq. (5) shows the attenuation to be 325 db. Going back to Eq. (3) and substituting an optimistic 10°K and 10 cps bandwidth, the receiver noise power is found to be 1.38×10^{-22} watts, or -209 dbw. This means that a transmitter 10 light-years away must have a power output times antenna gain of about 116 dbw in order to develop a unity signal-to-noise signal at the receiver, since

$$P_r = P_t - \alpha \qquad (6)$$

where $P_r =$ received signal power (in dbw)

$P_t =$ transmitted power (in dbw)

Expressing this figure in another way, a 1-Mw transmitter would have to be using a 56-db gain antenna in order to be detected under the assumed conditions.

Figures 2 and 3 show plots of required output power times antenna gain as a function of receiver bandwidth, for a 10°K receiver and a 1°K receiver, respectively, for a receiving range of 10 light-years. Plots are shown for various antenna sizes from 100 ft in diameter to 10,000 ft.

Quite obviously at the present state of the art, most of the so-called giant antennas are too small to be very effective as interstellar snooping devices. Most antennas over 100 ft in diameter are designed for relatively low frequencies, and are mechanically unsuitable for operation in the kilomegacycle frequency range. It is expected that this situation will be alleviated somewhat in the future, however, through the use of new design techniques. One of the most encouraging prospects for the future is a 600-ft-diameter antenna now under construction, designed with mechanically compensating servomechanisms which make it possible to receive signals well up into the kilomegacycle frequency range. With the techniques used in the design of this an-

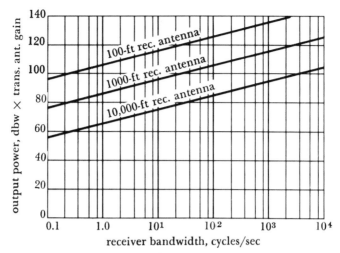

Figure 2

Transmitter output power required for a 10°K receiver, operative at a range of 10 light-years.

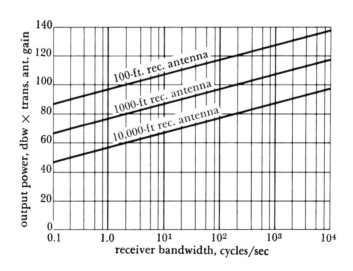

Figure 3

Transmitter output power required for a 1°K receiver, operating at a range of 10 light-years.

tenna, it is theoretically possible to construct antennas of virtually unlimited size.

The mechanical tolerance problem is a direct function of the gain of the antenna. In the past, 40-db antenna gain has been considered as the beginning of moderate difficulty in maintaining mechanical design tolerances. In optical telescopes, however, much higher gains are not only possible, but are rather commonplace. An extreme example of this is seen in the 200-inch optical telescope on Mount Palomar. If the "antenna gain" for this telescope is calculated at 4400 A (the approximate center of the visible spectrum), it is found to be about 180 db!

Perhaps a comparison of this sort is a little unfair, since it tends to draw conclusions from two somewhat dissimilar situations. It will, however, serve to illustrate a point, in that optical systems are at a considerably more advanced state of development than are their radio counterparts. Until recently there was very little interest in giant antennas. Radio astronomy provided the first requirement for these devices, as an aid to optical telescopes. Now it appears that space communication and interstellar snooping may ultimately require even more advanced radio telescopes. Actually, there is no "ultimate" size antenna to supply these needs. Just as in the case of optical telescopes, there will always be further mysteries which might be unfolded through the use of a larger antenna.

In satellite orbits around the earth it may be possible to design antennas of appreciably greater size than that which is possible at the surface of the earth. All is not gravy in this scheme, however, and a great many problem areas still remain. For example, the logistics of construction will require a fairly advanced space technology. Low-altitude earth orbits will experience additional problems of gravity gradient and atmospheric drag on such large, light-weight structures. High earth temperature and earth shadowing will pose additional operational problems. Higher altitude orbits will experience increased radiation and greater logistics problems, but less gravity gradient, earth shadowing, and atmospheric drag. In both cases the solar wind and unequal solar heating will have to be contended with. Solar heating might be so severe as to require that the entire antenna be encased in a giant balloon radome so that the thermal stresses can be controlled more accurately.

Finally, it might be advantageous to consider the surface of the moon as a likely construction site for a giant antenna. Atmospheric attenuation is negligible at the surface of the moon, and the lunar gravity is only about one-sixth of that at the surface of the earth. Still the lunar gravity is not negligible, and the problem of unequal solar heating is still there. Lunar surface temperature also poses a problem for very low temperature receivers, just as in the case of low-altitude earth satellite orbits. The reason for this is that the antenna sidelobes cannot be completely suppressed, thus producing limitations in minimum antenna temperature achievable.

Despite the impressive array of automatic devices, it is highly likely that the more advanced extraterrestrial radio observatories will be manned. Although both the earth orbit and lunar observatories have severe logistics requirements, the lunar station has very definite advantages in that housing, storage, and other facilities can be obtained under more familiar conditions. The advantages of a stable base of operations is certainly significant to such an operation.

Granted that it is possible to construct giant antennas, it might be desirable to examine further the chances for interstellar contact with other intelligent beings. Table 1 is a tabulation of the 55 stars nearest the sun, in order of their distances. The nearest star, α Centauri, is about 4.3 light-years away, but there are a large number of stars within 10 to 20 light-years distance. The number of stars in the sample increases very rapidly with distance from the sun. Statistically speaking, therefore, the chances for detecting intelligent life should increase very rapidly with increasing radio telescopic range.

Concerning the possibility of planets around other stars, Briggs (3) has said, "Determination of the rate of rotation of any particular star is possible by examination of the 'profile' of the lines of its spectra . . . It is apparent that approximately 67% of the stars of our galaxy are slowly rotating, which implies that they are accompanied by planets." He goes on to say, "Although there is no complete agreement amongst biologists concerning the origin of life, the work of Oparin and others in this field indicates that life arises by complex physio-chemical processes on any planet with suitable conditions."

Going back for a moment to the attenuation plots in Figures 2 and 3, only static conditions have been considered. For example, the planet transmitting a signal may be using a fairly high gain transmitting antenna. Unless that antenna happens to be pointing in the direction of the solar system and stabilized in inertial space (i.e., compensated for planetary rotation), then the signal can only be received for some limited time as the antenna beam crosses the solar system. The time during which this signal can be received will depend upon the antenna gain and the planetary rotation rate. Antenna gain G can be expressed

Table 1

Distance and Magnitude of Stars Nearest the Sun

(Stars nearer than 5 parsecs)

No.	Name	Visual magnitude	Spectrum	Distance, light-years	Abs. vis. mag.	Visual luminosity
1	Sun	−26.9	G0		4.7	1.0
2	α Centauri A	0.3	G0	4.29	4.7	1.0
3	α Centauri B	1.7	K5	4.29	6.1	0.28
4	α Centauri C	11	M	4.29	15.4	0.000052
5	Barnard's star	9.5	M5	5.98	13.2	0.0004
6	Wolf 359	13.5	M8	7.74	16.6	0.000017
7	Luyten 726-8 A	12.5	M6	7.9	15.6	0.00004
8	Luyten 726-8 B	13.0	M6	7.9	16.1	0.00003
9	Lalande 21185	7.5	M2	8.2	10.5	0.0048
10	Sirius A	−1.6	A0	8.7	1.3	23
11	Sirius B	7.1	A5	8.7	10.0	0.008
12	Ross 154	10.6	M6	9.3	13.3	0.00036
13	Ross 248	12.2	M6	10.3	14.7	0.0001
14	ε Eridani	3.8	K2	10.8	6.2	0.25
15	Ross 128	11.1	M5	10.9	13.5	0.0003
16	61 Cygni A	5.6	K3	11.1	7.9	0.052
17	61 Cygni B	6.3	K5	11.1	8.6	0.028
18	Luyten 789-6	12.2	M7	11.2	14.5	0.00012
19	Procyon A	0.5	F5	11.3	2.8	5.8
20	Procyon B	10.8		11.3	13.1	0.00044
21	ε Indi	4.7	K5	11.4	7.0	0.12
22	Σ 2398 A	8.9	M4	11.6	11.1	0.0028
23	Σ 2398 B	9.7	M4	11.6	11.9	0.0013
24	Groombridge 34 A	8.1	M2	11.7	10.3	0.0058
25	Groombridge 34 B	10.9	M5	11.7	13.1	0.00044
26	γ Ceti	3.6	K0	11.8	5.8	0.36
27	Lacaille 9352	7.2	M0	11.9	9.4	0.013
28	BD + 5° 1688	10.1	M4	12.4	12.2	0.001
29	Lacaille 8760	6.6	M0	12.8	8.6	0.028
30	Kaptcyn's star	9.2	M0	13.0	11.2	0.0025
31	Kruger 60 A	9.9	M4	13.1	11.9	0.0013
32	Kruger 60 B	11.4	M6	13.1	13.4	0.00033
33	Ross 614	10.9	M7	13.1	12.9	0.00052
34	BD − 12° 4523	10.0	M5	13.4	11.9	0.0013
35	van Maanen's star	12.3	G	13.8	14.2	0.00016
36	Wolf 424 A	12.6	M4	14.6	14.3	0.00014
37	Wolf 424 B	12.6	M4	14.6	14.3	0.00014
38	Groombridge 1618	6.8	K6	14.7	8.5	0.03
39	CD − 37° 15492	8.6	M4	14.9	10.3	0.0058
40	CD − 46° 11540	9.7	M4	15.3	11.3	0.0023
41	BD + 20° 2465	9.5	M5	15.4	11.1	0.0028
42	CD − 44° 11909	11.2	M5	15.6	12.8	0.00058
43	CD − 49° 13515	9.0	M3	15.6	10.6	0.0044
44	AO 17415-6	9.1	M4	15.8	10.7	0.004
45	Ross 780	10.2	M5	15.8	11.8	0.0014
46	Lalande 25372	8.6	M1	15.9	10.2	0.0063
47	CC 658	11.0		16.0	12.5	0.0008
48	o² Eridani A	4.5	G5	16.3	6.0	0.3
49	o² Eridani B	9.2	A	16.3	10.7	0.004
50	o² Eridani C	11.0	M6	16.3	12.5	0.0008
51	70 Ophiuchi A	4.2	K1	16.4	5.7	0.4
52	70 Ophiuchi B	5.9	K5	16.4	7.4	0.083
53	Altair	0.9	A5	16.5	2.1	8.3
54	BD + 43° 4305	10.2	M5	16.5	11.7	0.0016
55	AC + 79° 3888	11.0	M5	16.6	12.5	0.0008

as a function of antenna beamwidth θ in degrees according to the following relation (4):

$$G = \frac{27,000}{\theta^2} \tag{7}$$

However, for a time-varying antenna gain, $(\Delta\theta/\Delta t)\Delta t$ may be substituted for θ, so that

$$G = \frac{27,000}{[(\Delta\theta/\Delta t)\Delta t]^2} \tag{8}$$

Now comes the problem of assigning a rotation rate to the prospective planet. Of the earth's nearest neighbors, Mars is found to have a rotation rate similar to earth, and the rotation rate of Venus is still uncertain (5). Perhaps there is something magic about the 24-hour rotation rate of earth and Mars. At any rate it is a start, and with this assumption Eq. (8) can be expressed in decibels as follows:

$$G = 92 - 20 \log \Delta t \tag{9}$$

Figure 4 is a plot of Eq. (8), showing the maximum time expected for an antenna beam to be pointing toward earth, as a function of antenna gain. It is assumed that the planet rotates once in 24 hours, and that the antenna is pointed along the equatorial plane.

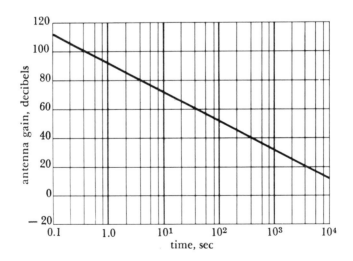

Figure 4

Transmitter output power required for a 10°K receiver, operating at a range of 10 light-years.

Of course it would be nice if the transmitting antenna were pointed directly toward earth, either stabilized in inertial space, or by being pointed parallel to the planetary polar axis. If such were the case, however, it would happen either as a pure coincidence, or due to an intentional transmission toward the solar system for purposes of radio contact. Since it has been agreed that the latter is a rather unlikely circumstance, a limited time contact is probably a more usual case to look for.

Figures 2, 3, and 4 provide little information on the possibility of interstellar contact unless the data bandwidth requirements are specified in a bit more detail. Although this is far too complex a subject to be discussed in detail here, certain generalizations can be made on the basis of communications experience already gained.

Probably the easiest wave form to detect would be a simple cw carrier. The data bandwidth required to detect a cw carrier is determined by the stability of the transmitted signal. With high-quality crystal oscillators available on earth, 10-cps spectral line width or instability bandwidth represents a very stable oscillator at the centimeter wavelengths. A high-stability atomic resonance frequency source, however, might provide appreciably greater frequency stability, thereby allowing even lower bandwidths to be used.

Although high-intensity cw waveforms may be searched for, the chances for detecting intelligent signals can certainly be increased by looking for more complex waveforms. Radar pulses, cw tracking radars, telemetry, television, voice transmission, digital telegraphy, or facsimile, are only a few possibilities. Unfortunately, most of these waveforms require appreciably greater data bandwidths than that which is possible to detect on earth. New detection techniques are now being developed, however, which show great promise in reducing the bandwidth requirements for repetitive waveforms such as radar pulses (6). Another interesting radar development is "chirp" or pulse compression radar. This requires, however, that the transmitter knows how to chirp.

Generally speaking, the detection problem may be described as a search for any non-Gaussian characteristic in the received signal. Searching may be made in amplitude and frequency, and over both narrow and wide receiver bandwidths. "Adaptive" filter techniques may be used to methodically search over a number of variables in an effort to detect any non-Gaussian signal characteristics, and to selectively detect any signal present. To facilitate this effort, the receiver intermediate frequency signal may be recorded on tape so that various types of selective filtering techniques may be applied "off line," to conserve radio telescopic receiving time, and to preserve the evidence of any signal which may be detected in this manner.

In Conclusion

It is difficult to specify what types of signals may be emanating from some planet in our general neighborhood of the galaxy. There is substantial evidence, however, that the chances for life, and very possibly intelligent life, are fairly high among our neighboring stars. It is also quite likely that any advanced society will make some use of the microwave portion of the electromagnetic spectrum. It is considered rather unlikely that any intelligent beings will deliberately try to contact the solar system, although this possibility should not be discounted entirely. A much more likely prospect is that of listening for microwave transmissions intended for defense, communication, or other normal commercial purposes.

Although there exists some possibility of interstellar radio contact at the present time, the chances for success will increase rapidly with man's increasing capabilities in low-temperature receiving techniques, large-diameter radio telescopes, and adaptive filtering techniques. Although the absence of intelligent life in any stellar system cannot be established by this method, it may be possible to establish the presence of intelligent life in one or more stellar systems. Since a relatively large statistical sample of stars exists within less than 20 light-years from earth, it may be possible to "play the odds" successfully in searching for intelligent life.

References

1 J. A. Webb, Satellite World Communications, *Telecommu. J. (Geneva)*, March 1961.
2 J. A. Webb, Space Communication, *Astronaut. Sci. Rev.*, April-June 1960.
3 M. H. Briggs, The Detection of Planets at Interstellar Distances, *J. British Interplanet. Soc.*, March-April 1959.
4 *Reference Data for Radio Engineers*, 4th ed., International Telephone and Telegraph Company.
5 Science and The Citizen (editorial), *Sci. Am.*, July 1961.
6 Robert Price, The Venus Radar Experiment, presented to AGARD (NATO), Aachen, Germany, Sept. 21, 1959.

Additional Remarks by J. A. Webb, October 16, 1962

It might be well to consider the possible character of intelligent emissions from an alien world. The following is a partial list of signals

Table A

Frequency, Gc/sec	Pulse width	Power output, Mw	Use
1-10	1-100 μsec	0.1-100	Aircraft detection
0.1-2	100-1000 μsec	10-1000	Antimissile, antisatellite radar
0.1-10	0.1 sec-cw	0.01-1000	Interplanetary surveillance radar
1-10	Code or cw	0.01-100	Space communications

which might be searched for, based upon present knowledge of technically feasible systems on earth within the foreseeable future (Table A). The aircraft detection radars need little further explanation, except to say that the 100-Mw upper limit for output power and 100 μsec pulse length are perhaps on the optimistic side owing to the fact that the horizon, rather than power output and pulse length, usually limits aircraft detection range.

Antiballistic missile and antisatellite radars of 1000 μsec pulse duration and 1000 Mw power output are theoretically feasible today, using phased-array antennas and multiple coherent transmitters. Early-warning radars are at the present time not much more than an order of magnitude below this power level.

The interplanetary search and surveillance radar postulated here is a possible requirement for an advanced civilization, where it is desired to keep track of various objects within the vicinity of the planet, either for defense or scientific purposes. This radar could be expected to have a very long pulse length and high output power.

An advanced civilization would undoubtedly have a requirement for interplanetary communications within their stellar system. This transmitter would have high power output, be pulse-coded or modulated cw, and would incorporate relatively high antenna gain.

From Figure 2 of my preceding article, assuming a 10°K receiver and a 100-ft-diameter receiving antenna, it would require almost 140 dbw of transmitter output power plus antenna gain to receive a 1000-μsec pulse (1 kc bandwidth) at a range of 10 light-years, for unity signal to noise ratio on a single pulse. This condition could be satisfied with 1000 Mw output power and 50 db of transmitter antenna gain. Detection of such a signal therefore, while not impossible, must be considered a rather unlikely event.

This brings up a rather interesting point of speculation. Suppose a radio telescope were trained on a likely stellar system intermittently over a rather long period of time, say for several weeks. Chances are that at some time during this period a rather unlikely event may just happen to occur. Once this event has occurred, it is almost certain that a more intensive search will produce more data, resulting in more certainty as to the reality of the event, and data on the characteristics of the signal.

Unity signal to noise ratio of course does not provide a sufficiently good probability of detection for a single pulse, but the probability of detection can be improved substantially by observation of multiple pulses [W. M. Hall, *Proc. Inst. Radio Engrs.*, **44**, 224 (1956)]. Although the detailed handling of the data is slightly different in the detection of a cw signal, the same basic principles of detection probability can be applied to cw detection.

To implement a search for a signal of unknown character, special filtering techniques are required. These techniques will require long, tedious search through noise. Probably the best way to accomplish this is to record the "noise" from the telescope on wide-bandwidth tape, digitize the output, and search for any non-Gaussian signal in the noise by means of a digital computer. Digital adaptive filters can be designed to apply various "randomness criteria" to the noise, and provide probability figures for any detectable non-Gaussian signal.

Whereas we can conclude that it would be generally unlikely that a 100-ft radio telescope, operating at 10°K, could detect a civilization comparable to that on earth at a range of 10 light-years, the possibility is certainly worth looking for, and a "lucky break" just might occur. Larger diameter telescopes, however, greatly increase the possibility of detecting other civilizations, for two reasons. First, they permit a deeper search for signals among our immediate neighboring stellar systems, and, second, they provide a larger statistical sample of stellar systems to search through, by providing greater search range. For example, our nearest stellar neighbor is 4.29 light-years away, but there are 55 stars within 16.6 light-years.

In space, or possibly even on the surface of the earth, it might be possible within the next few decades to construct radio telescopes 1000 to 10,000 ft in diameter. These telescopes would prove very useful for studying natural radio emissions from various portions of the galaxy, and could be readily justified for this purpose alone. The use of such powerful instruments for the detection of intelligent signals from space could almost certainly detect civilizations comparable to our own out to ranges of tens of light-years. Such search would probably be conducted "off line," from prerecorded tape, examined leisurely, and checked for possible errors. This proceedure also provides for more economical use of the large radio telescope; where, especially in the case of the very large telescopes, observation time will be at a premium.

I leave it to the astronomer and biologist to speculate on the probability of life in other stellar systems. As a communications engineer, however, I feel that it is technically feasible to search out our arm of the galaxy for intelligent radio emissions; and, if they are there, to detect such signals and determine their character. To me, this is a very exciting possibility, since it provides essentially the only hope that within the lifetimes of some of us, it may be possible to look into the lives of alien intelligent beings.

M. J. E. Golay

I9 ✳ COHERENCE
IN INTERSTELLAR SIGNALS

NOTE ON COHERENCE VS. NARROW-BANDEDNESS IN
REGENERATIVE OSCILLATORS, MASERS, LASERS, ETC.

In several discussions with engineers and physicists engaged in pushing the art of generating coherent radiation to shorter wavelengths, I have noted that the narrow-bandedness of the radiation produced, if not confused with the coherence* of this radiation, is often considered to be a measure of the degree of coherence. I would like to point out that coherence is not a quantitative concept, but a qualitative one; either radiation is coherent, or it is not, regardless of bandwidth considerations. If the duration of the signal is not indefinite, owing to physical limitations such as the heating of a ruby laser, or of the source of pumping radiation, either the radiation is coherent during its ephemeral duration, or it is not.

Theoretical experiments, probably realizable at later times, may be useful to form a picture of the concept involved here.

Consider a source of narrow-banded radiation which must be tested for coherence, and designate its approximate center frequency by f. If the source output is heterodyned with two assumedly available perfectly monochromatic signals proportional to $\cos 2\pi ft$ and $\sin 2\pi ft$, respectively, the two components of a phasor are obtained.

The behavior of this phasor will constitute the criterion of coherence vs. noncoherence of the radiation studied.

If this radiation is incoherent, the phasor end will be observed to

* The term "coherence" is used here in the sense of cw radiation which can interfere with indefinitely delayed portions of itself. It should not be confused with optical coherence, which refers to the property which two light beams have of interfering with each other when they are obtained from a common source.

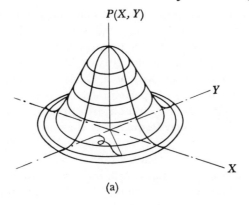

(a)

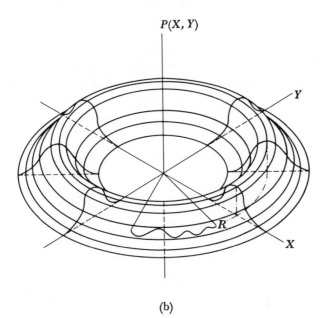

(b)

Figure 1

Probability distribution of the phasor representing the relationship between a narrow-band signal and a perfectly monochromatic reference signal, for two cases. (a) The signal is incoherent. The distribution is a "mole-hill" centered on the origin, showing no tendency toward regulation of amplitude. (b) The signal is coherent. The "mole-run" distribution shows a strong tendency to regulate amplitude to the value R but substantial random drift in phase may occur.

execute a two-dimensional random walk at a rate inversely proportional to the bandwidth of this radiation, and if the experiment is continued over a sufficiently long period of time, the statistical location of this phasor end will be describable by a probability distribution which, in most instances, will be a Gaussian "mole-hill" centered at the origin (Figure 1a). Superimposed on the random walk of the phasor end, there will be a circular drift proportional to the departure of f from the exact center frequency of the source spectrum.

On the other hand, if the radiation studied is coherent, the phasor end will be observed to execute a random walk statistically describable by a probability distribution which, in most instances, will be a circular "mole-run" centered at the origin, but with vanishingly small probability at that origin (Figure 1b). Any radial cross section of this mole-run will, in general, be approximately Gaussian. Radial excursions of the phasor end away from the center circle of the mole-run will resemble the excursions about zero of the thermal voltage on a condenser shunted by a resistance, for the regenerative property of the oscillator will tend to maintain constant the average length of the phasor. Conversely, circumferential excursions of the phasor end will assume the

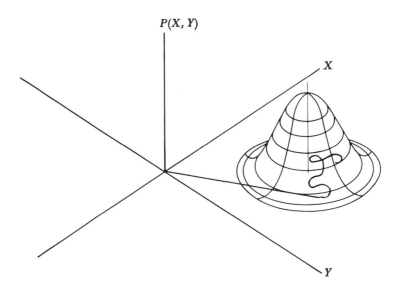

Figure 2

This probability distribution is not a possible result in the limit as observation time approaches infinity since it would imply "phase locking" with the hypothetical reference signal.

character of a random walk, the rate of which has been calculated in a former article (*1*). A slow average rotation will be superimposed on this circumferential random walk, the rate of this rotation being proportional to the departure of *f* from the exact center frequency of the source spectrum.

It is essential to note that there is no fixed phase reference to which the phasor may be brought back with a restoring force proportional to the departure of the phasor from this phase reference. Thus, a probability distribution of the phasor end describable by a mole-hill at a distance from the origin (Figure 2) is fundamentally impossible.

Experimental verification of the phasor's behavior for laser's outputs has not been obtained, but it may be speculated that when the radiation from two relatively stable lasers is caused to interfere on two photocells, with a quarter-wave difference between the two path differences from the two lasers to the two photocells, the photocells' outputs will represent a phasor, the phase of which is the phase difference of the two lasers. Whether or not the character of the probability distribution of the phasor end can be detected in such an experiment will depend upon whether the bandpass of the photocells' outputs exceeds or does not exceed the instantaneous frequency difference of the two lasers.

Reference

1 M. J. E. Golay, Monochromaticity and Noise in a Regenerative Electrical Oscillator, *Proc. Inst. Radio Engrs.*, **48**, 1473 (1960).

Note on the Probable Character of Intelligent Radio Signals from Other Planetary Systems

Experiments are now being planned (*1*) to detect radio messages aimed at the earth from planets of other solar systems—experiments which few believe will succeed, but which few would not want to see tried.

The spectral location, as well as the character of these signals, constitute subjects for stimulating speculation.

It may well be surmised that these hypothetic signals will have a spectral location related in a simple manner to the 1421-Mc line of hydrogen, and since this line is located in a relatively noisy region of the cosmic radio spectrum, a location at either half or at twice its frequency appears fairly probable.

It may be surmised further that these signals will contain a coherent component* at as nearly half or twice the hydrogen frequency as available accuracy permits. Following this line of reasoning, we may expect the senders to correct this frequency for the component of motion of their transmitter in the direction of transmission with respect to the center of gravity of their planetary system, as well as for the gravitational potential of that transmitter with respect to their "local" outer space; corrections which we should also make for our receiver.

Even when so corrected, the coherent signal postulated here will have to be further corrected for the nebular drift between the two solar systems, unless of course it is already corrected at the transmitting end. Thus, it would appear that there may be four likely spectral regions within which a search should be made for coherent signals, before any intelligent messages can be received: at half or at twice the hydrogen frequency, and with or without correction for nebular drift.

The extent of each search region will be determined mostly by our —or their—uncertainty in nebular drift, and to a lesser extent by the relative error of sender and receiver in determining the exact hydrogen frequency or the various corrections indicated above. It must be noted that the two search regions at half the hydrogen frequency are only a quarter as wide as the two search regions at twice that frequency and that this factor of four is exactly compensated by the fourfold smaller directivity of a reflector of a given size at the lower frequency. When such factors as easier power generation and greater space coverage are considered, the two half-frequency regions appear more favorable.

The bandwidth of search, Δf, within each region is a matter for much conjecture, but once this bandwidth has been decided upon, the manner of search appears straight forward. The signals received are heterodyned with $\cos 2\pi$ ft and $\sin 2\pi$ ft, respectively, where f designates a frequency within the search region, and the two outputs are filtered by two low-pass RC filters with a time constant of the order of

$$RC = \frac{1}{\pi\Delta f}$$

The filter outputs constitute the two components of a phasor, the behavior of the end of which should be studied for a time equal to a few times the time constant of the dual low-pass filters. If a "mole-run" tendency is detected for the statistical distribution of the phasor end, and if this tendency is confirmed by extending the time of search, the

* See the footnote on page 192.

presence of intelligent transmission within the $f \pm \Delta f/2$ region will be ascertained with a probability of error which decreases exponentially with time.

Since, for a given transmitting power, the bandwidth of search Δf decreases with the inverse square of the distance, and since the time required for searching a given region increases with the inverse square of Δf, the fourth power law relating total time of search and distance will require that several Δf-wide regions be searched simultaneously, in order to cover the total search regions in a reasonable time.

It is of interest to note the basic difference between the search procedure outlined above, and the search procedure which consists in recording a narrow spectral region, forming the autocorrelation function of the recorded signals, and taking the Fourier transform in cosines of this autocorrelation function. This latter method serves to reveal the presence of extra spectral energy within narrow bands, but does not preserve phase information. Thus, a coherent signal which is slightly phase modulated becomes indistinguishable from a spectral line with a width equal to the frequency excursion, whereas the mole-run character of the phasor-end statistical distribution which can be detected with the method discussed above serves to establish with increasing certainty that coherent signals are indeed coherent.

Reference

1   O. Struve, Astronomers in Turmoil, *Phys. Today*, **13**, 18 (1960).

COMMENT ON COHERENCE

Some of the confusion still surrounding the meaning of coherence appears to be due to the different viewpoints of the optician and of the communication engineer, whom the advent of the laser has obliged to communicate more with each other.

Taking the optical viewpoint, I have defined coherence as the essentially qualitative characteristic of a cw signal when compared to an optical emission line or to a narrowly filtered band of white noise (1), for an optician will say he is dealing with a coherent light source when he observes that this light source forms a sharp interference pattern with indefinitely delayed portions of itself, even if this pattern is not stationary. This is because the optician has, in the past, termed coherent two interfering optical beams derived from the same light source and finitely delayed with respect to each other. On the other hand, the communication engineer, long familiar with cw signals, takes for granted the existence of sharp interferences between two portions of the same signal which are indefinitely delayed with respect to each other, and may prefer to reserve the term coherence to designate a measure of some desirable property of the signal source, such as the degree of stationarity of the interference pattern, or of the phasor by said two portions.

At this point the communication engineer runs into some interesting problems. For instance, if his source is an ideal cw generator installed on a planetoid having its own orbit around the sun, the communication engineer will attempt to track the weak signal he receives with a phase-locked loop, the behavior of which may be described by the differential equation of a damped system such as

$$\left(1 + T\frac{d}{dt}\right)^n \phi_s = \phi_r$$

in which ϕ_s and ϕ_r are the phase of the received signal and of the slaved signal, and in which n and T have been selected so as to optimize the SNR.

Since a large T means a very narrow bandwidth of reception, T may be taken as a measure of the coherence of the received signal, even though there is a rapid rotation of the interference phasor formed by two portions of the signal delayed with respect to each other. Furthermore, the order n of the characteristic differential equation should be taken into account, which might lead to the view that coherence is a multidimensional quantitative concept.

The concept of coherence as I have defined it is not without its own questions. For instance, should we term partially coherent signals characterized by a phasor-end distribution having the aspect of a mole-hill depressed at the top, and is coherence, even as an optician would define it, a quantitative concept after all?

Reference

1 M. J. E. Golay, "Note on Coherence vs. Narrow-Bandedness in Regenerative Oscillators, Masers, Lasers, etc.," *Proc. Inst. Radio Engrs.* (correspondence), **49**, 958 (1961).

R. N. Bracewell

20 ✳ RADIO SIGNALS
FROM OTHER PLANETS

The 1420-Mc line of hydrogen can hardly be said to be located in a relatively noisy region of the cosmic radio spectrum (*1*). The average sky brightness temperature amounts to a few degrees Kelvin. There are some very limited regions in the direction of the center of the galaxy, and to each side along the galactic equator, where the brightness temperature is higher, reaching 50°K or more depending on the size of the antenna. At double the wavelength, these temperatures would be six or seven times higher. In addition to this continuum emission there is line emission, generally fairly close to the nominal hydrogen-line frequency, but also concentrated fairly heavily toward the galactic plane.

However, the planets from which signals are expected must not be so remote as to lie in the galactic plane (*2*), and therefore the brightness temperatures in the colder parts of the sky are more appropriate. At present the noise contributions of the receiver and ambient medium are thus more important than the cosmic noise. Consequently no case has been made for avoiding 1420 Mc. There are, however, reasons (*2*) for not using 1420 Mc or other microwave frequencies, if the distance to the nearest community more advanced than our own is 100 light-years rather than the 10 light-years investigated by Project Ozma.

Under circumstances where signaling by radio waves seemed reasonable, it would not seem worthwhile to correct out the various Doppler shifts. A stable transmitter on a remote planet would give us a signal from which we might hope to deduce the length of the day and the year, the radius and inclination of the planetary orbit, the radius of the planet, the latitude of the transmitter, and even other parameters. As a first harvest during the interval before a signal could be acknowledged, this would be much more exciting news than a string of prime numbers. The latter would only prove that the designers of high-power transmitters can also count, and is not appropriate to signals in the precontact phase.

References

1 M. J. E. Golay, Note on the Probable Character of Intelligent Radio Signals from Other Planetary Systems, *Proc. Inst. Radio Engrs.* (correspondence), **49,** 959 (1961).

2 R. N. Bracewell, Communications from Superior Galactic Communities, *Nature,* **186,** 670 (1960).

Su-Shu Huang

2 I ❋ PROBLEM OF TRANSMISSION IN INTERSTELLAR COMMUNICATION

Communication in general is a two-way process and interstellar communication should be no exception. If everyone is trying to detect signals from other beings without sending out his own, no one will receive a signal. Actually the situation goes deeper than this. Even if someone is willing to inform other people, we still cannot receive the full information without being supported by a transmitting station which can reach the place where these particular people live. This can be seen in the following way.

Let the total number of transmitting stations these people have for the sole purpose of interstellar communication be N_t and the total number of the receiving stations which are solely used for interstellar communication be N_r. If we further let $N_s{}^0$ be the number of stars per unit volume that have a higher-than-average chance of supporting life of an advanced form, the total number N_s of such stars is given by

$$N_s = \frac{4\pi}{3} N_s{}^0 R^3 \qquad (1)$$

where R represents the distance that *they think* they can reach according to *their ability* to transmit and receive signals. From the star count in the immediate neighborhood of the sun (*1*) and from the criteria of life-supporting ability of stars (*2*), we might expect $N_s{}^0 = 0.006$ if R is expressed in parsecs.

Let us now examine the behavior of R. It is evident that R increases rapidly with the advance of technological capability, because each step in the process of transmitting and receiving signals is improved with the advance of technology. For example, the power of transmission, the diameter of the transmitting antenna and radio telescope, the sensitivity of the receiver, etc., all increase at the same time as we improve our technical skill. Also, by moving the telescope outside of the earth's atmosphere we can gain another factor because of a reduction in noise.

From our experience on the earth, the technical skill in radio communication is progressing fast. Thus, any civilization that exists at present in other worlds in our galaxy is most likely either at a stage of complete incapability for radio communication or at a stage of technological perfection in the sense given by F. D. Drake that "The limits on communication system sensitivities are not set by deficiencies in the apparatus, such as receiver noise, but by natural phenomena over which man has no control" (3). From the invention of radio communication to the stage of technological perfection, the transition may take 100 years in the case of our own civilization. Compared with the time scales we are talking about, this interval is negligibly short. Accordingly, we may write

$$
\begin{aligned}
R &= 0 \qquad t < t_0 \\
R &= R_p \qquad t > t_0
\end{aligned}
\tag{2}
$$

where t_0 represents the time at which the transition takes place and may be regarded as a point on the time axis. R_p may be practically taken as a constant for all civilizations which have reached the stage of technological perfection in radio communication. Our own technological civilizations, which lie at present in the transitional period from complete incapability to technological perfection, appears to yield a value of R of the order of 5 parsecs from the discussions by F. D. Drake (3), and by G. Cocconi and P. Morrison (4). Therefore, it is entirely within our understanding that R_p can reach more than 500 or 1000 parsecs.

It should be noted here that the interest for establishing contact with other civilizations in the galaxy decreases with R because it will take longer and longer times to send signals from one to the other. For example, at $R = 1000$ parsecs, the interchange of an idea would take 6600 years, which is of the order of the entire period covered by written history on the earth. Thus, for our present discussion, we will take a value of $R = 500$ parsecs. Then it follows from (1) that $N_s = 3 \times 10^6$. We do not know the average total number N_t of transmitting stations that each civilization possesses. But it cannot be a large number because the construction of such stations is expensive, and more seriously, its operation yields no visible and reportable result. Whatever the result in the search for an interstellar message, one can always report something. But, the person who is transmitting signals to other worlds can report neither success nor failure year after year. On the other hand, he has to explain his long silence to people who have financed the project. Moreover, although the detection for the interstellar signals sent by intelligent beings has its scientific challenge, because it is a process of searching the unknown, the actual transmission of messages to interstellar space does not have the fascination and spirit of searching the unknown for scientists. Now, if scientists shy away from it because it lacks the excitement of challenge, who else will promote the project, which requires a large amount of money over a long period of time of thousands of years? Thus, here on the earth we have already started the project of Ozma (3) to detect signals from intelligent beings in other worlds but we have not yet sent out signals ourselves. It can safely be said that on the earth those who are either directly engaged, or simply interested, in the search for intelligent signals from outer space will eventually promote the construction of stations transmitting signals to stars. The present paper may perhaps be regarded as a step in this direction.

In any case, it is reasonable to say that the number of transmitting stations for the sole use of interstellar communication in each civilization will never be large. Thus, we may write down the following inequalities:

$$N_s \gg N_r > N_t \tag{3}$$

and N_s/N_t is perhaps of the order of 10^6 if we take $R = 500$ parsecs; i.e., we expect N_t to be less than 10. From the large value of N_s/N_t we can immediately see the dilemma facing the beings who are transmitting signals to other worlds. It is evident that they cannot afford to beam their transmitting antenna indefinitely toward one single star. The only way that they may have a good chance to contact civilization in other worlds is to divide the antenna time and beam the signals successively to all stars which are within their reach and which are believed to be able to support life of an advanced form. Thus, if they spend on the average one day on each star, it would take about 3000 years to send signals to all candidates if we take N_s/N_t to be 10^6 and if the beam width is narrow enough to scan each star individually as we may reasonably expect them to do.

Also, it is reasonably sure that if intelligent beings on any planet should transmit messages to other worlds at all, they must at least divide the message into two classes: (1) probing message, which signals others to recognize and then to contact them, and (2) informative message, which will be sent only to those who have responded to their signals. Such a division of messages is necessary and inevitable because they cannot waste their time to have a long "talk" with mute people. Thus, in order to receive significant signals, we must be prepared to transmit some kind of response to them. It follows also from this argument that we must be prepared to wait a certain period of time, depending upon their distance from us, before we may receive from them some significant and informative messages even if we transmit signals to them immediately after we have received their probing message.

They may not divide the time of transmitting antennae equally to all candidate stars that may support intelligent beings. Rather, they could beam signals to the nearest stars more frequently than to the faraway stars, because it takes a shorter time to obtain a response from the nearby stars if a response is indeed forthcoming. An efficient way of sending out the signals to their nearby stars under this argument is to space them in such a way that the time between two successive trials of transmission is of the order of $2r/c$, where r is the distance of the star and c is the velocity of light. This constitutes a "persistent inquiry," because the time interval thus specified is allowed only for signals to travel forth and a response to travel back. According to this scheme, a star at a distance of 5 light-years is beamed at a short interval (say 1 day, as in the previous example) every 10 years. Hence the frequency of beaming at nearby stars is increased greatly, and if a technological civilization is indeed developed in the neighborhood of a nearby star, such a transmission pattern definitely uplifts the chance of success in establishing interstellar communication. It is in this case that the search for signals from stars in our own immediate neighborhood, such as project Ozma, has its greatest chance of success. On the other hand, more frequent transmissions to nearby stars must be done at the expense of faraway stars, because the total time of transmitting antennae is limited. Therefore, this pattern of transmission suppresses the chance of detection of their signals by faraway stars.

In short, if the average separation of two contemporary civilizations in the galaxy is less than a certain value, say 10 parsecs, this uneven distribution of transmission times for different stars has its advantage. But if the average distance is more than a certain value, say 100 parsecs, this pattern of transmission has disadvantages. A priori, we don't know which is the case. Since our present technology is perhaps inferior to that of others who can communicate with us (5), we can avoid this choice by not sending out probing signals. Our transmitting station will be used solely, at least for the next hundred years or so, for making responses to some intelligent messages from interstellar space that have been detected.

The short time interval with which any being in other worlds may beam signals directly toward us in each scan also makes our detection and identification of them very difficult. Following our numerical example of sending signals toward us one day every 300 years, we may not be able to interpret conclusively the reception of their messages, even if we happen to point our radio telescope in the right direction at the right time, because when we try next time we will receive nothing until another 300 years has elapsed. Here we see once more the importance of having our own transmitting station as a support to the search for interstellar messages. If some signals should have been suspected to be coming from intelligent beings near some star, we could immediately beam our responding signals to them. Any civilization that is able to transmit signals must have the common sense to search for signals from the star toward which they had beamed their waves previously, allowing, of course, for a time interval due to the travel of signals back and forth between the two stars.

One may argue that the other beings may send signals toward any one particular star for a longer time than one day at each trial, say of the order of 1 year. Indeed, the receiving side may find it easier to recognize the nature of the source of signals. However, we then have to wait 10^6 years before we may have another chance to receive signals from them if we miss the previous one. If we were in the position of transmission, we would certainly not undertake an operation which takes 1,000,000 years to complete one single cycle. Most likely we would scan a star each time with an interval even shorter than 1 day. The optimum length of signaling time should be just long enough for the receiving party to disentangle messages from noise. Thus, it appears that the signalling time should be longer for the distant stars than for the nearby ones because it takes a longer time to detect a weak signal than a strong signal.

In any case, our chance of receiving signals from any being who is *actually* transmitting signals to other worlds in interstellar space is on the average equal to N_t/N_s, or of the order of 10^{-6} if $R = 500$ parsecs. This basic difficulty, which is caused by the disparity of the two numbers N_t and N_s, is not new to astronomers. In fact it is intrinsic to all astronomical observations. As a dramatic example, the total number of stars in our galaxy is of the order of 10^{11}, while the total active astronomers on the entire earth is perhaps of the order of 10^4 and the total number of telescopes used every night for astronomical researchers may be of the order of 10^2. It is natural to conclude that we cannot require astronomers to examine every star in the galaxy aside from the fact that most of them are too faint to be observed.

In order to initiate interstellar communication, on the other hand, we do require the transmitting antennae to scan all stars that are possible to support an advanced form of life. From what we now understand, emergence of life and intelligence is likely a cosmic event which comes naturally just as the formation of stars, if the physical environment is suitable for its development (6). Thus, the success of interstellar communication may depend more than anything else upon the problem of facing a large number of stars with a limited means of transmission and reception.

Acknowledgment

I wish to thank Dr. J. E. Kupperian, Jr., for valuable discussions.

References

1   P. van de Kamp, *Publ. Astron. Soc. Pacific,* **65,** 73 (1953).
2   S.-S. Huang, *Am. Scientist,* **47,** 397 (1959).
3   F. D. Drake, *Sky and Telescope,* **19,** 140 (1960).
4   G. Cocconi and P. Morrison, *Nature,* **184,** 844 (1959).
5   P. Morrison, *Bull. Phil. Soc. Wash.,* **16,** 58 (1962).
6   Discussions at Green Bank Conference on Interstellar Communication (see Chapter 28).

B. M. Oliver

22 ✳ SOME POTENTIALITIES
OF OPTICAL MASERS

Not long after the development of the microwave maser by Townes, Bloembergen, and others, it became apparent that the same principles could be applied to the generation of radiation of far higher frequency. In an historic paper in the *Physical Review* for December 15, 1958, entitled "Infrared and Optical Masers," Schawlow and Townes predicted the possibility of extending maser principles into the optical region, described general types of structures which would be required, and speculated upon the performance possible. Very few developments in recent years have excited the imaginations of so many scientists and engineers as has the optical maser, or "laser." The reason, of course, is that this device offers for the first time means for producing and amplifying coherent light and therefore opens up the optical spectrum for exploitation by all the techniques currently used in the radio spectrum.

In July of 1960 Maiman (*1*) of Hughes Laboratories announced the first successful production of coherent light on a pulse basis using optically pumped ruby. Early in 1961 Javan, Bennett, and Herriott of Bell Laboratories announced the successful cw operation of a gaseous optical maser (*2*). In addition, there has been a great deal of activity in this field at many other laboratories, and the effort is increasing.

The basic principles of the optical maser are the same as those of the microwave maser. Figure 1 illustrates in schematic form the essential ingredients of an optical maser. First of all there must be a resonant cavity. In an optical maser this is formed by two precisely oriented mirrors, one of which is slightly transparent. It can be shown that resonant modes will exist between these mirrors at frequencies for which the spacing is an integral number of half wavelengths. In

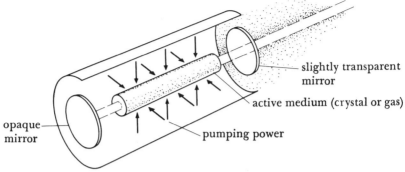

opaque mirror

slightly transparent mirror

active medium (crystal or gas)

pumping power

Figure 1
Elements of an optical maser.

this space between the mirrors is placed an active medium which may be either a gas or a crystal doped by certain atoms (such as chromium in the case of ruby). The medium must possess two atomic states separated in energy by an amount corresponding to the frequency desired, and it must be possible to overpopulate the upper of these states with respect to the lower. This is done by "pumping" the atoms from a ground state to a higher energy state either electrically or optically. From this higher energy state the atoms usually decay nonradiatively to the upper of the two energy states involved in the desired transition. From this upper state some atoms will decay spontaneously to the lower state and emit light just as occurs in any neon sign. The light caused by such spontaneous emission is incoherent and is radiated in all directions at random. However, in the presence of the resonant cavity some of this spontaneous emission will excite one of the resonant modes of the cavity, and the field associated with the resonance will induce emission in the medium. This induced emission is phase coherent with the field which induces it, and, as a result, if the interaction is strong enough, a coherent electromagnetic wave will build up corresponding to one of the modes of the resonant cavity. Some of this energy will leak through the partially transparent mirror forming one end of the cavity and emerge as a sharply defined beam of coherent light (Figure 2). The significant thing is that this beam of light is a plane-coherent electromagnetic wave just as would be produced by a radio transmitter, but of vastly higher frequency.

There are two aspects to wave coherence: spatial and temporal. A wave is *spatially* coherent if there exist surfaces over which the wave

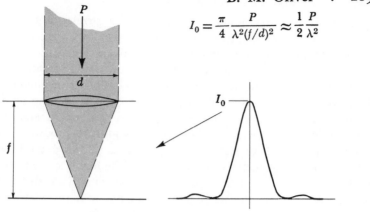

$$I_0 = \frac{\pi}{4} \frac{P}{\lambda^2 (f/d)^2} \approx \frac{1}{2} \frac{P}{\lambda^2}$$

Figure 2

Focusing of coherent light.

amplitude as a function of time is highly correlated. If the coherence is complete, the correlation will be unity, and the voltage at the one point will be proportional to the voltage at other points on the surface. As an example of spatial coherence, consider the voltage at any two points on an equiphase front in the light from a distant star. The voltage at two points is the same function of time, and, similarly at a given time, the voltage along different rays is the same function of distance.

A wave exhibits *time* coherence to the degree that there is correlation between the amplitude of the wave at a given point at one time and at some later time. A single frequency represents the extreme of time coherence; so does any combination of single frequencies, harmonically related. If the line components of the spectrum are broadened due to random modulation, the time coherence is lessened and in the extreme; when the spectrum of the wave consists of a smooth distribution of frequencies, as is true of black-body radiation for example, time coherence virtually disappears. Spectral purity (i.e., the degree to which the spectrum approaches a line spectrum) is thus a measure of time coherence.

The following analogy may be helpful in visualizing the difference between coherent and incoherent radiation. Incoherent radiation may be thought of as the three-dimensional analog of the pattern of waves on the surface of a swimming pool in its usual state just after the swimmers have left. Waves of all different wavelengths are racing every which way at random, and there is little correlation between the time functions representing the amplitudes at two widely separated points. If the pool were surrounded by quiet water at the same level and the walls suddenly removed, the agitation would spread out in all directions in a way which resembles the radiation of incoherent light. By contrast, if the surface of an otherwise quiet swimming pool were set in motion by the up and down oscillation of a float extending clear across one end, a series of plane waves would be produced. These would exhibit high spatial coherence, because the wave amplitudes as a function of time at different points would be highly correlated. And if the motion of the float is periodic the waves will exhibit time coherence as well. If the walls were again removed the wave pattern would propagate out in a beam normal to the float, and, if the wavelength were short compared with the length of the float, the beam would exhibit very little spread with distance.

Ruby lasers operate on a pulse basis and give quite high peak power output. Characteristically, pulses on the order of 10-kw output power and pulse durations of the order of 1 msec are obtained. The total energy per pulse is therefore on the order of 10 joules. Although the spectral line is clearly narrowed by the maser action, the time coherence is still relatively poor in the ruby laser. Spectral line widths on the order of 1000 Mcs being typical. The spatial coherence also is far from perfect and is thought to be limited by optical imperfections in the ruby crystals themselves. Hopefully, these are defects which will be eliminated with further research, and in our discussion to follow we shall assume ideal coherent operation to be possible. The cw gaseous masers operate at relatively low power levels—on the order of 20 mw—and exhibit excellent coherence. Line widths of less than 1 kc have been reported, and the spatial coherence seems to agree with what would be expected theoretically. There is every reason to believe that the power output of the gaseous laser can be increased, and these devices look very promising for communication applications.

Coherent Optics

The availability of coherent light greatly increases the scope of things that can be done with optical systems. In particular, the spreading of beams of light becomes limited only by diffraction. In an ordinary searchlight the beam spread is principally due to the finite size of the source of light. A point of the source lying on the optical axis produces a beam parallel to the optical axis, while various points of the source lying off the optical axis produce beams at various angles with respect to the axis. The totality of all these beams thus spreads at a rate determined by the greatest extension of the source and by the focal length of the objective. By contrast, plane waves radiated by an optical maser spread in the same fashion as would the beam from an antenna having the same size measured in wavelengths. Having coherent light is tantamount to having a point source.

When the light from a star is imaged by a telescope objective under ideal seeing conditions, a diffraction pattern called an Airy disk is formed. It consists of a central patch of light surrounded by a series of rings, the intensity as a function of radius, r, being given by

$$I(r) = I_0 \left\{ \frac{2J_1[(\pi d/\lambda f)r]}{[(\pi d/\lambda f)r]} \right\}^2 \tag{1}$$

where d = diameter of the objective, f = focal length of the objective, λ = wavelength, and J_1 is the first-order Bessel function. This same diffraction pattern is formed when the light from an optical maser is brought to focus with an ideal lens, assuming the beam illuminates the lens uniformly. In general the diffraction pattern is the (two-dimensional) Fourier transform of the aperture illumination. The intensity at the center of the spot is given by *

$$I_0 = \frac{A}{\lambda^2 f^2} P \tag{2}$$

where A = area of objective and P = power in light beam

Taking a value of 10 kw for the power output of the ruby laser and the wavelength of 0.7 μ, we find the power density at the center of the image to be about 10^{16} watts/m². This is an energy density far in excess of anything normally obtained in the laboratory. As a comparison, the energy density at the surface of the sun is 10^8 watts/m²; thus the ruby laser is theoretically capable of producing an energy density one hundred million times that of the surface of the sun! This high-energy density is accompanied by a correspondingly high electrical field strength given by

$$E = \sqrt{\eta I_0} \tag{3}$$

where $\eta = 120\pi$ = impedance of free space.

* This relation can be derived directly from the radio-transmission expression, Eq. (5), by setting $D = f$, $A_T = A$, $P_T = P$, and $I_e = P_R/A_R$. Again it assumes a uniformly illuminated aperture.

For the above case we find

$$E = \sqrt{120\pi \times 10^{16}}$$

$$\approx 2 \times 10^9 \text{ volts/m}$$

$$\approx 2 \text{ million volts/m}$$

At such fields it should be possible to produce many effects heretofore unobservable. Such possibilities as the alteration of the construction of molecules, the disruption of chemical bonds in small regions inside homogeneous substances, etc., suggest themselves.

If, after having been brought to a focus by an initial lens, the light from the diffraction pattern is allowed to propagate further, it can illuminate a much larger lens, which can in turn recollimate the light as shown in Figure 3. Such an arrangement will be recognized as the simple astronomical telescope used in reverse. Just as the resolving power of a telescope is increased in proportion to the diameter of its objective, so the beam spread of the emerging beam from this "optical antenna" is inversely proportional to the diameter of its objective. In fact, the width of the major lobe from the peak to the first null is found from (1) by setting $J_1 = 0$, and is the usual formula for the resolving power of a telescope:

$$\frac{\pi d}{\lambda} \frac{r}{f} = \frac{\pi d}{\lambda} \theta = 3.8317$$

$$\theta = \frac{3.8317}{\pi} \frac{\lambda}{d} = 1.22 \frac{\lambda}{d} \tag{4}$$

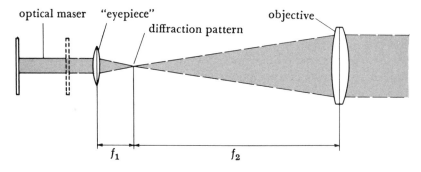

optical maser   "eyepiece"   objective

diffraction pattern

f_1 f_2

Figure 3

Optical "antenna" with power gain of $(f_2/f_1)^2$.

As a result of the decreased beam spread, distant points will be illuminated more intensely, and the antenna will exhibit a power gain equal to the square of the normal magnification of the device as a telescope. Used as a searchlight, a laser followed by a telescope can produce a remarkably small spot of light at great distances. As an example, a 12-inch-diameter telescope would produce a spot of light only 8800 ft in diameter on the moon. The illuminated patch, of course, corresponds to the figure of confusion of the same objective when used as a telescope.

The extremely small beam spread possible at optical frequencies with coherent light suggests that it should be possible to transmit power over considerable distances with relatively little loss. This turns out to be the case. For a given maximum size of antenna (considering both the receiving and transmitting antenna) the least power loss will occur if the beam intensity as a function of radius off axis is properly shaped. This distribution is approximately Gaussian in shape and is, in fact, the distribution which arises naturally when the resonator of

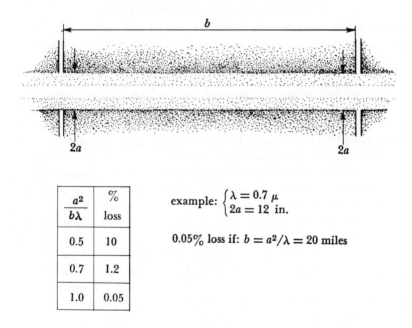

$\dfrac{a^2}{b\lambda}$	% loss
0.5	10
0.7	1.2
1.0	0.05

example: $\begin{cases} \lambda = 0.7\ \mu \\ 2a = 12\ \text{in.} \end{cases}$

0.05% loss if: $b = a^2/\lambda = 20$ miles

Figure 4
Transmission between apertures.

the laser consists of two confocal concave mirrors as described by Fox and Li (3). The beam from a laser employing such a resonator 1 m in length is only about a millimeter in diameter: a fine thread of light. However, its radial intensity distribution will be preserved after passing through an antenna of the type shown in Figure 3, and so it is simple to create a beam of large cross section having this Gaussian distribution. If the diameter of the transmitting aperture and receiving aperture are both 2a and if the distance between them is b, as shown in Figure 4, then, with such a beam, the power loss will be as given by the table and example in that figure. A loss of one-twentieth of 1 per cent of the power in a 20-mile hop is less than occurs with the average transmission line. However, this low loss can only be achieved if scattering and refraction in the medium are absent, and hence can be realized only in free space or if a controlled atmosphere is provided in a pipe connecting the two apertures. The possibility of transmitting power by optical means from earth to a satellite or from one space vehicle to another is a very real one.

Communication by Coherent Light

The use of coherent light for communication purposes is an obvious application, and in this section we shall consider the potentialities of lasers in this service. The factors which must be considered are the bandwidths afforded by the new type of channel, the transmission loss, the inherent noise, and the cost. Let us look at these in turn.

In the red end of the spectrum the frequency of light is approximately 4×10^{14} cps. Thus a 1 per cent band in this portion of the spectrum will have a bandwidth of 4 million Mcs: enough for a billion simultaneous telephone conversations. Thus it should be possible in theory to transmit all the conversations going on anywhere in the world simultaneously over a single thread of light 1 mm in diameter. Apparently we have bandwidth to burn. This is especially true when one considers the fact that because of the extremely directional beams that can be produced, many simultaneous channels can exist in the same frequency band without mutual interference. The problem is not one of lack of spectrum space, but of how to make use of it: of how to modulate the optical maser or its output so as to fill up the spectrum. Work in this direction is going on at the present time, and beams from lasers have been modulated at frequencies up to X-band, so that channels 10,000 mcs wide have been achieved but at the cost of large modulating powers. There seems little doubt that ways will be found to produce extremely wide band modulation and thus utilize the bandwidth capabilities of optical channels, but even on a less ambitious bandwidth basis, these channels are still attractive as we shall see.

The transmission loss in an optical channel is of course reduced because of the very directional beams easily achieved, as illustrated by the example of power transmission. The basic formula of transmission loss in the optical region is the same as in the radio region, namely*:

$$\frac{P_R}{P_T} = \frac{A_T A_R}{\lambda^2 D^2} \tag{5}$$

where

$P_T =$ transmitted power
$P_R =$ received power
$A_T =$ area of the transmitting antenna
$A_R =$ area of the receiving antenna
$\lambda =$ the wavelength
$D =$ the distance between the antennas

This formula assumes uniform illumination of the transmitter aperture, which indeed gives the least power loss on axis. The λ^2 in the denominator shows that the power received is proportional to the square of frequency, and this reflects the increasing concentration of energy by the transmitting antenna as frequency is increased. It is important to remember that with fixed antenna sizes any improvement in transmission with increased frequency comes about from this cause alone.

There are practical limits to the directivity of beams which can be achieved even in the optical region. In order for the theoretical beam spread to be attained, an objective mirror must be well within a quarter wavelength of the true figure over its entire surface. While the surfaces of a lens are less critical, there are more of them. As the size is increased this accuracy requirement becomes increasingly difficult to meet. The 200-inch telescope, for example, is nowhere near perfect enough to realize its full resolving power.

* Equations (1), (2), and (5) may all be derived from Huygens' principle. Equation (5) also follows from the fact that the aperture of an isotropic antenna is $\lambda^2/4\pi$, as may be proved thermodynamically.

Even if the optical surfaces were perfect, the turbulence of the atmosphere would limit the usable beam sharpness. It is very seldom that seeing conditions are good enough to permit the resolution of points separated by less than one-half second of arc, so that beams sharper than this would not be suitable for communicating from the earth's surface to space. Along the earth's surface the situation is even worse because of the greater length of high-density airpath, so that unless a controlled atmosphere or vacuum is provided, beams of angular spread of at least a few seconds must be used.

If we now further assume that atmospheric refraction effects are absent, as in an evacuated pipe or free space, there still remains the problem of pointing an exceedingly sharp beam in the right direction. Vibration of mounting structures, bending of supports by thermal expansion, and, in the case of free bodies, changes in the moments of inertia due to motions of the parts will all introduce pointing errors difficult to reduce below one second of arc.

In addition to turbulence troubles in the medium, a great deal of power can be lost over a long path through molecular scattering and scattering due to suspended particles. Again, the use of vacuum or perhaps a filtered helium atmosphere would reduce this loss. Further, any terrestrial path must be bent to conform to accessible routes and to the earth's surface. This can be done through the use of mirrors or prisms disposed along the path at frequent intervals. It is difficult to make such a beam bender with less than 1 per cent loss, so that an attenuation on the order of one or more napiers per 100 bends is to be expected.

Quantum mechanical analyses have shown that even an ideal amplifier has a noise power spectral density referred to the input which is given by

$$\psi(\nu) = \frac{h\nu}{\exp(h\nu/kT) - 1} + h\nu \qquad (6)$$

The first term in this equation represents thermal noise, and at low frequencies, for which $kT \gg h\nu$, this term approaches the familiar kT watts per cps, while the second term is negligible by comparison. At high frequencies such that $kT \ll h\nu$, thermal noise disappears, but by then the second term is dominating, so that the total noise is greater than at low frequencies. Thus at high frequencies more signal power must be received to achieve a given signal-to-noise ratio. This is true regardless of whether coherent or incoherent detection is used, and basically stems from the fact that the energy per quantum increases with increase in frequency. At optical frequencies the signal-to-noise ratio is given by

$$\frac{S}{N} = \frac{P_R}{h\nu B} = \frac{W_R}{h\nu/2} = 2\bar{n}$$

where W_R = average energy received per pulse or per Nyquist interval, $1/2B$

$\bar{n}$ = average number of quanta per pulse or per Nyquist interval.

Thus the number of quanta received per pulse (or per Nyquist interval) is directly related to the signal-to-noise ratio.

The linear increase of noise power density with frequency detracts from the square law increase of received signal power with frequency (with fixed antenna size) so that only a first-power improvement in signal-to-noise ratio with frequency is obtained.

It appears that optical masers and associated equipment will not be particularly more expensive than other terminal equipment for present-day communication channels. The big question mark in the application of optical masers to telephone communication would seem to be in the expense of the construction and maintenance of the light pipes required. Not enough is known about this at the present time to make even a rough guess as to the cost per mile. Suitable light pipes will probably not be cheap compared with coaxial cable, for example, but if very wide band modulation means can be devised, their cost can probably be cheap per channel of communication.

A Terrestrial Example

Using the equations presented in the last section it is possible to compute the performance of any given channel aside from the unknown of losses in the medium. As a particular example let us assume that we have a gaseous cw maser with a power output of 80 mw at 1 μ wavelength. We wish to use transmitting and receiving apertures no bigger than 1 inch in diameter; we want a 4-Mc channel and a signal-to-noise ratio of 40 db at the receiver. It then turns out that the maximum distance over which this can be done is 1000 miles. This figure does not at first seem very surprising since coaxial circuits exist over greater distance today, but what is impressive is that this distance is achieved without repeaters. Losses in the medium and beam benders would reduce this distance perhaps by as much as ten to one.

Space Communication

It is interesting to compute the communication capabilities of optical masers over long paths such as are involved in space communication. Here let us assume a pulse code channel so that we can use devices such as the ruby maser with its higher power output. Using the preceding transmission formulas the curves of Figure 5 were computed. The ordinate in this chart is the geometric mean of the diameter of the objective at the transmitter and receiver, i.e., $\sqrt{d_T \, d_R}$. The curves show the value of this mean objective diameter required as a function of distance between transmitter and receiver. The parameter n_1 attached to each curve is the expected number of photons received per joule of radiated energy. Thus if a pulse of energy W joules is radiated, a number of photons $\bar{n} = n_1 W$ will be received on the average. With an ideal receiver, Eq. (7) shows the signal-to-noise ratio in deci-

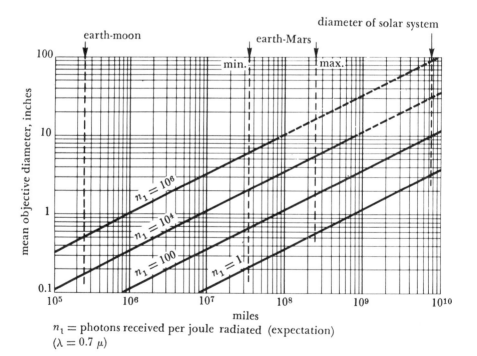

n_1 = photons received per joule radiated (expectation)
$(\lambda = 0.7 \, \mu)$

Figure 5

Coherent optical transmission over interplanetary distance.

bels would be $3 + 10 \log n$. Allowing for less than ideal performance in the receiver we may take (S/N) db $\approx 10 \log n$.

As a first example, let us assume a ruby maser with 10 joules output per pulse. We see that the mean objective diameter required for a 60-db circuit between earth and moon is only 0.3 inch. In other words, the ruby rods themselves without any associated optical system would be sufficient for communication. As a second example we see that a 3-inch objective is sufficient to provide a 40-db signal-to-noise ratio channel between earth and Mars, even when the latter is at superior conjunction (that is, on the opposite side of the sun from the earth). Finally, we note that 10-inch telescopes would suffice to provide a 30-db signal-to-noise ratio clear across the solar system. From these figures it would appear that optical masers are ideal for interplanetary communication, and this is probably true.

The question now arises: What happens if we attempt to use the lasers for interstellar communication? The situation we find here is depicted in Figure 6. We now note that n_1 ranges from unity to 10^{-6},

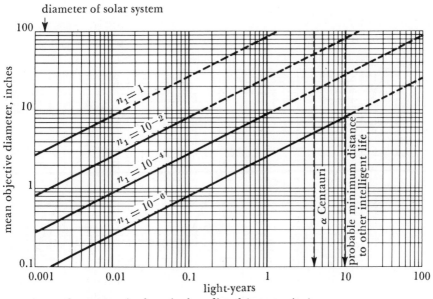

$n_1 = $ photons received per joule radiated (expectation)
$(\lambda = 0.7 \, \mu)$

Figure 6

Coherent optical transmission over interstellar distances.

so that for points on the lowest curve a million-joule pulse is required to receive one photon on the average. Above 10-inch diameter the curves are shown dotted, because it is very doubtful that the tightness of the beams involved for larger diameters is practical, for the reasons stated earlier. Although it was quite practical with lasers of present performance to communicate across the solar system, we see from Figure 6 that the solar system is only a milli-light-year in diameter. By contrast, the nearest star, α Centauri, is 4 light-years distant. This star is a binary and so probably has no planetary system. In fact, we have to go out to 10 light-years before we find solar-type stars such as ϵ Eridani, and so it is not until this distance is reached that there is more than an infinitesimal likelihood of encountering other intelligent life. It is obvious from the curves that a tremendous increase in optical maser power output must occur before interstellar communication by this means is feasible. Figure 7 shows a comparison between the per-

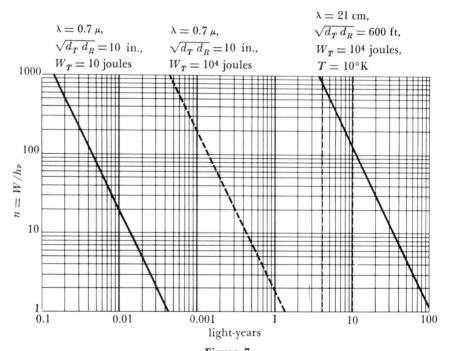

Figure 7

dx performance—optical maser versus microwave system.

formance of optical masers and a practical, high-power 1420-Mc system at interstellar distances. The ordinate here is the expected number of photons per pulse in the case of the optical system and the quantity W_R/kT, which has the same significance for the radio system. The curve at the far left is for the present ruby maser and 10-inch antennas, the middle curve shows the effect of increasing the power per pulse to 10^4 joules, and we see that even here the expectation is far less than one photon per pulse at 10 light-years. By contrast, a radio system near the hydrogen-line frequency ($\lambda = 21$ cm) using 600-ft antennas such as the one currently under construction at Sugar Grove, a transmitter power of 10^4 joules per pulse (for example, 10 Mw for 1 msec) and a receiver noise temperature of $10°$K would have the performance shown by the curve in Figure 7 and would be able to achieve a signal-to-noise ratio of over 20 db at 10 light-years. The radio system has about 417 times the beam spread of the optical system in Figure 7. The reason for the superior performance of the radio system in spite of this poorer directivity is twofold. First, the receiving antenna has 720 times the diameter and therefore picks up $(720/417)^2 = 3$ times the power. Second, the noise power per cycle is some 2000 times less at the radio frequency than at the optical frequency. Thus at a given range the signal-to-noise ratio for the radio system is 6000 times that of the optical system. For a given S/N the range is therefore $\sqrt{6000} = 77.5$ times as great.

Conclusions

Optical masers appear to offer exciting possibilities in several areas. First they make it possible to achieve tremendous power densities in tiny regions of space. They are thus a research tool for investigating the effects of such densities on physical and chemical processes. There are also undoubtedly hundreds of industrial processes in which extremely high energy densities could be used. Examples suggest themselves—such as microengraving to produce complex semiconductor devices, and ultraminiature circuit components of various sorts. For example, grids for klystron tubes might be formed by evaporating the metal in a thin film in a regular pattern of holes.

Pulses of parallel light from optical masers may be imaged by the lens of the eye onto the retina, where they will produce scar tissue as a result of steam formation and consequent tissue damage. This is attractive as a means of preventing retinal detachment without surgery, as is necessary in cases of advanced glaucoma. It also presents the less attractive possibility of blinding enemy troops.

Optical masers also offer the possibility of producing far tighter beams of radiation than have heretofore been possible. Such beams will allow efficient communication over great distances. Small antennas suffice even for interplanetary distances, but for interstellar distances the larger antennas required are impractical, and optical systems are not competitive with decimeter and microwave radio systems. Highly directive beams make possible optical radar and detection schemes of heretofore unachievable resolving power. For certain space applications where the receiver may be in an inaccessible location such as a satellite, coherent optical beams may be economical for the transmission of power. There has been much speculation that the development of the optical maser might make possible the proverbial death ray. It is clear that enormous increases in the amount of radiated power would be required before such a ray would be effective, although as noted above, such a beam can do retinal damage even though its unfocused thermal effects are negligible.

Optical masers make available tremendous communication bandwidths both because of the enormous number of cycles in a small percentage of the visible spectrum and because of the space diversity resulting from the tight beams. Finally, it should be added that optical masers are so new and so revolutionary that other uses will undoubtedly develop which cannot be foreseen at the present time. Some of these uses may far exceed in importance anything which has been discussed.

References

1 T. H. Maiman, *Nature,* **187,** 493 (1960).
2 *Bell Lab. Record,* **39,** No. 3 (1961).
3 A. G. Fox and T. Li, Resonant Modes in a Maser Interferometer, *Bell System Tech. J.,* **40,** No. 2 (1961).

R. N. Schwartz and C. H. Townes

23 ✳ INTERSTELLAR AND INTERPLANETARY COMMUNICATION BY OPTICAL MASERS

Long-range communication by radio waves is already well known, and the possibility of interstellar communication by radio waves in the microwave region has been suggested in several interesting proposals (1-3) to search for signals from intelligent beings on planets associated with nearby stars. The supposition is that curiosity such as our own would motivate advanced civilizations associated with stars other than our sun to make determined efforts to communicate with whatever other intelligent life might exist on neighboring planetary systems. Radio waves have, because of our present state of technological development, dominated the field of very long distance communication, and perhaps for this reason these proposals gave particular attention only to the radio region. It appears, however, that we are now not very far from the development of maser oscillators and other appropriate apparatus in or near the optical region which will also allow detectable light signals to be beamed between planets of two stars separated by a number of light-years.

Our own maser techniques in the optical and nearby spectral regions are still in a rudimentary stage; no such operating device was known a year ago (4, 5). Another 10 years should bring very marked development. Further, only historical accident seems to have prevented discovery of optical masers 30 or more years ago, in which case they would probably already have been in an advanced stage of development. This implies that a separate civilization might have inverted our own history and become very sophisticated in the use of optical or infrared masers rather than in the techniques of short radio waves.

We propose to examine the possibility of broadcasting an optical beam from a planet associated with a star some few or some tens of light-years away at sufficient power levels to establish communications with the earth. There is some chance that such broadcasts from another society approximately as advanced as we are could be adequately detected by present telescopes and spectrographs, and appropriate techniques now available for detection will be discussed. Communication between planets within our own stellar system by beams from optical masers appears *a fortiori* quite practical.

Optical Maser Characteristics

Present ruby masers have produced pulsed optical beams of 10-kw power (6), or still shorter pulses of perhaps 100-kw peak power. This radiation is concentrated in a bandwidth of about 0.02 cm^{-1}. Another type of maser, operating continuously at about 0.02 watts, emits a wave which has been shown to be in phase over the entire maser reflector surface (about $\frac{1}{2}$ inch in diameter) and to be concentrated in a frequency interval of about 10 kc/sec (7). The latter case is much closer to theoretical expectations (4) for an ideal maser in so far as coherence is concerned. There seems to be no general reason, other than the necessary dissipation of power, why solid-state optical masers cannot operate continuously at high power and with a short-term monochromaticity close to theoretical expectations, or hence with frequency widths very much less than 1 Mc/sec.

Now consider directivity of the beam from an optical maser. If a maser produces a wave of wavelength λ with constant phase over a surface of diameter d, the angular width of the radiating beam is approximately λ/d. However, it is obvious that its angular width can be still further reduced if it is operated in conjunction with an auxiliary optical system. Imagine that an ideal lens is put in the beam of focal length d and diameter d. Then, at the focal point the entire beam has a diameter approximately λ. If this focal point is made to coincide with that for a much larger ideal lens or reflecting mirror of diameter D and focal length D or larger, the beam emerges from the latter with an angular diffraction width determined by its aperture, or λ/D. To obtain this result, it is not necessary actually to focus the beam to a small spot; this was assumed only for heuristic purposes. The limiting factors in achieving an intense, directed beam probably reside, not in the source, but in the more familiar technical problems of producing large mirrors of the required accuracy and controlling the optical distortions due to heating by the beam.

For the sake of discussion, two optical maser systems will be assumed with the following characteristics:

System (a). Power level, 10 kw continuous; frequency, ~5000 A; bandwidth, ~1 Mc/sec or 3×10^{-5} cm^{-1}; diameter of reflector (D), 200 inches (maximum size of present telescopes); beam width (λ/D), 10^{-7} radian.

System (b). A group of 25 masers, each of the same maser characteristics as system (a), but with an effective system aperture, D, of 4 in. (and therefore a beam width of 1 sec of arc, or 5×10^{-6} radian). The entire group is to be pointed in the same direction within the accuracy of the beam width.

The beam width of system (a) could be attained in a system operating from a platform above (or in the absence of) a planetary atmosphere and of such accurate dimensions that diffraction is the limiting factor (see following discussion). When operating from within an earth-like atmosphere, the atmospheric turbulence restricts the effective bandwidth to that which would be achievable in a 4-inch telescope system, suggesting system (b) in this case as a more reasonable choice.

Detectability of Maser Signals

Two primary criteria for detection of a maser beam emanating from near a star are: (1) it must produce enough photons per unit area at the receiver to be detectable with a lens of practical size and in a reasonable time; (2) it must be distinguishable from the background of stellar light.

The maser system operated from above an atmosphere [system (a)] would produce a beam of intensity I, where: $I = \text{flux}/\lambda(D)^2 = 10^{18}$ watts/steradian at 5000 A or per wave number; $I_v = I/\Delta v = 3 \times 10^{22}$ watts/steradian cm^{-1} in a bandwidth $\Delta v = 3 \times 10^{-5}$ cm^{-1}.

The intensity of radiation from system (b) would be less by a factor of 100. Under the most favorable conditions, a star of magnitude 8.3 can be seen by the naked eye; hence, the system (a) beam could be seen by eye at 0.1 light-year. With ordinary binoculars against the normal sky, the range would be about 0.4 light-year. Corresponding distances would be less by a factor of 10 for system (b).

From a distance of 10 light-years, the system (a) could be seen visually through the Hale 200-inch telescope or could be photographed with ordinary techniques with an exposure of about 1 min. This time of detection gives about 10^6 quanta of signal, and presumably could be much shortened by special effort. The distance of 10 light-years is significant because, as noted by G. Cocconi and P. Morrison (1), there are seven stars of nearly the same luminosity and spectral character-istics as our sun within the comparable distance of 16.5 light-years. System (b) would require correspondingly about a $1\frac{1}{2}$-hour exposure in the Hale telescope for detection at 10 light-years. Thus criterion (1) is well satisfied.

The beam intensities indicated here are quite sufficient to com-municate between planets of our solar system. They must, of course, compete with a background of light reflected from the planetary sur-face. The intensity of sunlight scattered by the earth's surface is less than $1/\pi \times$ cross-sectional area $\times$ solar constant $= 6 \times 10^{16}$ watts/ste-radian, so that the maser beams could be easily seen against the back-ground of the earth as viewed visually through an optical filter a few hundred angstroms wide, or as a bright spot superimposed on the im-age of the planet in a telescope of moderate size. This affords an alter-nate communications technique with some advantages for specific cases over radio communications. For example, because of directivity, light could be beamed from Mars or the moon to a particular part only of the earth. Furthermore, equipment for receiving simple signals need not be much more than the human eye.

Consider now the question of detection of such a signal from a distant planet against the background of light from its star. There is some, but little, hope of resolving the two spatially. The earth and sun subtend an angle of about $\frac{1}{2}$ sec of arc at a distance of 10 light-years. Hence light of equal intensity from the two might be resolved at this distance by a telescope of very high quality. However, one can perhaps more easily resort to high spectral resolution in order to dis-criminate between maser and stellar radiation.

We may take the spectrum of our own sun as representative of the light to be discriminated against. The intensity per unit wave number of the continuum has a maximum near 5000 A of about

$$I\gamma \, (5000\text{A}) = 1.2 \times 10^{21} \text{ watts/steradian cm}^{-1}$$

with a total intensity

$$I = 3 \times 10^{25} \text{ watts/steradian}$$

Here it is seen that the maximum stellar intensity per wave number is 1/25 that of maser system (a) or about four times that of maser sys-tem (b). The bandwidth of 1 mc/sec chosen for the maser might pos-sibly be reduced to increase the relative intensity of maser to star, but possible difficulty in obtaining high-power masers with this stability and some other considerations which will be mentioned later make use of such narrow bandwidths unattractive.

For the sun, I_v is lower than the value of 5000 A by more than an order of magnitude below 2500 A and above 15,000 A, two orders of magnitude below 2000 A and above 4 μ. Superimposed on this continuum is a discrete structure, the Fraunhofer absorption lines, and emission spectra in the far ultraviolet. The most pronounced absorption lines of Ca II, Sr II, and Na provide windows several angstroms wide in which the intensity is less by an order of magnitude than that of the continuum. Of course, it is to be remembered that the earth's atmosphere limits terrestrial observation to wavelengths between 2900 A and some few microns.

A logical selection in transmission frequency would be either to use a frequency as far in the violet as atmospheric absorption permits, or to pick a prominent Fraunhofer line (as the Ca II H or K line). In either case, a gain by a factor of about 10 to 20 in the ratio is to be had over transmission at 5000 A, the choice probably being dictated by the availability of a suitable maser material to produce the desired frequency. Were it only a question of the solar intensity, another two or three orders of magnitude could be gained by recording above the earth's atmosphere in the 1400 to 1800 A region. However, the loss of reflecting power in mirror systems and the anticipated difficulties in master operation at these wavelengths make the region unattractive—even if recording above the atmosphere were not already too awkward. The advantages of transmission in the infrared over that at 5000 A would be offset by the widening of the beam were diffraction the limiting factor as in system (a).

Assuming a maser system (a) operating, say, within the Ca II H or K absorption lines, the ratio of maser to sun intensity is about 300 in the narrow bandwidth of 3×10^{-5} cm^{-1}. A spectrometer with resolution comparable to 0.01 cm^{-1} (that is, somewhat better than a resolution of 10^6 at this frequency) would give a maser signal just equal to the stellar background. Present grating spectrographs of high speed and resolving power give a resolution close to this figure [for example, the echelle spectrograph of G. Harrison (8)]. The use of interferometric techniques can provide a resolution of a few orders better than this. An instrument comparable to the coudé spectrographs developed for use in conjunction with the Hale 200-inch telescope and with the required resolution appears capable of producing an acceptable photographic image with an exposure of a little more than an hour. Much less resolution than 0.01 cm^{-1} would still yield signals detectable against background, although the maser signal would then not be so obviously narrower than some spectral emission lines.

Maser system (b) would give an intensity just three times that of stellar background, again in the bandwidth 3×10^{-5} cm^{-1}. While convenient detectors operating within such a narrow bandwidth might be developed, none is yet available. A spectrometer of resolution 0.01 cm^{-1} would afford a maser signal 1 per cent as large as background, which might allow marginal discrimination.

One must consider the possibility that changes in Doppler shifts during the period of exposure will be larger than the spectral resolution used and thus weaken the image. The earth's orbital or rotational motion, the orbital motion of a satellite around the earth if such is used as an instrument platform, and corresponding motions of the transmitting source may all produce Doppler shifts which can change the frequency and smear out the maser signal. The maximum rate of variation of the fractional change of frequency due to a Doppler shift $\Delta \nu_D$ from a signal source following a circular path of radius r with angular speed ω is given by

$$\frac{1}{\nu} \left| \frac{d(\Delta \nu)_D}{dt} \right|_{max} = \frac{\omega^2 r}{c}$$

where ν is the frequency and c the velocity of light. Taking the motions within our own solar system as illustrative, one obtains maximum values of 2×10^{-10} per second for an earth-based transmitter mainly due to rotation of the earth and 10^{-11} per second for a moon-based transmitter. For these Doppler changes on both the receiving and sending end of the transmission to be contained within the required limits of resolution of 0.01 cm^{-1}, the times of photographic exposure in the visible spectrum, then, would be restricted to about an hour. This is, as already noted, the approximate time needed for a good spectrum if the transmitter were at a distance of 10 light-years. Alternatively, both sender and receiver might, of course, compensate for his own cyclical Doppler shifts, which would be well known to him.

The question of exposure, or integration time, has a different connotation depending on whether the observer is engaged in a search of the spectrum or has found a likely line. In the first situation, hundreds of angstroms of the spectrum can be examined in a single photograph and, consequently, the spectral search of a given star is not unduly hampered by fairly long times of exposure. The spectral line sought can be expected to be exceptionally narrow, at an abnormal frequency for the type of star in question, and varying in intensity. Observation of any of these characteristics should lead to closer examination. Once a likely line has been located, a photodetection system of higher sensitivity could be used to reduce the required integration times to minutes for the purpose of recording modulations in the signal. Actually, with a 200-inch telescope and an efficient dispersing system, the modulation could be visible to the eye.

Discussion

Thus, it appears that if one postulates the existence of an optical maser system beamed toward us of the characteristics of system (a) at a distance of the order of 10 light-years, it is within the state-of-the-art for us to detect it. System (b) is marginally detectable, or detectable with good signal to background, if very narrow band optical receivers are developed. One should hence consider the feasibility and expense of such systems as judged by our own experience, and of course in the light of any fundamental difficulties.

Advantages accruing from the coherence of radiation over a very large aperture, or from the theoretical possibility of obtaining coherence among several maser sources are nullified if the system is required to operate from within an earth-like atmosphere. In this case, system (b) above, perhaps augmented in either power level or numbers of system elements, appears most advantageous. An appreciable increase in the number of elements would not necessarily involve prohibitive expense. Accepting a criterion of minimum detectability as a signal of only 1 per cent of the background, system (b) as defined would be sufficient for the job. An added difficulty in working within an atmosphere should be noted. Local air turbulence caused by hot lens and mirror surfaces in contact with the atmosphere would widen the beam even more unless well controlled. The power density reflected from the mirror surface of system (a) is close to that of direct sunlight. Such problems, connected with handling a large amount of power in a carefully controlled optical system, would probably be some of the most troublesome ones.

The unique advantages of maser sources can be better utilized in operation from a very high altitude balloon, a space platform, or natural moon—a possibility that may not have been seriously considered a few years ago but should be more acceptable today. The capability of the ideal system (a) could possibly be met by using a single large mirror, although the very large mirrors with which we have had experience have not attained the highest angular resolution possible [the Hale 200-inch has an angular resolution of about $\frac{1}{3}$ second of arc (9)]. The task of obtaining the limit imposed by diffraction may be a difficult one. However, the beam intensities of system (a) might also be met by a bank of smaller mirrors of higher accuracy, perhaps operated in phase (the beam intensity varies in such case as the square of the number). In this connexion, it should be noted that the 36-inch mirror to be used in the current Stratoscope II high-altitude balloon program (10) is a casting of fused quartz which is expected to achieve its theoretical angular resolution of 1/10 second of arc.

It may be both an encouraging enlargement of possibilities, and at the same time an unwelcomed complication, to find that the frequency of the hydrogen line in the microwave region is not the only reasonable place at which to search for possible interstellar communications, and that the optical region also seems a logical one. What other methods are we overlooking which might appear natural to some other civilization? Far ultraviolet and infrared are absorbed by most imaginable atmospheres friendly to life, and hence would be avoided unless reception above the atmosphere is to be expected. Beams of charged particles would be subject to inconvenient bending in interstellar fields. We see no way of producing neutron beams or electromagnetic waves much shorter than the ultraviolet (4) with adequate intensity. On the other hand, the rapid progress of science implies that another civilization, more advanced than ourselves by only a few thousand years, might possess capabilities we now rule out—they may have already been able to send us an exploratory instrumented probe. Since none has yet been seen, perhaps it would be appropriate to examine high-resolution stellar spectra for lines which are unusually narrow, at peculiar frequencies, or varying in intensity.

Note added in proof: Dr. W. S. Boyle and Dr. R. J. Collins have independently arrived at similar conclusions (private communication).

References

1   G. Cocconi and P. Morrison, *Nature,* **184,** 844 (1959).
2   E. M. Purcell, Talk at Professional Group on Microwave Theory and Techniques, *Inst. Radio Engrs.,* June 1959.
3   O. Struve, K. T. Kompton Lecture, Massachusetts Institute of Technology, November 1959.
4   A. L. Schawlow and C. H. Townes, *Phys. Rev.,* **112,** 1940 (1958).
5   T. H. Maiman, *Nature,* **187,** 493 (1960).

6   T. H. Maiman, *Brit. Commun. Electron.*, **7**, 674 (1960).

7   A. Javan, W. R. Bennett, Jr., and D. R. Herriot, *Phys. Rev. Letters*, **6**, 106 (1961).

8   G. R. Harrison, J. E. Archer, and J. Camus, *J. Opt. Soc. Am.*, **42**, 706 (1952).

9   I. S. Bowen, *Publ. Astron. Soc. Pacific*, **62**, 91 (1950).

10   *Phys. Today*, **14**, 82 (1961).

R. N. Bracewell

24 ✳ LIFE IN THE GALAXY

Are We Alone?

For some time men have speculated on the possibility that there is intelligent life elsewhere in the universe. Most of these speculations have referred to the moon and to the other bodies of our solar system, especially Mars and Venus, but there is nowadays no expectation among astronomers that intelligent life exists on Mars or Venus, nor any life whatever on the moon. In this chapter we are going to consider intelligent life, and so we shall be concerned with regions of space far beyond the confines of our solar system, and shall be dealing instead with the planetary systems of stars other than our sun.

Do we really expect to find intelligent life out there? Well, man has often assumed that he occupies a special position in the natural scheme of things and often with humbling results. For example, it was apparently once thought that the Mediterranean was the center of the world. Later, when the earth's ball-like character was appreciated, it was thought that the earth was at the center and that the sun and planets moved about the earth. Then it was realized that the earth was a rather minor blob of stuff moving around a mighty central sun, and in due course we have learnt that our sun is in no way privileged, but is rather a common type of star moving with a billion others around the center of our galaxy. Until quite recently it seemed that our galaxy was larger than other galaxies, but the earlier experiences were enough to give cause for suspicion, and it was a relief when, more recently still, further astronomical studies made it possible to demote our galaxy to a more mediocre status.

So we see that it has been a good guiding principle to assume that we are not specially privileged, or unique, and on this reasoning alone we would be more prepared to accept the existence of other intelligent life in the universe than to deny it.

However, the cogency of this reasoning has been offset in modern times by opinion regarding the origin of the planetary system. Everyone has heard the theory that the earth and other planets were formed as a result of a collision, or near collision, between the sun and another star, and other catastrophic origins have been discussed, which have permeated our intellectual environment for over a century. One can estimate how often such collisions could occur and the conclusion is that they are extraordinarily rare. Hence, if the earth really did have its origin in this way, we might really be here on our own.

For various reasons, it is now no longer generally believed that the earth originated in this way. For one thing, modern calculations have shown that the fragments drawn out of the sun by a grazing star would fall back into the sun. Another difficulty is to explain how 98 per cent of the angular momentum of the solar system is contained in the planets, and why only 2 per cent resides in the sun itself. For these reasons, other types of explanation have been studied, and it is now widely considered that both the sun and planets condensed simultaneously out of the one original gas cloud. In other words, instead of a catastrophic mechanism, we now entertain one whereby the earth and planets are here as a normal byproduct of the process of star formation. We think all stars were formed in this way; consequently, planets should be a more or less general accompaniment of stars.

We do know that many stars are double, or have even more components, and this is explained by the accidental details of how the original cloud condensed. We also think that sometimes stars were formed that were not much more massive than Jupiter, our largest planet, and that there is no basic difference in origin between planets and stars.

The very massive stars, those that condensed from bigger gas clouds, have been found to be rotating about 50 times faster than would have been expected by comparison with the sun.

Possibly, the strong gravitational attraction and physical extent of the central condensation allowed it to engulf the forming planets, and to keep the whole angular momentum of the cloud. We therefore think that the rapidly rotating stars have no planets and that the rest do.

We can now make an interesting application of the principle that we are only average. Of the other intelligent communities that have evolved on other planets in the galaxy, some will be more advanced technologically than we are, and some will be less advanced. But those that are more advanced may be very much more advanced indeed. We have only to look at the rate of technological development to see that it is accelerating, that the advances of the last century outdistance those of previous millennia and that the advances of the last two decades surpass those of the preceding century. I am referring here to advances in our understanding and control of our physical environment, and not to moral or political advances. It is impossible to predict what will have been done a century hence. The weather may be under control, the night sky may be illuminated, there may be international television with simultaneous machine translation, disease may have been eliminated, and so on.

Let us now go on to consider what we could do to make contact with these communities. If we embark on exploration of the neighboring planets, will we find them? The answer to this is given by the experience of Columbus. He did not find in the Americas a civilization that was technologically more advanced than that of Europe. Had there been one there, it would have discovered Europe. In general then, when we go out exploring, we discover inferior things—for example, we expect at the most to discover lowly forms of vegetation on Mars. The startling conclusion to this reasoning is that the more advanced communities, whose existence we have surmised, ought to be here discovering us. Have they discovered us, were they here long ago, and if so, might they have left some sign of their visit? These questions will now be followed up.

The Galactic Club

As there are about one billion stars in our galaxy, the number of planets would be about 10 billion, if astronomers are right in thinking that stars like the sun normally possess planets. Now not all of these would be habitable, some would be too hot and some too cold, depending on their distance from their central star; so that on the whole we need only pay attention to planets situated as our earth is with respect to the sun. Let's describe such a situation as being within the habitable zone.

This is not to imply that no life would be found outside the habitable zone. There may very well be living things existing under most arduous physical conditions, and it has often been conjectured that some exotic forms of life might depend on the chemistry of the silicon atom, instead of the carbon atom on which all terrestrial life depends. But carbon is a plentiful atom all through the visible universe and we may confidently expect the bulk of living things to have made use of the rich chemistry of molecules containing carbon. However, if there are any silicon communities it would certainly be fascinating. Instead of breathing out carbon dioxide as we do they would breathe out silicon dioxide, which is sand.

After elimination of frozen planets, and planets sterilized by heat, we estimate that there are about 10^{10} (or ten thousand million) likely planets in the galaxy. We also leave out the planets of double stars because we do not think that such planets would remain in stable circular orbits, and at a steady enough temperature, for the millions of years needed for organisms to evolve.

Of the 10^{10} likely planets, we frankly do not know how many of them support intelligent life. Therefore, we explore all possibilities, beginning with the possibility that intelligent life is abundant and in fact occurs on practically every likely planet. In this case, the average distance from one intelligent community to the next is 10 light-years. For comparison, the nearest star, of any kind, is about 1 light-year away.

Ten light-years is a very large distance. A radio signal would take 10 years to cover the distance, and as far as is known at present, signals of every kind would take at least as long. Consequently, communicating with someone 10 light-years away would not be like a telephone conversation, with its rapidfire question and answer. It would not be a conversation at all, but rather a two-way flow of information. It should better be regarded as contact between communities rather than between individuals, because human lives are not long enough for one individual to interact.

Before going into this, however, are we sure that we can send a radio signal as far as 10 light-years? A definite answer can be given to this question. We are sure that space itself presents no impediment to the passage of radio waves, because we have already received radio waves from much greater distances—not signals of intelligent origin, but naturally occurring emissions from radio stars. From the facts available it is clear that we can communicate over 10 light-years by radio today if we use very powerful radio transmitters, very sensitive receivers, and very large aerials such as the familiar large radio telescopes.

How do we first make contact? Well, first of all we must realize that it is pointless trying to contact communities less advanced technologically than ourselves. For instance, if they haven't got command of radio, the radio method would fail. But we have only had radio ourselves for a few decades and so any community that is lagging us is unlikely to be of interest to us just now. On the other hand, the communities that are ahead of us are likely to be very much ahead of us in view of the accelerating rate at which technology develops.

Furthermore, we should not expect that, when we do make contact outside, it will be the first occasion on which it has ever occurred. It will have occurred many times before, so that even as I write a chain of communication may exist between communities in the galaxy, who have passed the stage of development where we are. Furthermore, they are experienced at locating emerging communities such as ours and bringing them into the circle.

Consequently, we shall not be contacting them. They will be contacting us, but we must be on the alert to receive their signals. This is the reasoning behind project Ozma, an American enterprise aimed at seeing whether any attempt was being made from ϵ Eridani or τ Ceti, two nearby stars, to contact us by powerful radio transmissions. The 85-ft radio telescope at Green Bank, West Virginia, was pointed at these stars for a month but if there are any people up there radioing to us at this time, they were not received in this first attempt.

Thus a very intriguing guessing game is being played in which we depend on the superior powers of the other player (in this case on his superior radio-transmitter power), and try to guess what he would presume us to do, when we arrive at the stage of surmising that he is there. We have not yet made this contact, but I believe we are on the eve of plugging in on the galaxy-wide communication network.

Whether project Ozma was the right move, and whether there are other things we should do, will now be considered.

The Life Phenomenon

We have seen that conditions suitable for intelligent life are believed to be widespread in our galaxy, and the main gap in our knowledge is that we don't know whether life has evolved on the planets where the conditions are favorable. But there is no reason to think it couldn't happen elsewhere if it has happened here. Of these other communities, some would be more advanced technologically than ourselves, some less so, and just as we expect some day to make contact with other communities, so others will already have done so and created a network of communication that is in existence now.

If they are so advanced, will they be interested in us? Well, some of the intelligent communities may have developed a Yoga-like philosophy and be spending their time merely in meditation. Others may have solved all political problems and just be watching television. We had better limit ourselves here to communities that have not lost their scientific curiosity about the universe they inhabit.

Now it has been suggested that we should be very careful about making contact with other civilizations because they may want gold or some other valuable mineral that is found here, or they may just want us for beef cattle. But I do not think that this is a serious risk because of the enormous cost of transporting material objects over interstellar distances. It is undoubtedly cheaper to synthesize steak from its elements or to be a vegetarian than to import meat from another star. Very large rockets are needed to lift even small things out of the earth's gravitational well.

The most interesting item to be transferred from star to star is information, and this can be done by radio. I think that the information we could furnish would be valued by some other scientific community. After all, we send expeditions to inhospitable places to explore them, and are contemplating expeditions to the moon. But on our expeditions, we have to extract the information we want by laborious observation. How much richer the return would be to outsiders investigating our earth to receive our full report on the nature of our planet. How much more worthwhile antarctic expeditions would be to us if the penguins had kept weather records.

What would these other people be like? For the purposes of the present thread of reasoning it is not necessary to know. We can be content to discuss communities that are more advanced in control of their physical environment than we are, and we can say sufficiently precisely what we mean by this, namely, that they should already have gained the ability to launch rockets from their planets, to send out radio waves, to explode atom bombs, and to understand all the other things that man on earth has achieved.

Still it is nice to speculate on their physical appearance. They might be as different from us as dinosaurs or dolphins, or, to be more extreme, they may be like ants or mosquitoes, or even bacteria.

Now it has sometimes been argued that man as a tool-using animal was greatly favored by possessing hands and prehensile fingers, and that dogs, for example, were handicapped by inability to pick up a stick, and to use it as a weapon or implement. But I think that the brain is more important and that other intelligent beings not only need not have hands but may be very strange indeed. It is hard, of course, to imagine living communities that are quite unlike anything we have seen. But for all we know the inhabitants of some other planet may be spherical—just round balls—and may have adopted that shape because of peculiarities of their physical environment. Instead of handling things as we do, they might have to ingurgitate them and manipulate them as we can manipulate things with our tongues. Perhaps their tongues would be luminescent and there would be an eye in the roof of their mouth, or a microscope. Such speculations may seem most implausible, but we may be sure that the facts would be at least as strange.

The key thing as regards future contact with advanced communities is that they should have gained control over their environment by understanding it, just as we are doing on earth. These are the only communities at stellar distances that we may hope to contact, and in due course they may inform us about their physical shape, and vice versa. This will not be as important a part of the information exchange, however, as the flow of more fundamental knowledge about the universe. It is on our understanding of nature that our control of it depends; for example, our ability to look inside ourselves with X rays and take the proper steps to keep ourselves healthy, depends on our knowledge about electron beams and the structure of atoms. So it is apparent that the acquisition of new information from a more advanced planet would be a tremendous experience in the culture of the human race.

Just what our destiny is as a biological phenomenon of the physical universe, no one knows, but it may very well be that we are to play a role in a grander, galaxy-wide, production than we have envisaged. Life, as an undeniably present phenomenon of the galaxy, may have more than an ephemeral significance and intelligent consciousness may ultimately exercise control over the evolution of the galaxy. It is clear that humans have changed the face of the earth, as may be seen by flying over it, and we may soon be extending this influence to the moon, Mars, and Venus.

The extremes to which some scientists think the life phenomenon may go in altering its surroundings are exemplified by Dyson's generalized Malthusian hypothesis. He says that we are converting the inorganic matter of the earth into living protoplasm and will not stop until we have utilized all the earth and all the available power that comes from the sun.

Messenger Probes in Space

Although there is reason to think that we are not alone in the galaxy, and that there are other communities more advanced than ourselves in their control over their environment, we do not know how far it is to the nearest one. If such life is abundant, the nearest could be at a distance of about 10 light-years. In this case, radio signals offer a good means of making contact, and attempts to receive such signals from ϵ Eridani and τ Ceti have already been made.

But if life is less abundant, and the nearest, more-advanced community is, say, 100 light-years away, then things are different. Making contact will be more difficult, although once contact is made radio communication will be feasible. The difficulty lies in knowing where to beam the radio signals. There are about a thousand equally likely stars within the spherical volume with 100 light-years radius, and so we have to face a difficult choice. Furthermore, the other party has to choose between the thousand equally likely candidates centered on itself. The probability that we are listening in their direction at a time when their signals are arriving in our direction clearly works against success. Consequently, it seems to me that some other technique might be more effective, especially as, if such a signal were received, the answer would arrive with a 200-year round-trip delay, at least, which seems a very precarious way of initiating relations.

To obtain a clue as to conceivable moves that might be made, we might consider what we ourselves are now planning. As is known, space probes have already been despatched toward Venus and others to Mars will shortly depart. Plans for flights to the orbit of Jupiter and beyond are being worked on, and several types of low-thrust engine suitable for sustained journeys of many years' duration are being tested. It does not seem unlikely that by the end of the century a space probe may have left our solar system for the nearest star. Such a flight would take a very long time, and the full information resulting from it would not become available in the lifetime of the launchers of the probe. Although there are practically no human enterprises that are planned ahead so far, we shall have of necessity to contemplate such long-lived projects in connection with stellar exploration. And I think that such an imaginative project would have a good chance of being supported with the necessary funds.

Various items of interest about conditions in interstellar space would be signalled back by the probe while it was in transit, but I wish here to draw attention to one good and very simple experiment that could be performed by the probe on arrival at its destination. Suppose that a reserve rocket was used to kick it into orbit about the distant star. It could then attempt to detect the presence of technological life, by listening for radio stations. To do this, it would not need to know where the planets were, but might hope in the course of a few years to pass close enough to one to pick up any radio waves emanating from it. It is very hard to think of a simpler and more positive experiment establishing the existence of intelligent life. The question of furnishing the complicated equipment for locating a planet and the massive rocketry needed to approach and land on it is completely bypassed. What if the probe heard evidence of radio communication? It could signal back to earth. But it could do another very simple and very exciting thing. It could make its own existence known by playing back some of the transmissions it intercepted, on the same wavelength. A moment's thought will show that the recipient of the original transmission would be aware of something resembling an echo.

Now the point of this digression about our own plans was to help in suggesting clues as to possible moves that might be made to attract our attention to the presence of a galactic chain of communities, the nearest of which was so distant that direct first contact by radio seemed hopeless. My proposal is, then, that messenger probes might be launched to the thousand surrounding stars. One might be in our solar system now, and if this is the case then we should be very careful not to overlook unexplained radio signals that may be received. There is a great danger of such an oversight, because radio operators and other users of the radio spectrum are listening for some particular program and deliberately reject the unexpected. It would be a tremendous experience to be the recipient of the first message from outside.

In view of the great inconvenience occasioned by 200-year round-trip delays in direct communication over a distance of 100 light-years, there would be a great advantage in loading the messenger probe with lots of information to convey to any listener with which it established contact. In view of the present and projected developments of automatic computers and miniaturization techniques I do not think it is exaggerated to expect that a tremendous fund of information could be stored in a computer the size of a man's head. Indeed, it may not be unreasonable to assume that suitable preprogramming could produce, to us, the appearances of dealing with an intelligent being. If we contemplate the resources of biological engineering, which we have not begun to tap yet, it is conceivable that some remote community could breed a subrace of space messengers, brains without bodies or limbs, storing the traditions of their society, mostly to be expended fruitlessly but some destined to be the instruments of the spread of intragalactic culture. Such a procedure would be unacceptable with us; we would prefer to fabricate such a brain from inanimate material by the microminiaturization techniques of molecular electronics. My main point is that a probe encountered at stellar distances from its place of origin may be expected to be packed with information and to be capable of reacting intelligently to interrogation.

Now it may be that even 100 light-years is an underestimate of the distance to the nearest more advanced community, and in that case I think the contacts will be made between probes—a computer from one planet engaging with a computer from another. This is a rather humbling thought for us humans. I can see these probes being launched in all directions from the parent planets, making occasional contacts, reporting back home, until ultimately the home planets are in direct communication. The attenuation of signal strength over such great distances presents no insuperable difficulty, once contact is established, since the relay principle, already used in transoceanic cables and telephone lines, is available also in space.

Now if our nearest neighbor is as far away as 1000 light-years the situation begins to change. This would mean that there were only about 2000 advanced communities in the whole galaxy, or only one in ten million of the likely planets; and this has a surprising implication. We don't know how long it would take for life to evolve to the technological level on another planet, but we do know that in our case it took about one thousand million years. Suppose this is so in general. Then most of the ten thousand million planets resembling the earth will be supporting nothing more than primitive microbes, with millions of years of evolution still ahead of them. When they ultimately achieve our level of technology, it will flourish for a time, let us for the sake of argument say 500 years, and under these conditions about one in 10 million of the likely planets would be in flower at any given moment. There would only be about 2000 in all, spread throughout the galaxy, and from this we can verify by calculation that the distance to the nearest more advanced community would be around 1000 light-years. If it is true, therefore, that technological communities are so rare that it is as much as 1000 light-years to the nearest advanced neighbor, then such rarity may be ascribable to the lack of longevity of technological communities. It would imply a lifetime of 500 years beyond the stage we have reached. Of course you will have noticed that this would not give us time for even one round-trip exchange, since our community would be extinct before the first answering message could arrive, and so we would never join in an intragalactic club.

It is a solemn thought that after the expenditure of so many years to evolve into a state of consciousness of the surrounding universe, and to gain partial control of its forces, technological communities may be going off pop in different parts of the galaxy, without ever knowing their neighbors, at the rate of one or two a year.

Many natural reasons leading to the extinction of living communities can be mentioned; most, however, involve the long time scales of geological change. For example, the climate must ultimately deteriorate to a point where it would be unlivable for our present society. But a short lifetime is also conceivable if the development of technology contains within itself the seeds of destruction. Unfortunately, it is only too apparent at the present time what this seed might be.

It seems at present to be a matter of chance whether we succeed in stabilizing the political situation, but apparently the achieving of this stability for a long-enough period is a prerequisite to formation of, and membership in, a galactic chain of communities.

R. N. Bracewell

25 ※ COMMUNICATIONS
FROM SUPERIOR
GALACTIC COMMUNITIES

Since Morrison and Cocconi (*1*) published the suggestion that there might be advanced societies elsewhere in the galaxy, superior to ourselves in technological development, who are beaming transmissions at us on a frequency of 1420 Mc/sec, Drake (*2*) has described equipment under construction to look for such transmissions. The confidence necessary to commence actual observations is based on an opinion that planets are a common byproduct of the formation of stars. One argument among others is that stars of spectral type later than F5 have low angular momenta, just as the sun has; and in the case of the sun we know that it is because the momentum (98 per cent of it) resides in planets (*3*). Of the thousands of millions of planets in the galaxy likely to be situated similarly to the earth in relation to their star, it is hard to dismiss the possibility that some have more advanced civilizations than ours. In view of the acceleration with which technology develops, advanced societies could be incredibly more advanced.

Any simple test of this possibility would be well worthwhile. Drake plans to look at τ Ceti and ϵ Eridani. Of the list of likely neighboring stars given by Morrison and Cocconi, these two, and ϵ Indi, are the only ones left when we eliminate double stars. Because of orbital perturbations, the planets of double stars are, with some exceptions, not expected to possess equable climates over the geological periods deemed necessary for evolution (*4*).

But do we really expect a superior community to be on the nearest of those stars which we cannot at the moment positively rule out? Unless superior communities are extremely abundant, is it not more likely that the nearest is situated at least ten times farther off, say, beyond 100 light-years? Let us assume that there are one thousand likely stars within the same range as the nearest superior community. This makes it hard for us to select the right one. Furthermore, if this advanced society is looking for us, we can only expect to find them expending such effort as they could afford to expend on the thousand likely stars within the same range of them. It does not seem likely that they would maintain a thousand transmitters at powers well above the megawatt estimated by Drake as a minimum for spanning only 10 light-years, and run them for many years, and we could scarcely count on them paying special attention to us. Remember that throughout most of the thousands of millions of years of the earth's existence such attention would have been fruitless.

Would not this other more advanced society, on the contrary, be doing what we ourselves are now discussing and are on the point of doing, probably during this century, namely, sending probes to nearby stars? Their exploration and other activity would be intense in their immediately neighboring planetary systems. Beyond their immediate neighborhood, it might be feasible for them to spray some number of suitable stars, say, one thousand, with modest probes. Each probe would be sent into a circular orbit about one of the thousand stars, at a distance within the habitable zone of temperature. Armored against meteorites and radiation damage, and stellar powered, the probes could contain durable radio transmitters for the purpose of attracting the attention of technologies such as ours.

Using this plan, our hypothetical advanced neighbors could lay down a stronger signal here than they could with a home-based transmitter handicapped by inverse-square attenuation over interstellar distances. They would also eliminate their dependence on our ingenuity in selecting the right star and the right wavelength.

For this reason we might better devote our efforts to scrutinizing our solar system for signs of probes sent here by our more advanced neighbors. In this way we would be effectively paying attention to all stars capable of reaching us. We need not expect, however, that any community other than the nearest is trying to reach us, because the superior communities throughout the galaxy are probably already linked together into an existing galaxy-wide chain of communication. They will act in concert and avoid duplication in searching. Our impending contact cannot be expected to be the first of its kind; rather it will be our induction into the chain of superior communities, who have had long experience in effecting contacts with emerging communities like ours.

For suggestions as to how the superior communities may detect us, consider what we might do to detect them. A very good first project for us, when we come to probe outside the solar system, would be to seek the presence of technological development on τ Ceti and ϵ Eridani by means of a probe that would listen for the existence of monochromatic radio communication, and report back by star-to-star relay. We would see whether there is in those solar systems a radiofrequency line-emission spectrum such as the earth now emits. It is possible, in fact, that the hypothetical feelers sent out in large numbers by our nearest superior community did no more than listen for this radiation. If so, a positive answer could have been on the way back to the home star several decades ago, and we may look forward in due course to the arrival of a more sophisticated mission.

However, since interstellar transfer of material things is time-consuming, and transfer of information is in any event more important, it would be commensurate with the effort of delivering a material probe into our solar system if the very first probe sent here contained a quite elaborate store of information and a complex computer, so that it could not only detect our presence, but could also converse with us. Such a probe may be here now, in our solar system, trying to make its presence known to us. For this purpose a radio transmitter would seem essential. On what wavelength would it transmit, and how should we decode its signal? To ensure use of a wavelength that could both penetrate our ionosphere and be in a band certain to be in use, the probe could first listen for our signals and then repeat them back. To us, its signals would have the appearance of echoes having delays of seconds or minutes, such as were reported 30 years ago by Størmer and Van der Pol (5) and never explained.

To notify the probe that we had heard it, we would repeat back to it once again. It would then know that it was in touch with us. After some routine tests to guard against accident, and to test our sensitivity and bandwidth, it would begin its message, with further occasional interrogation to ensure that it had not set below our horizon. Should we be surprised if the beginning of its message were a television image of a constellation?

These details, and the matter of teaching the probe our language (by transmitting a pictorial dictionary?), are fascinating but present no problems once contact has been made with the probe. The latter is the main problem. The important thing for us is to be alert to the possible interstellar origin of unexpected signals. We must avoid relegating them, if they are there, to the fate of the very strong emissions from Jupiter (of the order of 1000 Mw/Mc/sec) which were heard and ignored for decades (6).

If after a few years of careful attention we find no signs, radio or other, of such probe, we shall have to admit the possibility that our nearest superior community is beyond the range where attempts at contact with us would be assured of much certainty of success.

To survey the possibilities of there being a superior community within reaching distance of us, consider Figure 1, which shows the number of superior communities in the galaxy, N_C, plotted against the distance to the nearest superior community, d, in light-years. This graph is obtained from the broken curve which shows a quantity N_L, the number of likely stars at a range less than d. By likely stars I mean those 5 per cent (4), here taken as 10^{10} in number, that cannot be ruled out at present as unsuitable to support life. The curve is based on a galactic mass-distribution model and cannot be considered accurate to better than an order of magnitude.

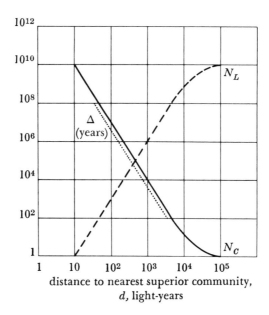

Figure 1

N_C, total number of communities in the galaxy the technology of which is superior to ours; N_L, total number of likely stars out to a distance d; Δ, average lifetime of a superior community.

Now consider the consequences if $N_C = 10^7$. Then $d = 100$ light-years, and the number of likely stars within this range is 10^3. The frequency of occurrence, p, of superior communities among likely stars, is 10^{-3}. Although we have no evidence for intelligent life elsewhere, yet if we consider that on the average it takes 5×10^9 years for a likely star to produce one superior community, which then endures for an average lifetime Δ measured in years, then $p = 10^{-3}$ implies a Δ of 5×10^6 years, assuming that we are in a state of secular equilibrium. This would seem to offer ample time to explore the 10^3 stars out to 100 light-years and establish a chain of communication.

Consider the consequences, however, if technology in our galaxy is less abundant, for example, take $N_C = 10^3$. Then $p = 10^{-7}$, $N_L = 10^7$, $d = 2000$ light-years, and $\Delta = 500$ years. The duration of communities which can maintain a frequency of occurrence of only 10^{-7} is thus, on the average, too short to permit interstellar traffic.

If intelligent life does develop on other likely systems at the same tempo as ours has developed, and if some superior community has not made contact with us, it may simply be that the mortality rate for advanced civilizations is too high for them to become abundant in the galaxy. Even so, it is rather striking that there would be a thousand superior communities present in the galaxy at any time even though it takes as long as five thousand million years to produce a technological community that is viable, on the average, for only 500 years beyond the point we have reached.

Even in the event of technology being rare, there is, however, the possibility of a chain existing. Thus, in a galaxy supporting only 10^3 superior communities with brief expectation of life, there may be some communities that have achieved durability, even quasi-permanence, perhaps by gaining control of the circumstances that lead to short average lifetimes. Aided by accidental proximity due to random spacing, some of these could be in contact. Presumably such an ancient association would be very able indeed technically, and might seek us out by special means that we cannot guess. Whether they would be interested in rudimentary societies which, in their experience, would usually have burnt themselves out before they could be located and reached, is hard to say. Such communities would be collapsing at the rate of two a year (10^3 in 500 years), and they might already have satisfied their curiosity by archeological inspection made at leisure on sites nearer home. On the other hand, the prospect of catching a technology near its peak might be a strong incentive for them to reach us.

References

1 G. Cocconi and P. Morrison, *Nature,* **184,** 844 (1959).

2 F. D. Drake, *Sky and Telescope,* **19,** 140 (1959).

3 O. Struve, *Sky and Telescope,* **19,** 154 (1960).

4 S.-S. Huang, *Am. Scientist,* **47,** 397 (1959).

5 C. Størmer, *Nature,* **122,** 681 (1928); B. Van der Pol, *Nature,* **122,** 878 (1928). For later discussion, see K. G. Budden and G. G. Yates, *J. Atmospheric Terrest. Phys.,* **2,** 272 (1951).

6 B. F. Burke and K. L. Franklin, *J. Geophys. Res.,* **60,** 213 (1955); C. A. Shain, *Australian J. Phys.,* **9,** 61 (1956).

Philip Morrison

26 ✳ INTERSTELLAR COMMUNICATION

It is a great honor indeed to address the 1496th meeting of any organization, and particularly one founded by the man who was the second of the famous American physicists, after Benjamin Franklin, Joseph Henry.

I should like to put very clearly the thesis to which I wish to speak and concerning which I hope to present a very plausible case. I propose to assert that near some star rather like our sun there now exists a civilization with scientific interests and with technical possibilities much greater than those now available to us. Moreover, to the beings of such a society, our sun must appear as a likely site for a similar civilization. It is probable that for a long time they have awaited specific development of science near the sun and I believe that they look forward patiently to signals from our solar system which would make known to them a new society ready to enter the community of intelligence.

I would like to ask what sort of communication channel is open? What are the circumstances in those remote spaces, into which now, for the first time with some understanding, we begin to probe? Can we expect the extraordinary encounter with another civilization to which it seems to me we must inevitably come?

The idea is not a new one. It has had a lengthy history, and a kind of efflorescence in fiction in the recent past. There is also some scientific literature—about a half dozen papers in the last year or two. But the first references—and I hope to quote one of the most eloquent at the close of my remarks go back at least to the thirteenth century, and indeed this view prevailed in those great times, at the turn of the seventeenth century, when that science which we today serve was in fact born.

Tonight, I would like first to speak to the question of whether or not we could recognize living things of a very different form from our own. I shall set up, if you like, a criterion of conservatism. Suppose we make a graph (Figure 1), plotting on the horizontal axis some measure of complexity. On the vertical axis we present the population of some region as a function of the complexity of systems in the population. In general, if we look at a sterile sample, grabbed at random from an imaginary world without life, or from a part of our own world without life, taking for instance a sample of sea, beach, or sky, we would find a curve similar to curve I (Figure 1). In a random distribution of atomic structures of all kinds we must expect that complex forms will very rarely exist. Whether indeed there is ever enough time to permit the chance existence of even one genuinely complex form such as we find in a fern or a tree or a man, I very much doubt. But, in principle, such a curve should contain an entry for any complex thing, *but* with a very small probability for extremely complex systems. This is the curve for a sterile world where no life has ever been seen.

The coming of life, I think, could be characterized quite objectively, without reference to its chemical nature or the place in which it is found, by modifying this curve in a very characteristic way. We will cut off the tail of the curve, replacing it by a rather rapid decline toward zero; but we will replace the missing tail by a pip (curve II). At first the pip is small and, as time proceeds, gradually increases, representing the accumulation of living forms, who derive their sustenance by operating on the environment. They prevent the establishment by chance processes of the intermediately complex products

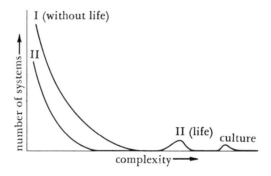

Figure 1

which, before the existence of life, would have filled in the part of the curve between the pip and the main section.

I suspect that such a two-piece curve would adequately characterize the existence of living forms. I would, however, go further. If we imagine now that living forms evolve, as they have evolved on our own planet, to a certain capability of manipulating the free energy of the environment beyond that which with their own tentacles, they can touch, then we will find the growth of still another pip. This part of the curve represents still more complex systems, and if our experience is any guide, it will grow still more, reflecting the cultural product of this second step. This is a third set of complexities. Here we include, for example, the books of the libraries of the world or, for that matter, the automobiles or the woven textiles or the architects' constructions. The presence of such breaks in the series of complexities, is, I think, a characteristic feature which we have to require for the existence of living forms, and then also for the existence of what we call cultural activities.

As you see, I have made no reference whatever to whether the systems are liquid, solid, or gaseous, whether they are magnetic or made of fluorine or carbon. We are dealing in matters in which we are at the moment simply too ignorant to be able to characterize them with even slight reliability. We are lucky if we can simply formulate a general program of such research.

I should like now to make a much more modest yet less general proposal. I should like simply to say that if to the process which unites familiar atoms into complexes, there is available an adequate stream of free energy, then we must expect to obtain curves similar to curve II of Figure 1.

There *are* more speculative thinkers who are not yet writing in serious journals but in, I assure you, quite serious works of fiction! Mr. Fred Hoyle, for instance, has described to us in his extremely suggestive and imaginative work, *The Black Cloud,* the emergence of a form of complexity built out of plasma, i.e., of magnetic fields, hot gas, and dust. I only mention this to show how far one can carry such speculations.

No more imaginative discussion! Everything from now on is done with analogies of the most timid kind, avoiding any serious extrapolations. I shall look for precisely the material basis which we ourselves see on the earth, forming what I have called a scientifically capable society. I shall look first for the existence of the abundant light elements: hydrogen, carbon, nitrogen, oxygen, magnesium, phosphorus, sodium, potassium, chlorine, calcium, iron. Hardly anything else is needed. We know that in the process of nucleogenesis their incidence is high.

I would like to go so far as to assume that the chemical reactions which will lie at the base of the structures, unlike the plasma beings, are probably based on water in the liquid phase or, at the extreme of an extrapolation, to some other mode of utilization of the flexible and convenient hydrogen bond.

This places severe limitations upon the physical environment in which such forms could evolve; namely, the limitations through which we ourselves have evolved. If the temperatures are very much below zero degrees centigrade the process involving hydrogen-bond formation in solid water solutions are much too slow to give a very wide split of the original curve in the times available. So, with too low temperatures, while something may go on, it may be very slow indeed. With too high temperatures, one cannot make any such structures very easily: the structures involving the rather weak but flexible and highly manipulatable hydrogen bonds are next to impossible. Therefore we have a severe requirement on temperature.

Besides thermodynamic temperature, we have to worry about the presence of currents of free energy of such concentrated kind that they can destroy complex structures, even though they may not represent a large contribution to the over-all thermal content of the environment. Here, of course, I refer to fluxes of high-energy particles, ionizing radiation, and the like: quanta of energies large compared to energies of chemical bonds. Such bombardment must be severely limited compared to chemical formation rates or those structures cannot evolve. We know we must have something like the atmosphere of the earth for this protection. Open exposure to the indiscriminate currents and fluxes of space will prevent elaboration of molecularly based complexities of the sort I describe.

Let us consider (frontispiece) the great nebula in Andromeda in the north sky. It is a circular mass of unresolved stars some 120,000 light-years across and appears to us as a tilted disk. We know that we live in a galaxy almost the twin of this one. Such a galaxy contains on the order of one hundred billions of stars, appearing to be merged together only because they are so far away that the photographic plate and the optical train through which the plate has been exposed cannot separate the images.

If someone looks at our galaxy from the outside, he sees such a relatively bland, slightly spiral, lightly marked disk of whirling stars, rotating once every three hundred million years. Not far from the center of this light patch there is the sun, an inconspicuous member of a population typical of the entire galaxy. Around the sun there whirl, among others, two planets which may be suitable for life; namely, the earth and Mars. On the earth is a clear and present instance of the development of the society of modest scientific capability in the very recent past; and on Mars, a strong indication that conditions favor the independent evolution of life, not indeed to any stage of technical capability but (very plausibly) to a stage of considerable chemical elaboration.

It is upon this sample of two that I think the argument we make must rest. I would like to stress the probable existence of some form of life on Mars—some form of growth of complexity at the expense of the free energy of the environment—because otherwise we are left to the uncomfortable sample size of one, the unique example of earth. I learned in statistics that it is very hard to make a conclusion from a sample so small as one. Anything can happen once, but about things that happen twice—one can at least say each is not unique. This is the main reason I would like to see growing in the Smithsonian Institution a little sample of that Martian vegetation which Dr. W. Sinton has made so plausible from his magnificent work with infrared spectroscopy.

Have we any certain knowledge of what goes on outside the solar system? I do not think so. But we have some conjectures and some plausible inferences which I should like to list briefly in order to establish the rest of my argument. We wish to look for those environments, resembling to a considerable degree the terrestrial environment and the Martian environment, which are hospitable enough to allow the elaboration of chemical complexity in the form of living beings. We are going to look therefore for terrestrial planets, with atmospheres, with free energy supplied by the sun, and with a temperature regime like our own.

In spite of considerable effort we have not yet found a really sound basis for the origin of the planetary system. We could not, for example, calculate clearly the distribution and mass and position *a priori* from the knowledge of the type of star we have. But we do have, besides some rather plausible inferences of this kind, some observations which are not difficult to describe.

Here again a graph (Figure 2), on which is marked the familiar letters which indicate to the astronomer, roughly speaking, a scale of temperature from about 50,000°K on the left to about 2500°K on the right, with our own sun being at the letter G. Next I would like to

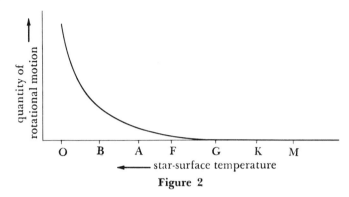

Figure 2

plot the measure of rotation of typical stars of these various classes. There is a great deal of rotation among the stars of classes of O, B, A, but we do not see much rotation in the F, G, K stars.

If we look at the distribution of the angular momentum in our present solar system we find that 99.5 per cent of the angular momentum lies, not in the sun, which has 99.9 per cent of all the mass, but in the planets which go about the sun.

Thus the angular momentum, which was presumably present in the whirling gases from which the sun condensed billions of years ago, now resides not in the massive sun but in the tiny planets. It is a plausible inference that the reason why the angular momentum of these young stars is still in the stars themselves, as we can see by the spectroscope, is that they have not made planets. Similarly the angular momentum which the older stars must certainly have had, if they were formed by the same processes that made the younger ones, has been whirled off perhaps in many forms; it is not unreasonable to say that some of these stars have bequeathed their spin to planets.

Here the argument is of course uncertain. We cannot be sure that the conditions for condensation of planets were right. We can be fairly sure that the angular momentum went off with much gas. But since the angular momentum is still resident in the planetary system of our sun, it is plausible that most of the stars of masses like the sun, might well be surrounded by a suitable cortege of planets, which bear a small part of the mass of the original cloud but an appreciable fraction of its original endowment of angular momentum. Near stars of F class and fainter we then expect to find an appropriate distribution of planets. Let us imagine some considerable fraction do have planets. (We will recall the uncertainty in a final factor eventually.)

There *must* be enough light; otherwise we would find too low a temperature for life. The planets which we impute to the stars must be in the right positions, receiving neither too much light, so that they are sun-baked like Mercury, or too little light, so that they are cold and sodden with mists of methane and hydrogen, like Jupiter. They must be somewhere analogous to the Mars-earth region.

In all this I follow the work of S.-S. Huang. He draws this inference: Since the light from the sun is received here diluted by the spread of the light flux in free space—if you like, by the inverse square factor—we can scale all stars and their planets to have the heat and light of earthly conditions, provided we scale the distance to the planet according to the luminosity of its star. The planets' distance being called R, R^2 will have to be proportional to the luminosity of the star.

Let us say we have a spread of possible distance in our system something like the spread between earth and Mars, or even between Mars and Venus. If we imagine that whirling planets have always formed disks, this allowable area is in turn proportional to R^2. (The area of an annulus is proportional to the square of its radius.) In such an area a planet near any star would find conditions tolerably close to our own.

Moreover, the calculations of William H. Guier and Robert W. Hart at the Johns Hopkins University Applied Physics Laboratory have demonstrated that the distribution of masses in any "solar" system ought to be rather flat in this region. It is reasonable not to make any further correction, but simply to say the area available for earth-like orbits is the only measure of how lucky a planet has to be in order to receive the right amount of light.

Now, we see that a very faint star may have planets feeling the same light intensity as we enjoy on earth, but only if they lie in a little disk hugging the star, to gain the benefit of the small warmth of their faint furnace. Our argument simply has shown that these habitable areas are proportional to the luminosity of the star. It might well be that there are such systems near faint stars, but they must be few, because the volume allowed in space for the statistical distribution of habitable planets is not large, since one must live so close to a faint star. Therefore, we can be pretty sure that the very numerous faint stars are not likely seats for planets endowed with the kind of warmth that we have here.

One can calculate this nicely, using statistics on the distribution of stars in the galaxy, and we have done this, to find a curve rather like the one shown in Figure 3. The size of the zone of warmth, multiplied by the fraction of stars having that luminosity, gives the relative probability of finding a planet around a star, dependent on the luminosity of the central star. In the middle lies the sun, to the right are fainter and fainter stars, very numerous ones. To the left brighter stars, but conspicuous ones. On this consideration alone, each of these stars would be very likely to have planets because there is ample warmth; each has a big useful volume. But since they are few in number the total contribution cannot be large, and the brightest ones of all still spin. They have no planets.

The faint stars are not very important then; but the stars at the center of the range are not so important either because the brighter stars, even though they are not very numerous, are so much brighter that they make up for their scarceness by their favorable chance to have comfortable planets. So, if we have no other criterion, we would say the most likely thing is that such planets will be found in that very wide zone of tolerance near the very bright furnace of the high-temperature stars.

But we have one more indispensable requirement—time. No doubt the spontaneous process of energy degradation and the transfers of free energy require a large amount of time—if you will, geologic amounts of time. Indeed, that is the story of paleontology. We have to allow billions of years for the elaboration of those many forms which necessarily precede the kind of complex beings we are looking for.

This time is not available in the case of the bright stars, because they burn themselves out, and move off the sequence, perhaps to go

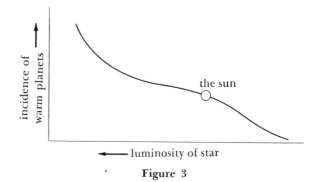

Figure 3

through all sorts of catastrophic changes. Only the conservative, smoothly flowing sources of radiation, the weak stars, will work. Suppose we want the star to remain without an appreciable change in temperature, during a time of three or four billions of years, like the time since the first signs of life appeared in our solar system. Then we must multiply this curve by the fraction of that time which the life of the star represents.

The very brightest stars do not live anything close to that time. Therefore, they contribute nothing. By the time we multiply this curve by an appropriate time factor we have produced the effect shown in Figure 4. This is the probability, taking into account both light and time, among only those stars with planets. Recall that the brightest stars do not have planets because they too still rotate.

The sun lies tolerably close to the maximum of the final curve. About 90 per cent of all the stars that are plausible homes of life in our hypotheses are contained in the small range of surface temperature which astronomers would call late F to K classes. These stars vary from our sun's temperature by perhaps 10 per cent one way or the other.

We should probably exclude multiple stars (an argument also due to Huang), although multiple stars may well have planets. They illuminate their planets so differentially that instead of mere seasons, the planets undergo extremely complex rhythms of heating, unlike our rather smooth evolutionary history. A skeptic might well say this would be a kind of stimulation and challenge to early life. But consistent with our determination to extrapolate hardly at all, we shall

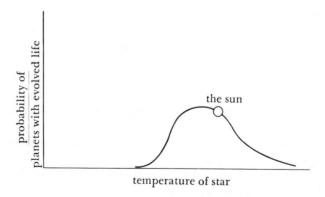

Figure 4

exclude all multiple stars as being possible sites of life like our own. Maybe they are sites for other forms, more suitable to a climate which may change enormously in a few million years and then change back a few million years later, but we shall not discuss them further.

We can say that around the simple dwarfs of the main sequence, from what are called dG0 to dK2, we subsume perhaps 90 per cent of all the possibilities for having planets with atmospheres and temperatures like the terrestrial planets of the solar system.

Now, the number even of these special stars is not small. The number of such eligible stars is a few hundred million in our galaxy alone. If we exclude the multiple stars, we cut this by a factor of three or four, to above a hundred million instead of several hundred million. If we allow that the galaxy is several times older than our sun and allow for the fact that some stars have played out within that time, we still come to many times 10^7, or say roughly one hundred million. Where are these stars located? They are stars of the disk population, found not far from the central galactic plane, anywhere from near the center quite far out to the rim.

One can compute that eligible stars are sitting 50 to 80 light-years apart throughout the whole bulk of the galaxy. A remote astronomer observing our galaxy sees a bright mass like the Andromeda nebula, with fifty to a hundred million star-spots at which he might plausibly argue that living forms occur. We now know he would be right about exactly one of those spots; namely, our own planet.

It seems to me an irresistible inference to say he may be right about many of those spots. There is no central feature; there is no great arrow in the heavens to mark where we live. We are but one mote in this enormous Keplerian ring that runs around the galaxy, democratically indistinguishable from our fifty million dG0 to dK2 counterparts.

Now we must ask: What is the history of life as we see it here? Can we not expect this to have some kind of counterpart in these other possible, still unknown seats?

I plot in Figure 5 time as abscissa and, as ordinate, the number, the population, the amount, or some other measure of quantity for a number of different interesting phenomena which we know to have gone on in time on the surface of a planet near our sun. Here we must be rather flexible. I will mention the significant features of the plots (which are not to be interpreted literally!).

At the right-hand end of Figure 5 is 1960. At the left is five billion B.C. I ask, for example, what would the expert observer, who knows everything, say about the plot of the planetary mass, the total

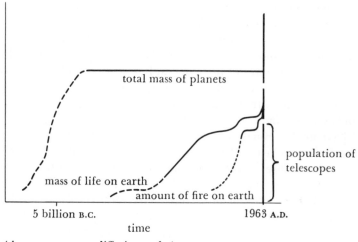

total mass of planets

population of
telescopes

mass of life on earth

amount of fire on earth

5 billion B.C.   1963 A.D.

time

(the curves are on differing scales)

Figure 5

mass congealed into good working planets around our sun? We know it has not changed very much for the last 4.5 to 4.6 million years and that earlier there was a time when there were no planets at all, but only a kind of gas. So the planets' mass had to rise from zero up to its final value along a curve something like the top one in the figure.

Next, I plot on the same axes the total mass, not of planets, but of living forms in the solar system, i.e., the mass of life upon earth (Figure 5, middle curve). Life itself begins much later than the planets. Things rapidly grew, and built up smoothly until the time when the first land forms began after life had filled the seas for a thousand million years. Here occurs a little bump in the curve. Then came the flowering of land life, which represents an increase in total life, but not a great one. Even to this day most life probably exists not on the land but still in the sea, the first home of life. Again experts may disagree whether the lands hold 20 per cent or 80 per cent of life but, broadly speaking, that does not change the look of the curve.

As we come close to the present I would like to add one more small increase, not easy to calculate. In the very last moments of geologic time, a little spike protrudes from the curve which represents the replacement of the forest by crop lands and the irrigation of new lands. It is the first effect of culture, the third rise in my original curve. The middle curve of Figure 5 then reports the total mass of living beings as a function of time.

I have also tried to estimate such a curve for flame. It is easy in principle for an observer to measure flame; he can distinguish the flame of a fire from most of the gases and glowing liquids of a volcano. When I thought this through, I was surprised to realize that long before there were men there was fire, burning in the grass lands and in the forests where lightning ignited it, over much of geologic time.

I have made a rough, but reasonable extrapolation, based on present experience in remote countries, which would lead me to believe that the plot of fire would look something like the bottom curve of Figure 5. It begins when the land forms begin. When there was no life on land there was not much fire. Fire grew nicely as the forests and grass became well developed; then it grew very much indeed when first men came on the scene. Thereafter it did not grow much until rather recently, when agriculture and then cities were invented. In the last couple of hundred years, when industry was developed, it went up again, though yet not very far. Of course this last time interval cannot be shown in the figure; there is actually a spike at the end.

Finally, I will show one more curve which is really the key to what I am driving at. It is a very easy curve to draw, the steepest possible. That is the curve for the population of telescopes in the solar system. Up to 300 years ago, there were absolutely none; and then, whatever number there are, now appear effectively all at once. You cannot fairly represent the time since Galileo by the thickness of a fine line; the curve is an absolute step function.

I take the population of telescopes to be a very good representation of the beginnings of a technically competent cultural inventory. Therefore, no matter what we think is the distribution of the histories of cultures in these other parts of the universe, since the rise time of science is so small compared to the spread in their starting times, to spread in the rates of evolution, and to every other cause of spread that we can imagine, the starting points of culture are distributed more or less uniformly over a time very large compared to the difference between Galileo or even the Chaldeans and 1960. That means if one simply assumes the cultures of these stars we talk about did not have *exactly* the same starting time and *exactly* the same evolutionary rate as our own—that is, unless the synchronization is exact to a wholly unreasonable degree—because of this very short rise, we can be sure, that if civilizations exist, then about half of them are far older culturally than our own. But what is the probability that these older cultures also have an appreciable longevity? They might, of course, give up science or even die out.

Here we come to points still harder to calculate than the very difficult problems of evolution and planetary formation with which I began. We are trembling on the edges of speculation which our science is inadequate to handle. Our experience, our history, is not yet rich enough to allow sound generalization.

I beg those who are historically minded and socially trained to consider whether any general remarks may be made to form some guide for us in this problem. How likely is it that populations of men, or manlike things, would evolve along that curious path which leads to the swift succession of those steeply rising functions which I think are characteristic of the artifacts of man? I do not know. We will say, then, that a certain number, say $\epsilon \times 10^7$ stars in the galaxy contain living forms superior in culture to us. Of those some may continue to exist, some may still be scientifically interested, some may have remarkable scientific ability.

The factor ϵ conceals the following probabilities which we know nothing about: (1) The probability that under the same conditions something like "men" will rise from other living forms; (2) the probability that those societies will remain interested; (3) that they maintain technical capabilities of an increasing sort; and (4) that those societies have a longevity great compared to the span of human history, if not comparable with the span of geologic time.

Let each person put in his own guess for ϵ. Those who are very pessimistic will say $\epsilon = 0$. I think if we approach the problem with the usual hopeful hypotheses of scientific investigation, we will say: "no reason to put it zero." I do not know what ϵ is, but we ought to try some schemes of measurement to find out. Therefore, we argue that near a number which may be somewhere up to 200 million stars, at most, certainly not much more, and perhaps as small as one, certainly not less, somewhere near this number of stars in our galaxy there are astronomers, telescopes, and the rest, and most of them understand much better than we do stellar evolution, planetary formation, radio propagation, etc. They do so not for any reason intrinsic to the mental forms with which they may describe these things, but for reasons intrinsic for the survival of these organisms in a bath of sunlight, protected by an atmosphere. These reasons force them, step by step, if they are to investigate their environment, to carry through the same sort of measurements and to obtain the same sort of information about the spaces between the stars and about the stars themselves as we have, only very likely much more.

That, then, is the situation in which we place ourselves when we look at the problem: Do these beings communicate, and how will they choose to send their communications?

First, what kind of communications would such advanced societies be likely to undertake? Would they go traveling? I submit that the motives for travel, even in a less advanced culture like our own, are becoming fewer and fewer from the point of view of the explorers of old time. Explorers seeking sources of raw material, like migrations of people seeking new crop lands, have relatively less importance each decade.

The major explorations of today, even the major travel of today, is for gathering information, even here on the surface of the earth. On a much larger scale, if one must dispatch a rocket ship to the Pleiades to bring back a carload of plutonium iodide, it simply is not worth it. If you are in a position to do something like that, you are in a much better position to make your plutonium, or to do without it. To dream of bringing back that cargo is to put the thinking of the merchant adventurers of the sixteenth century into the framework of a technical capability enormously greater than that of our own day.

There is only one real motive for travel (aside from ceremonial or symbolic travel, involved say in Mr. Khrushchev's visit to the United States) and that is to gain information. But to gain information, it is not necessary to travel; it is necessary only to *signal*. And the signal has one great advantage over every possible means of travel; information can be transmitted, as no travel can be carried out, at the speed of light itself.

The maximum rate of information gain will be obtained from a system which transmits, not things or people, but signals at the speed of light. Therefore, I think that, perhaps after a few temporary explorations in the near neighborhood, these $\epsilon \times 10^7$ stars around whom these superior fellows are now living, have long been in intercommunication, over splendid channels of high complexity, using light-velocity signals, carried by fields of some sort, probably electromagnetic (although for all I know they may use neutrinos). The question is: Are they interested in doing anything besides that?

There is not much more science left to do at their level, if one studies, say, stellar evolution. What is still interesting is clearly the experience of our fellows, because we know that the most complex and the most unpredictable of these forms of complexity are the things that we plotted at the far right of Figure 1, in the cultural area. What are the novels? What are the art histories? What are the anthropological problems of those distant stars? That is the kind of material that these remote philosophers have been chewing over for a long time. Do they want to know about the earth? I would say if there are many of these stars, if ϵ is a largish number, comparable to 10^{-4} or 10^{-3}, then they do not specially want to know, because they have already seen many new societies emerge. But there may be, however, a little corner of interest still retained, and there are many societies who might be seeking.

If I may risk a somewhat frivolous statement, I will say that our earth is not the concern of the great enterprises of knowledge among those far societies, or even of their great enterprises of art; rather, it is the activity of a Department of Anthropology. They may well maintain a certain small subsidiary interest in looking around for new entrants into their great community.

Of course, if there are very few of them, if ϵ is a number comparable to 10^{-6} or 10^{-7}, then they will be strongly interested in finding us; but they will likely live very far away; the means of contact will be difficult, and even very advanced civilizations will have a hard time making many round trips across the galaxy in search of this curious planet.

They would therefore try electromagnetic signaling as the simplest means to call the attention of even the most primitive fellows to what is going on. We need not look for sophisticated means of signaling. If we wish to land on the Queensland coast near Port Darwin and communicate with the Australians (I do not mean the Australian astronomers from Sydney, but the aboriginals), we would hardly set up a TV station and broadcast a program. We would rather use some simple audible means, like a steam whistle and a drum. Then these people who are sure to have that kind of communication will come to see what it is we have to sell, give, or trade, or what news we have to spread. So it is with the civilizations of the universe.

Their Department of Anthropology will maintain primitive signaling devices meant to catch those people who cannot do very much better. The anthropologists will feel that it would be nice to see how the primitives could enter their interesting society. Here the points of view diverge. I will mention the opinions of three different authors on this subject.

First, Professor R. Bracewell, who has what appears to me a rather tendentious scheme, not so good as one that will come later. He asks: How would I go about this? I would dispatch automatic probe ships to every plausible solar system in the neighborhood, to idle about each solar system like satellites. They would listen; when they heard radio signals or TV debates from their near neighbors, these satellites would mount up a big antenna and report home. He says, moreover, that such satellites would try to encourage communication directed at themselves by echoing what they heard; e.g., if they heard dot-dash they would echo back dot-dash; if they heard a commercial, they would echo back a commercial.

This, it seems to me, is a frightening degree of pessimism! I do not think that any drone in orbit would simply echo. Mr. Bracewell *does* point to the fact that echoes of mysterious origin are well known. They were unmistakably heard 25 or 30 years ago. Nobody knows their origin for sure. He thinks perhaps these were drone-orbiters echoing back to show they heard us. I would not, myself, build such unintelligent orbiters. If I heard a signal I would send back, not an echo, but something unmistakably meant to attract attention.

I agree his is a *possible* scheme. It does not depend on the abilities of the local people to do anything very good. If they can reach a neighboring drone by accident, that would be enough to tip off the news of their existence. However, it is very expensive to maintain the drones; to maintain them in space is perhaps relatively easy, but to maintain them in time, against the erosion of space, is very difficult, since they must sit in orbit for millions of years before they have the expectation of hitting the evolution of science.

I think it is better to mount signal beams at home, beams of a simple and unmistakable kind, directed preferentially toward those points where we think listeners may sooner or later arise. The beams should be of a kind best suited to attract attention, and to carry the information over the distance of galactic space.

Figure 6 is a demonstration of the kind of transmissions which might succeed in space. Here you see the transmission in per cent plotted all the way from very slow frequencies, like turning on and off light switches, up to gamma rays. We notice the two famous windows through the earth's atmosphere explored by terrestrial astronomers. Here we have, at the bottom of Figure 6, the absorption of interstellar space. There are two very wide windows, but the ultraviolet and soft X rays are cut off by the atmospheres of planets, which will also cut off radiation in the millimeter and the decameter ranges.

If we look at these plots, then, it seems likely that we will want to use one of these windows which we ourselves find, either in the far gamma-ray region or in the radio region, or possibly in the visible. Certainly no one will use the UV and soft X-ray region. The designer of such equipment will choose some optimum. On which of these frequencies is the random noise of space most serious? Since he knows

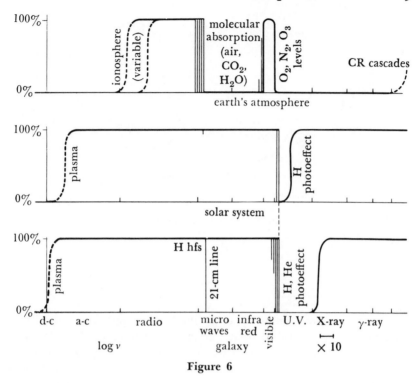

Figure 6

the conditions in space, he will choose rationally. If we too understand his rationale, we can predict his design.

There are two important kinds of noise in space. We know the
visual Milky Way and the radio Milky Way. We are looking at a
sunlike star, because the planets of life are in orbit around such stars.
It turns out that the noise from the star itself both in the visible and
the gamma-ray regions is high, and the much more plausible channel
appears to be in the radio region. Now in the radio region, at very
low frequencies, the sky is very bright; at very high frequencies, the
sky becomes dark, but the stars become bright. Therefore, there is an
optimum for simple receivers, which are not capable of resolving star
from sky, namely, the broad intermediate radiofrequency region, somewhere near a few thousand megacycles (Figure 7).

If we had to look at random for such signals, we would be searching indefinitely. But there is right here a unique frequency, as every-

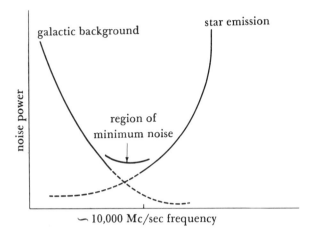

Figure 7

one knows, the one major spectral line in the radio band, the 21-cm emissions from neutral hydrogen atoms. This line, at 1420 Mc, or 21 cm, is a frequency for which there must be sensitive receivers in use on the part of anyone who would understand the nature of galactic space and matter in it. I suggest that for a signaling distance between ten and a few hundred light-years, this channel remains indispensable.

If you want to communicate to someone who does not know you are sending, you usually choose a frequency near the frequency he is already prepared to listen to. If I want people to listen to my illegal radio station, I always choose a frequency close to the frequency of the official broadcasting station, because I know listeners at that frequency can become listeners of a frequency close to it. They will hear me call from the Sierra Maestra. That is exactly what these remote people would do (though I would welcome detailed historical or social study of how one makes signals known to persons who do not expect to find them).

Therefore, set at 1420 Mc. Look as Dr. Frank Drake very courageously did last year, with his rather small mirror but good receivers, at a few nearby stars, to see if he was lucky enough to pick up the ethnological beams from τ Ceti or ϵ Eridani. He was not successful, but one cannot expect to be so lucky the first time. We cannot expect to have neighbors as close as 20 light-years. Maybe we will have to go to a thousand years if we are to find any at all. This is the Ozma project.

I would very much like to lend my support to this investigation. I do not think it in the least foolish. I think it is worthwhile. I feel that there is no more philosophical or practical conclusion to be derived from astronomy than the conclusion that such signals would immediately bring.

I should like now to devote only a few paragraphs to suggest how the code would be sent. Writers often say it is indispensable for communication that the partners have something in common. Communication is not possible between completely isolated systems. This is indeed true, but it is only a tautology. Communication is possible only when there is something in common, but there is always one thing in common whenever there is communication; namely, the signal.

A signal is by definition some common physical properties of the transmitter and the receiver. Therefore, by denoting in the signal itself we can make communication; we can invent a language, so to speak, by pointing. What we point at is not some other object. We point at and with the signal itself.

How would I point? I am now going to present a little experiment. I am going to pretend that I am communicating to others without the use of language. I want to formulate it very simply, in a few moments, but realize that in fact this project could employ cryptographic computing machines, and many clever people; then, even a much more difficult problem could be solved in no time at all. The

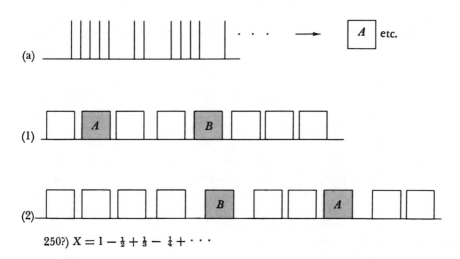

$$(250?) \; X = 1 - \tfrac{1}{2} + \tfrac{1}{3} - \tfrac{1}{4} + \cdots$$

Figure 8

decoding probably would be relatively trivial. I can go a long way in three minutes. I will show that I can send signals which would elicit guaranteed response. But I cannot in this restricted space do anything very abstract. I must be allowed a few ground rules. Since the receiver would in reality be getting pulses at the rate of ten thousand or more a second, he would have much more information than I can illustrate. Therefore, I will use symbolic boxes, which I will call A, B, C, and so on (Figure 8). These lettered boxes stand for many pulses in a certain repeated pattern. Any pattern will do; if the receiver hears, say 200 pulses, then the same series comes again, I will call the whole series of 200 pulses pattern "A" (Figure 8a). I will use other distinct patterns "B," "C," and so on.

From these we will infer what the statements mean and what the meanings of the patterns are. Figure 8 represents the voltage on the output of the receiver. In Figure 8(1) is the first continuous sequence. Imagine the sequence occurs a few thousand times in a few seconds.

The next sequence (Figure 8(2)) too goes on a few hundred times or a few thousand times. Do I have any takers for what I would mean by A and B? It is, of course, clear that "A" is *plus,* "B" is identical with *equals.* I can skip the rest. I could have gone through all the algebraic symbols in the same way. When I have zero, minus, equals, I have no trouble signaling multiplication and division.

Now we receive another pattern block X and the pattern block for *equals,* followed by a series of pattern blocks and numerics. We evaluate this series and we find the series says 3.14159265358979323846. If X equals that series, what then is "X"? We have a name for it. X equals π. Other series are then transmitted to us and each of them defines the number π. These people have shouted at us for many seconds, "pi, pi, pi, pi," using infinite expansions.

Then we get the following signal. A narrow pulse, a long time with nothing, and another high narrow pulse. The next signal, the high narrow pulse, but the same time elapsing before another high narrow pulse. Again a high narrow pulse, and then a little pulse in the middle.

Then a high narrow pulse, and then two spaced pulses in the middle, like Figure 9, and then more and more of such spaced pulses.

Now, this is a curious thing. I will give a slight hint. In the first pictures, we saw pulses whose numbers changed, but their spacings showed no interesting features. Now, these pulses are distinct. There is a constant numerical pattern. Here is one pulse, then two, two, two, two, hundreds of these pairs of pulses, but spaced more and more.

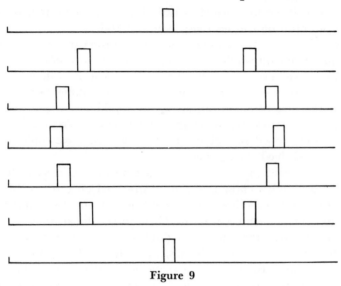

Figure 9

Of course I get the cryptographers to work. They begin to do all kinds of operations on these spacings. Maybe if the group is clever, after a while, some physicist plots the way these spaces vary with the number of these high pulses. Soon they start coming together again as in Figure 9. Then the signal shouts "pi" at us again, and it is all algebraic forms, pi equals, pi equals, and the whole rigmarole starts again. What then is going on? As you have guessed, it is a circle. We now know the TV code.

Of course, they may not scan linearly. Maybe they scan in logarithmic spiral. It makes no difference to the method. As long as they supply us with a simple geometric pattern and some algebraic clue to it, we cannot take very long to make out the nature of their scanning raster. Once the television pictures enter, I retire from the field in favor of linguists, language teachers, and elementary-school teachers.

Can pictures alone convey adequate information? Teaching a language seems not at all hopeless. Guessing what will be in these pulses is not very profitable. We had better look for them, and not merely guess. (H. Freudenthal of Leiden has done the whole job even without pictures, by symbolic logic alone—in my view, too hard.) There is, at least, no intrinsic difficulty in communicating, to the level of being able to send decodable two-dimensional scans (even three-dimensional if we like) which a little bit of algebraic ingenuity and geometric intuition can lead anybody to decode.

We will have, say, two weeks of pulses to work on; it is not a hard problem. Then we would see displayed before us animated films, so to speak, of whatever it was they wanted to teach us. I do not think it would be very long before we would have a rudimentary language. This is the first communication, which would last a few years. Of course, we cannot expect to answer in a few years. We would be doing at least pretty good secondary-school work before we could hope to have acknowledged the first signal.

Someone said to me, "This would tend to divide scientific questions in two kinds: Those that can be answered on earth within twice the transit time, and those that should be put on this channel—very much in demand—and sent off to Them to get the answers."

I have spoken too long, but I think that one can demonstrate the probable existence of these beings, in what number I do not know. Their communications are most plausible; and it is even likely they will try to communicate with us. We should listen only, and not yet try to do anything more ambitious. It is worthwhile at least mentioning the problem of communicating to the Andromeda galaxy, that neighbor collection of a hundred billion stars. It is very hard for me to believe that nowhere in its great disk, containing a hundred billion stars, 250 million of them likely to have planets like terrestrial ones, is there any scientifically competent civilization. I can think of only one or two ways to signal them, which sound far beyond the capacity of men. Maybe one of the stars can be modulated by interposing an opaque screen. It would have to weigh about 10^{20} grams (the mass of a comet), distributed in micron-size particles over a five-degree zone of a sphere surrounding the star, and moving in an orbit like the orbit of a planet.

If this could be modulated every six months or so, taken away and put back again, or changed to affect the interstellar intensity, we could make it beam a series of algebraic equations at us. Perhaps in that remote galaxy, some patient signalers have for fifty million years tried to modulate a star. These ideas are real ones, and not meant wholly lightly. I should like to conclude with that impression. I think I am not producing science fiction, but legitimate speculation of demonstrable plausibility.

I should like to close with an early reference to these ways of thought. Teng Mu, a scholar of the Sung Dynasty in China, wrote this. I cannot close more fittingly than by reproducing the words now seven hundred years old, of a man who thought as we think, but who lacked the technical capability to verify in real life what his imagination was capable of foreseeing:

> Empty space is like a kingdom, and earth and sky are no more than a single individual person in that kingdom.
>
> Upon one tree are many fruits, and in one kingdom there are many people.
>
> How unreasonable it would be to suppose that, besides the earth and the sky which we can see, there are no other skies and no other earths.

Sebastian von Hoerner

27 ✳ THE SEARCH FOR SIGNALS
FROM OTHER CIVILIZATIONS

A search for extraterrestrial signals from an intelligent source should be guided by two estimates, one of the probable nature of such signals and the other of the distance from which they might come. We cannot search for something without at least a rough idea of what to look for, and we cannot detect an object if the range of our means of perception is too short. The present article is concerned in large part with the distance. The objective in making such estimates is not to make statements about other civilizations but solely to lead to a working hypothesis which could guide a search.

Because we have no knowledge whatsoever about other civilizations, we have to rely completely on assumptions. The one basic assumption we want to make can be formulated in a general way:

> Anything seemingly unique and peculiar to us is
> actually one out of many and is probably average (1)

As a demonstration of the power of this method one can show that even the ancient Greeks could have estimated the distance of the sun from the earth, and even the distance between neighboring stars, if they had just applied the foregoing assumption to the earth, assuming it to be an average planet, and to the sun, assuming it to be an average star. They would have assumed that the earth was of average diameter, albedo, and distance from the sun; comparison of the average apparent brightness of the five known planets with that of the sun, together with the Greeks' knowledge of the diameter of the earth, would have given them a distance to the sun which is too large by a factor of 2. They would have assumed that the sun had average absolute brightness; comparison of the average apparent brightness of the ten brightest stars with that of the sun, together with the distance of the sun as derived above, would have yielded a distance between neighboring stars which is too small by 5 per cent.

All that is needed in this approach is the right classification and one absolute value to start with (in the foregoing examples, the diameter of the earth). The resulting estimate can be, of course, completely wrong, but the probability that it will be is very small, and the probability that the result will be right is high. This is the best we can demand.

The basic assumption in the present article is that our planetary system and our civilization are about average and that life and intelligence will develop by the same rules of natural selection wherever the proper surroundings and the needed time are given. This includes the assumption that the average civilization will reach our present level of intellectual concern or state of mind (science, technology, search for interstellar communication) after about the same length of time as we did and will face about the same difficulties as we do. However, we should also assume that our present state of mind is just one of many possibilities and that it will be succeeded by other interests and activities.

We should not underestimate the power of two critical factors that can terminate the life of a civilization once the technical state has been reached. Science and technology have been brought forward (not entirely, but to a high degree) by the fight for supremacy and by the desire for an easy life. Both of these driving forces tend to destroy if they are not controlled in time: the first one leads to total destruction and the second one leads to biological or mental degeneration. In summary, we assume that a state of mind not too different from our own will have developed at many places but will have only a limited longevity.

Distance between Civilizations

All the following quantities are supposed to be average ones within a solar neighborhood of, say, 1000-parsec radius.* We call v_0 the fraction of all stars which have planets where life can develop, T_0 the time needed to develop a technical civilization (defined, for example, by the presence of highly advanced radio techniques), l the longevity (l) of the technical civilization, T the age of the oldest stars, and v the fraction of all stars which at present have a technical civilization.

* 1 parsec = 3.26 light-years = 3.086×10^{18} cm = 1.95×10^{13} miles.

If we assume, for the present purpose, that the rate of star formation has been constant over the time T, we then have

$$
\nu =
\begin{cases}
\nu_0(T - T_0)/T & \text{if } l \geqslant T - T_0 \\[2mm]
\nu_0(l/T) & \text{if } l \leqslant T - T_0
\end{cases}
\tag{2}
$$

If we call D_0 the mean distance between neighboring stars, then the mean distance between neighboring technical civilizations, D, is given by

$$
D = D_0 \nu^{-1/3}
\tag{3}
$$

In order to obtain the average longevity l, we have to go into some detail. We adopt the following five alternatives by which the longevity of a technical civilization (or of its technical state of mind) might be limited: (1) complete destruction of all life; (2) destruction of higher life only; (3) physical or mental degeneration and decay; (4) loss of interest in science and technology; (5) no limitation at all. In cases 2 and 3, another civilization might develop on the same planet out of the unaffected lower forms of life, and we assume that the time needed for such recurrence is small compared with T_0. Now, we call $l_1 \cdots l_5$ the average longevity in the above five alternative cases and $p_1 \cdots p_0$ the probability of their occurrence. If $l_1 \cdots l_4 \leqslant T - T_0$, we have

$$
\nu = \nu_0 \{[(p_1 l_1)/T] + \cdots + (p_4 l_4/T) + p_5(T - T_0)/T\}
$$
$$
\times [1 + (p_2 + p_3) + (p_2 + p_3)^2 + \cdots]
\tag{4}
$$

or

$$
\nu = \nu_0 Q(l/T)
\tag{5}
$$

with the average longevity l defined by

$$
l = \sum_{i=1}^{4} p_i l_i + p_5(T - T_0)
\tag{6}
$$

and a recurrence factor Q, defined by

$$
Q = 1/[1 - (p_2 + p_3)]
\tag{7}
$$

Another interesting question is the following: At what stage are the first civilizations we meet most likely to be? We call t the time from the beginning of their technical phase (defined by advanced radio techniques) to the present. The probability that the first civilizations we contact will be of group i is given by $P_i = \nu_i/\nu$, and their average "technical age" at the moment of contact is $t_i = l_i/2$. The most likely value for their technical age, then, is

$$t = \Sigma\, P_i t_i = (\Sigma\, p_i l_i{}^2)/2l \tag{8}$$

The probability is

$$p_r = p_2 + p_3 = (Q - 1)/Q \tag{9}$$

that there will have been other civilizations before them on the same planet.

The foregoing analysis seems to be fairly straightforward up to this point, but it tends to become a matter of personal opinion when one begins to adopt numerical values for the average longevities, l_i, and the probabilities of occurrence, p_i, of the various alternative cases. As a justification for doing so at all, I mention two arguments. First, one cannot design an adequate receiving system without some estimate of this kind. Second, the uncertainty of l enters Eq. (3) only with the power $1/3$:

$$D \sim l^{-1/3} \tag{10}$$

In Table 1 appear the values which in my opinion are the most likely ones, and for the sake of brevity I omit all the long discussions which led to these values ($p_5 = 0$, for example, means that I do not believe in this one at all). Maybe this very subjective guess seems a little pessimistic, but I want to be on the safe side. From these values we find

$$l = 6500 \text{ years} \quad \text{and} \quad Q = 4 \tag{11}$$

Table 1
The Most Likely Values for l_i and p_i

Alternative	Estimated range for l_i, years	Value adopted l_i, years	p_i	$p_i l_i$, years
Complete destruction	0–200	100	0.05	5
Destruction of higher life	0–50	30	0.60	18
Degeneration	10^4–10^5	3×10^4	0.15	4500
Loss of interest	10^3–10^5	10^4	0.20	2000
No limitation	$\geqq T - T_0$	$T - T_0$	0.00	0

If we adopt $T = 10^{10}$ years, $\nu_0 = 0.06$ [somewhat less than the estimate of Su-Shu Huang (2)], and $D_0 = 2.3$ parsecs (as the average distance of the ten nearest stars from the sun), we get

$$\nu = 2.6 \times 10^{-7} \tag{12}$$

as the fraction of stars which have technical civilizations at present, and

$$D_0 = 360 \text{ parsecs} \tag{13}$$

as the average distance to the ten nearest technical civilizations. Furthermore, we find from Eq. (8) that the first civilization we receive signals from will have a most probable "technical age" of

$$t = 1.2 \times 10^4 \text{ years} \tag{14}$$

and thus will have weathered the first crisis (destruction) a long time ago; and there is a probability of

$$p_r = 75 \text{ per cent} \tag{15}$$

that it will be the successor of older, extinct civilizations on the same planet. On the other hand, the chance of meeting a civilization in exactly the same phase that we are in [still confronted with the crisis of destruction (groups $i = 1$ and $i = 2$)] is only 0.4 per cent. Finally, we define the average longevity of the most frequent civilizations by $L = 2t$ and obtain

$$L = 2.4 \times 10^4 \text{ years} \tag{16}$$

First Conclusions

As mentioned earlier, this estimate should be regarded only as a working hypothesis for the purpose of guiding a future search for extraterrestrial signals. If we assume that the values adopted in Table 1 are not too wrong, and if we neglect the "feedback effect" discussed in the next section, we can draw the following conclusions.

1. The value $\nu = 2.6 \times 10^{-7}$ means that only one in 3 million stars will have a technical civilization, and this implies that we cannot search for signals from a certain number of individual, conspicuous stars; we must scan the whole sky continuously.

2. This value also implies that no other civilization will send contacting signals (intended to attract attention and to establish con-

tact) in the direction of our sun as one of the conspicuous stars. But such contacting signals might be sent from beacons in all directions over the whole sky.

3. The value $D = 360$ parsecs means that the antenna-receiver system to be used for a search should be able to reach a distance of at least, say, 400 parsecs, and this also demands an estimate of the probable nature of the signals and the power emitted.

4. The civilizations we find will very probably be much older than we are, and they will be more advanced. Our chance of learning from them might be considered the most important incentive for our search.

5. Since 360 parsecs is about 1000 light-years, the waiting time t_w for an answer to a question will be about 2000 years on the average; this implies three consequences: (a) the contacting signals would already contain messages (including an introduction to a language); (b) there would be no need to hurry in "speaking," and relatively slow pulses might be used; (c) there might be some "speaking" and "listening," but "mutual exchange" of ideas would be rather limited because of the long time scale involved.

Possible "Feedback" Effect

The mutual exchange of ideas just mentioned leads to the consideration of a feedback effect of the longevity, via radio communication, on itself. Suppose that the estimated value for the unaffected longevity l [Eq. (11)] is too large, so that in reality the waiting time for answers, t_w, is greater than the longevity of the technical state of mind. Then nobody will ever get an answer to his call. Some still-hopeful civilizations (after having made too optimistic an estimate for l) might, for a while, send signals which might be picked up occasionally by others. But if the search for signals, on the average, is not successful, then loss of interest will usually come soon. This we call case A. On the other hand, suppose that our estimated value of l is too small and that a real exchange is possible. This will have a tendency to keep interest alive over a very long period and might even lead to civilizations helping one another to solve problems and weather crises. This we call case B. Thus, in my opinion, there is a high likelihood that there will be either no exchange or a great deal, but a low likelihood of an in-between situation. A small amount of exchange is, so to speak, a nonequilibrium state. Unfortunately, our estimate for the unaffected longevity just happens to fall into this unstable region, so it is hard to tell which one of the two alternatives is the one which will prevail.

The governing quantity in this problem is the ratio of the average longevity of the most frequently occurring civilizations, L, to the average waiting time for answers, t_w. This ratio is

$$K = L/t_w \tag{17}$$

where $L = 2t$, t is given by Eq. (8), and $t_w = 2D/c$ (c is the velocity of light). From the values of our estimate [Eqs. (13), (14), and (16)] we obtain

$$K = 10.2 \tag{18}$$

Ten conversations per lifetime of a civilization would mean some exchange, but not much, and the question still remains open whether this is enough to trigger, through feedback, case B. In order to show more clearly in what way the quantity K depends on the assumption made, we write

$$K = c/2D_0[(\nu_0 Q)^{1/3}(\Sigma\, p_i l_i^2 / T^{1/3} l^{2/3})] \tag{19}$$

and for simplicity we will assume that, from the various alternate groups of Table 1, only one group, index k, has a high value of the product $p_i l_i$ as compared with the values for the other groups. We then have $L = l_k$ and

$$K = (c/2D_0)(\nu_0 Q p_k)^{1/3}(L^{4/3}T^{1/3}) \tag{20}$$

We see that, unfortunately, the most uncertain quantity, L, enters with a high power, while the remaining somewhat less difficult quantities Q, ν_0, and p_k enter only with the power $\frac{1}{3}$. Therefore, we throw all uncertainty into L and write

$$K = (L/L_0)^{4/3} \tag{21}$$

with a critical longevity L_0 defined by

$$L_0 = (8D_0 T/c^3\nu_0 Q p_k)^{1/4} \tag{22}$$

If we use the values $D_0 = 2.3$ parsecs, $T = 10^{10}$ years, $c = 3 \times 10^{10}$ cm/sec, $\nu_0 = 0.06$, $Q = 4$, and $p_k = \frac{1}{3}$, Eq (22) finally gives

$$L_0 = 4500 \text{ years} \tag{23}$$

Because of the exponent $\frac{1}{4}$ in Eq. (22), I think the value for the critical longevity [Eq. (23)] should not be too far wrong. Everything depends, then, on the question of whether the unaffected longevity is great compared with 5000 years. If it is, the feedback will be triggered,

Table 2

Variation of $1/\nu$, D, t_w, and K with Longevity L

L, years	$1/\nu$	D, parsecs	t_w, years	K
100	1.3×10^9	2,480	16,200	0.006
300	4.2×10^8	1,720	11,200	0.027
1,000	1.3×10^8	1,150	7,500	0.13
3,000	4.2×10^7	796	5,190	0.58
10,000	1.3×10^7	534	3,480	2.9
30,000	4.2×10^6	370	2,420	12.4
100,000	1.2×10^6	248	1,620	61.7
300,000	4.2×10^5	172	1,120	268
1,000,000	1.2×10^5	115	750	1,330

generating case B, and this will increase the longevity L considerably, up to some limiting value L_m.

At this point, however, we have reached the limit of our method of estimate, because, having had no communication with other civilizations, we have nothing to start with and we cannot know how strong the effect of the feedback will be. It is purely a personal belief if we think that L_m will not be higher than, say, a million years and that it will probably be much less than that.

In order to illustrate the variation of the different quantities with the longevity L, I have made some calculations, with the results given in Table 2. Using the values that we used for Eq. (23), we get

$$\nu = \nu_0 Q p_k K / T = L/(1.25 \times 10^{11} \text{ years})$$

$$D = D_0/\nu^{1/3} = 2.3 \text{ parsecs}/\nu^{1/3}$$

$$K = (L/L_0)^{4/3} = (L/4500 \text{ years})^{4/3} \tag{24}$$

$$t_w = 2D/c = 15 \text{ years}/\nu^{1/3}$$

I wish to emphasize that the longevity L is the one extremely uncertain quantity, while all the other quantities in equations (24) may be trusted to a fair degree. Thus, whatever L we choose requires that the answers of Table 2 for this L then be accepted.

Especially, we must accept very long waiting times t_w (of at least 1000 years and probably more) if L is to stay within reasonable limits, and this is a rather disappointing result. It means that the feedback and case B can be triggered only if the more highly advanced civilizations are able to think, to plan, and to act in terms of thousands of years. This is extremely different from our own situation, in which we would be happy if we could solve the problems of the next 5 years. But it is not impossible, either, that natural selection and increasing good sense might work in this way. Furthermore, even if the average value for K is too small to trigger case B, there might be large fluctuations of K in time and space; if the feedback has trigged case B once somewhere, the resulting effect then would tend to go on in time and to expand in space. It is amazing how similar this seems to be to the problem of the origin of life in general (and one might feel a strong temptation to draw some more parallels).

In summary, I think that the feedback effect will play an important role, in one direction or the other. The basic idea is just that of giving up if one is disappointed and of increasing the effort if one is successful. But I am unable to say in which of the two directions the effect is more likely to be felt. We expect to find either a high activity in communication at shorter distances (200 to 300 parsecs) between civilizations of extremely long time scales (case B) or very little if any activity at greater distances (600 to 1000 parsecs) from civilizations similar to our own (case A). We should be prepared for both possibilities.

Second Conclusions

If the feedback plays the role we think it will, then some of our first conclusions must be modified. Because we cannot decide as to the direction of the feedback, both possibilities must be considered.

1. No essential change is needed for Nos. 1, 2, 4, 5a, and 5b of our first conclusions; we cannot search for single stars, and nobody sends messages to us especially; the civilization we meet will be much more advanced than we are, and contacting signals will already contain messages which might use relatively slow pulses.

2. Our receiving system should be able to reach a distance of either 200 to 300 parsecs in case B or of 600 to 1000 parsecs in case A.

3. In case A there would be little or no interstellar communication. In case B we should expect a highly developed communication system and much activity.

4. According to the law of natural selection, a variety either has the will and the ability to maintain itself or it soon dies out. Thus, if the feedback effect has triggered case B and *still* maintains case B, this implies that some effective means exist for "beginners" to establish contact with other civilizations (contacting signals).

Nature of the Signals

In order to have a reasonable hope of success, we should be guided in our search by a definite idea of what to look for. This idea might turn out to be wrong, and we would then have to start with a better one. But it seems hopeless to search the whole sky, all the time, over all frequencies and with extremely narrow bandwidth, just for "something."

I suggest that we assume that the nature of the signals will be defined entirely by two things: (a) the purpose they serve; (b) the most economical way to achieve it. Both of these we might be able to guess. The argument that other civilizations could be completely different does not help at all in guiding a search, even if it is true, whereas the foregoing assumption will lead to a definite program, even if it is invalid; only by trying can we tell whether it is valid or invalid. To summarize, I think that a search has a fair probability of success if it is guided by the best guess we can make, but almost none if it is made without a definite plan. The following considerations are very incomplete and tentative; my main purpose in proposing them is to stimulate the formulation of better ones that finally could be used.

As to the purpose, we can think of three general possibilities: local communication on the other planet, interstellar communication with certain distinct partners, and a desire to attract the attention of unknown future partners. Thus, the things we should look for we might call local broadcast, long-distance calls, and contacting signals. The local broadcast has the highest likelihood of existing but may be extremely difficult to detect because of its relative weakness. Long-distance calls would not be intended for us but might hit us just by chance; the probability is small, however. Contacting signals would be intended for exactly the kind of search we plan to make, and therefore they should have the highest probability of detection, provided they do exist. Local broadcasts would exist in both cases A and B, as defined earlier, while long-distance calls and contacting signals would exist in case B only.

As to the frequencies used, those for the local broadcast might be not too different from our own, but for communication over interstellar distances, the range of frequencies would be limited by considerations of economy. Drake (3) calculated the combined influence of galactic and atmospheric noise and found a broad minimum between 1000 and 10,000 Mc. In a recent paper (4) Drake finds, even for sending and receiving from above planetary atmospheres, a very general rule for defining the most economical frequency. It should lie in the range from 1000 to 30,000 Mc/sec, most probably at about 10,000 Mc/sec ($\lambda = 3$ cm), a frequency which still could be observed from within our atmosphere.

Drake (*4*) has pointed out that the local broadcast would occupy a large number of narrow channels, distributed over a larger frequency range. He has worked out a very effective method of detection, a cross-correlation between two independent frequency scans. This method is not concerned with the single signal, with its frequency or its strength, but answers with increased sensitivity the question of whether or not there are a large number of signals at the same frequencies in both scans. This is the first thing to ask.

As for long-distance calls, we have estimated the probability of the earth's being hit by one. Because the answer is not very encouraging I shall skip the details and just give the result. If each civilization speaks, on a permanent basis (and listens, as well), to a number n of its neighbors, if the messages are sent with beamwidth β, and if we are able to detect these signals at q times the distance to which they are sent ($q > 1$ because detecting is easier than understanding), then the probability of our being hit by chance is about

$$P = (\pi/120)q^3\beta^2n^2 \cdots \tag{25}$$

a value which is independent of L and D.

If we regard $P = \frac{1}{2}$ as sufficiently large to warrant a search and regard $q = 5$ and $\beta = 1$ minute of arc as likely values, this would require that each civilization should speak, on a permanent basis, with $n = 1300$ others, and it seems very unlikely that this is the case. But if we regard $n = 50$ as a reasonable value, we would then need the somewhat extreme values $q = 10$ and $\beta = 10$ minutes of arc, which, again, are unlikely. Because all the unknown quantities enter Eq. (25) at high powers, we think that a chance hit is highly unlikely (though not impossible). Another difficulty is that the bandwidth probably would be extremely narrow and that we have no way of guessing the exact frequency used.

The contacting signals form a fascinating problem. Provided they do exist, they are intended to attract the attention of any new civilization. If we were able to guess the most economical method of doing this, we would know exactly what to look for; this would greatly increase the probability of detection and thus (to close the circle) would make this method the most economical. There is just one problem:

Sebastian von Hoerner : 283

how to define precisely the word *economical?* I have to admit that I have not found a definition worth writing down, and I must, at present, leave this problem open.

Suppose we had found the right definition. This would enable us to calculate for each method suggested the price C (or whatever we call measure of the effort on our side, on the other side, or on both) which has to be paid in order to yield a probability of detection P_d over a distance D_d within a time t_d. For P_d we might take $\frac{1}{2}$; for D_d, the average distance D (200 to 300 parsecs); and for t_d, half of the number of years after which most new civilizations would consider giving up their search if it had not been successful (some hundred years, perhaps). We calculate the value of C for all methods suggested and conclude that the one with the lowest value of C will be exactly *the* method used by the others, with one condition. The methods we can think of, as well as our definition of *economy*, depend on our present state of advancement. The other civilizations will be much more advanced than we are but will have had experience with beginners, and they will have set a certain standard of what a beginner should know and how much he should be able to guess in order to be considered a future partner. The condition, then, is that we already meet this standard. But whether we do or do not, we shall find out only if we try.

The value of C should be lowest when all power is sent in a single narrow channel at a certain frequency which can be guessed by the listener. As Cocconi and Morrison pointed out (5), the only "milestone" we know of in the interesting range of frequencies which might be used for this purpose is the 21-cm line. I suggest a modification. The background of a signal would be much stronger within this line than beside it—so strong as to drown out a small signal—and the boundaries of the line are not well enough defined for us to place the signal exactly beside it. The next suggestion, then, might be to use, for example, exactly *twice* the frequency of the 21-cm line. If this should fail we would have to look for more sophisticated methods of producing contacting signals.

Each method will consist of a general *plan* for distributing the transmitted power over space, time, and frequency and of a number of *parameters* governing these distributions. We should be able to guess this plan, and to evaluate those parameters which minimize the value of C. As for the parameters which do not influence C, we will just have to try them out until we hit the right values. Thus, the probability of detection has to be calculated under the assumption that the plan and the minimizing parameters are known on our side and that we vary the remaining noncritical parameters systematically over their possible range. These, then, are the rules of this fascinating game.

We should mention two more rules which possibly could play a role. First, because of the long waiting times, the contacting signals would probably contain messages. There are two possibilities: either the whole contacting signal would vary in the manner of a coded message, or its plan would be devised in such a way that it would direct our attention to the exact frequency where the messages were being sent. Because detection has higher priority than the message and detection is easier if no irregularity (code) is involved, and because there would be no requirement for haste, in "speaking," I think that the second case is the more likely, and that a few channels would be enough for the message. Second, the contacting signal should not interfere with other activities, such as already existing communication: this means, for example, that it should not occupy too much of the whole frequency spectrum. (Contacting signals and long-distance calls would have about the same range of most economical frequencies.) To give an idea of the way in which the contacting signal might direct attention to the message, I shall give one example. We distribute a large number of signals over the economical frequency range in a pattern which is symmetrical with respect to the center of this range. Toward this center we decrease the spacing between the signals (and their bandwidth) in proportion to the distance from the center, until we arrive at an extremely narrow channel at the very center of the pattern (all other details of the arrangement are defined entirely by minimizing C). In this center channel an introduction to the language is repeated every 10 years, say, and at the end of this time the listener is told at which frequency to find the next message, and so on, all these messages being sent simultaneously but being read in the right order. Finally, the listener is told at what frequency and with what power he should answer.

Third Conclusions

1. Our search should be guided by the assumption that the nature of the signals will be defined entirely by the purpose they serve and by the most economical way to achieve this purpose. We should try to guess both, in order to increase the probability of detection.

2. We have considered three kinds of signals, with different pur-

poses, which we called local broadcast, long-distance calls, and contacting signals. The local broadcast has the highest likelihood of existing but would be extremely difficult to detect. Long-distance calls would exist in case B only, and the probability of their hitting us by chance is very small. Contacting signals would exist in case B only, and these have the highest probability of detection because they would be devised for that very purpose. For this reason and because of conclusion No. 4 of my "second conclusions," I recommend that we begin the search under the assumption of case B and look for contacting signals. If this should fail, we might then increase our effort by searching, under the assumption of case A, for local broadcasts.

3. At present, no definite program can be given for the search for contacting signals. But the general reasoning required to arrive at such a program is given: to guess and estimate as much as we can about the nature of the signals and to assume that the sender knows how much we can guess, because this approach leads to the most economical kind of contacting signals.

4. The search for other civilizations will have either a tremendous result or none at all. Thus I recommend, hoping that the first case obtains, that we begin as soon as possible and try as hard as we can. But to be prepared for the second case, I recommend the design of a receiving system which can be used for ordinary astronomy as well, since, because of the size and sensitivity needed for its prime task, it will be extremely powerful. The observing time should then be allocated in equal parts between the two projects assigned to the instrument.

Should we really search for signals of other beings? I think: yes. But one should try to visualize, too, what a success would mean to us, in the light of the tremendous power of mental contact upon which our whole human existence is based.

It means a strong inner experience to become aware of the large amount of confidence presupposed by such a search: confidence in the universality of the thirst for knowledge, the wish for understanding, and the use of logic; confidence in the partner himself; and, finally, confidence in the universality of this very confidence.

Acknowledgment

It is a pleasure to thank F. D. Drake for many stimulating and helpful discussions and for reading the manuscript.

References and Notes

1 The importance of this quantity and its connection with the distance was first pointed out by R. N. Bracewell, *Nature,* **186,** 670 (1960).

2 S.-S. Huang, *Publ. Astron. Soc. Pacific,* **71,** 421 (1959).

3 F. D. Drake, *Sky and Telescope,* **19,** 140 (1959).

4 F. D. Drake, in preparation.

5 G. Cocconi and P. Morrison, *Nature,* **184,** 844 (1959).

J. P. T. Pearman

28 ✳ EXTRATERRESTRIAL INTELLIGENT LIFE AND INTERSTELLAR COMMUNICATION: AN INFORMAL DISCUSSION

The discovery of life elsewhere in the universe and a study of its characteristics is very likely to have momentous consequences for biology, whether or not the newly found organisms repeat exactly the chemical and physical patterns familiar on earth. On this point there is a substantial measure of agreement. But there, as a rule, the matter is allowed to rest. The growth of our capabilities in space travel and research will eventually settle the point, at least so far as the solar system is concerned. However, the arguments which lead to the proposition that the appearance of life is a normal accompaniment of certain chemical and physical conditions (themselves not particularly uncommon) are seldom taken to their logical conclusion. Unless we are prepared to postulate that terrestrial life is unique, the additional assertion that intelligent living forms may evolve in suitable extraterrestrial environments should at least be considered.

Having devoted some study to the probability of existence of extraterrestrial life and its detection at the simplest recognizable level, the Space Science Board of the National Academy of Sciences considered it appropriate to sponsor a preliminary examination of the problem of extraterrestrial intelligent life. An informal conference was accordingly held in November 1961 at the National Radio Astronomy Observatory at Green Bank, West Virginia, through the hospitality and good offices of the then Director, Dr. Otto Struve. Those attending were:

Otto Struve (Chairman), D. W. Atchley, Jr., M. Calvin, G. Cocconi, F. D. Drake, S.-S. Huang, J. C. Lilly, P. M. Morrison, B. M. Oliver, C. Sagan, and J. P. T. Pearman.

The purpose of the discussions was to examine, in the light of present knowledge, the prospects for the existence of other societies in the galaxy with whom communications might be possible; to attempt an estimate of their number; to consider some of the technical problems involved in the establishment of communication; and to examine ways in which our understanding of the problem might be improved.

The following is an account in general terms of the topics which were discussed and the conclusions which emerged. In such a far-ranging subject as this, the risk of misrepresentation is not to be ignored; for errors of this kind the present reporter alone is responsible.

To facilitate orderly discussion it was agreed to express and debate the several topics of particular relevance as successive terms in a formal, although schematic, equation. The expression accepted for this purpose (recognizing that many other formalizations are possible) was

$$N = R_* f_p n_e f_l f_i f_c \cdot L$$

In this equation N is the estimated number of communicative societies in the galaxy at any time, R_* is the rate of star formation, f_p the fraction of stars forming planets, n_e the number of planets per star with environments suitable for life, f_l the fraction of suitable planets on which life develops, f_i the fraction of life-bearing planets on which intelligence appears, f_c the fraction of intelligent cultures which are "communicative" in an interstellar sense, and L is the time spent in the communicative state.

The first three terms on the right-hand side of this equation are astrophysical in character and include the principal physical prerequisites to the more complex and tentative biological and social considerations expressed in the last four terms. Taken as a whole, the expression serves not only as a convenient statement of the problem but also as a vehicle for preliminary quantitative estimates. The discussions of these factors are summarized below.

Astrophysical Considerations

In the formulation adopted, the astronomical considerations are: the rate of star formation in the galaxy, the fraction of stars forming planets or planetary systems, and the average number of planets per star with environments suitable for the development of life. (The number, N, of communicative societies is the present number and is proportional to the product of the stellar formation rate and the time L during which the societies associated with them are communicative.)

If stars of solar type only are considered, a rough estimate of $R*$ is given by the total number of such stars in the galaxy divided by their average lifetime. Thus $R_* \approx 10^{10}/10^{10} = 1$ per year. This is perhaps a conservative estimate and less restrictive considerations permitting the inclusion of some Population II stars would give values as high as 10 stars per year.

Estimation of the fraction of stars which form planets (f_p) is subject to great uncertainty and, although several different arguments may be adduced, they are all weak. If all nonbinary stars of spectral class later than F5 have lost their excess angular momentum to the surrounding nebula, which has then formed planets, the value of f_p would be about 0.5. This is probably an upper limit, for the fate of the nebula after initial star formation is not known: from it may be formed another star, planets, asteroids, or perhaps it may be blown away by radiation pressure. If this series of alternative events is in order of decreasing probability, then f_p might be about 0.2, since the probability of binary formation is known to be 0.5. Alternatively, extrapolation of binary star statistics to the fraction of binaries having secondaries of mass less than 0.01 that of the primary gives $f_p \approx 10^{-2}$. Again, if the sample of stars out to the distance of 61 Cygni is representative, the available evidence on the proportion with dark companions (including the sun) gives a value of 0.4.

The great uncertainty in all these estimates argues strongly for systematic efforts to obtain more experimental data—the more so because there seems every possibility that this can be done. A careful and sustained program of observation of periodicities in proper motions and brightness using modern methods of autocorrelation and Fourier analysis would add greatly to our knowledge of the occurrence of planetary systems. The observation of only one more planetary system would be a very valuable contribution.

Estimation of n_e, the average number of planets per system with environments suitable for the development of life, is a matter of pure guesswork. Mass, composition, temperature, and many other factors are important. Little as we know of the probability of occurrence of planetary systems, we know nothing of the details of any other planetary system but our own. A statistical mechanical treatment of the distribution of mass in the solar system indicates that the minor planets are anomalous. However, the sun is quite unexceptional for a star of its type and the minor planets *do* exist. For the solar system n_e would appear to be at least 2 (earth and Mars)—and retention of ammonia and methane may, by the "greenhouse effect," lead to temperatures suitable for life of a kind on one of the major planets. For the galaxy in general a value for n_e of 1 to 5 was postulated.

Biological and Social Factors

The remaining terms f_l, f_i, f_c, and L involve, for the most part, biological and sociological inferences of considerable breadth and uncertainty. The exception is f_l, the probability that life will develop on a planet if the environment is favorable.

In the light of contemporary evidence and views on planetary evolution, the nonbiological formation of "biogenic" organic compounds, and bioporesis it was asserted and generally agreed that the most probable value of f_l is unity. The recent elucidation of the structure of the self-replicating compounds essential to terrestrial life and the demonstration of possible nonbiological routes to their synthesis; the ready production of a wide range of biogenic compounds from reactions between the constituents of the reducing atmospheres of primitive planets and the identification of biologically related compounds in meteorites all serve to strengthen the view expressed above. The term biogenic compounds used here signifies substances such as amino acids, sugars, purines, pyrimidines, and others which together may constitute the substrate on which life may later develop. It would appear that life (in terms of terrestrial biochemistry) is a virtually inescapable consequence in planetary environments similar to that of the primitive earth. The possibility of life arising in radically different environments and based on a different type of chemistry was not discussed.

Whether or not intelligence will appear once life has become established is a matter of conjecture. Since it has arisen in the human species and since both absolute numbers of individuals and their distribution have increased very markedly since early times, it may be permissible to conclude that, in this case, intelligence has definite survival value. However, the successful persistence of a multitude of simpler organisms from ancient times argues that intelligence may confer no unique benefits for survival in an environment similar to that of earth. Nevertheless, there does not seem to be any evidence for evolutionary selection against intelligence once it had begun to appear. Evidence for the existence of a remarkable level of intelligence among the Cetacea was noted with great interest. The level of their neurological development suggests that the appearance of intelligence (or, perhaps, the equipment for intelligence) may not be a very unlikely event. The present context, however, would appear to require the association of intelligence with manipulative ability. On balance, it was conjectured that although only one species on earth possesses this combination, the adaptive value of intelligence is high enough to make its eventual selection very likely. At the same time, it was recognized that variations in the environment might, in a repetition of terrestrial evolution, lead to the development of intelligent organisms otherwise devoid of recognizably human morphological characteristics.

Taking these factors into account and again with some appeal to the unexceptional nature of the sun and, by extension, the solar system, a value of about unity was postulated for f_i.

Development of the interest and ability in communicating over interstellar distances implies as prerequisites not only complex social organization but also elaborate technological capabilities. This has occurred on the earth only very recently. It was argued that the course of human history has seen between one and five largely independent attempts at organizing the same species into complex social associations. Independence here applies to the transfer of large amounts of nongenetic information. Examples are the cultures of China, the Americas, and the Middle East. A minimum of one of these has reached the communicative state; hence on this basis, f_c has a value of about 0.2. It was recognized that this argument is quite vulnerable on the question of independence besides being frankly anthropocentric.

Nevertheless, the opinion prevailed that technological development on a planet inhabited by intelligent beings might well occur with moderate probability, though modified by environmental features (for example, the relative scarcity of metals in the planets of metal-poor stars). Given the technological development, the essential requirements for development of the communicative state were felt to be high intelligence and good sensory channels for input from the stars.

Given the capability for interstellar communication, the question of interest still remains. It is easy to imagine a technologically advanced society completely devoid of any concern with such endeavors. Arguments to the contrary are likely to be classed as anthropocentric, but perhaps constitute the only basis available for making any estimate. With these conjectures in mind, a value for f_c of 0.1 to 0.2 was suggested.

The final term to be evaluated is the mean lifetime, L, in the communicative state of the postulated societies. Such a period began on the earth only a few years ago with the development of radio astronomy. Its duration depends on the proficiency with which the culture can survive the internal stresses which may tend to destroy it or to divert its attention to other problems. Fears that the value of L on earth may be quite short are not groundless. However, there is at least the possibility that a resolution of national conflicts would open the way for the continued development of civilization for periods of time commensurate with stellar lifetimes.

It would seem possible, therefore, that the distribution of L for a population of many technological societies might be bimodal. Some may destroy themselves in a relatively short time, say less than a thousand years, but others, having surmounted this crisis, may continue development almost indefinitely, perhaps for periods of the order of hundreds of millions of years. Thus, two values of L were considered: $< 10^3$ and $> 10^8$ years.

Conclusions

When the factors discussed above are combined to give an estimate of N, the present number of communicative societies in the galaxy, it is at once apparent that the value chosen for L has a decisive influence. Thus, for small values of L the average number of communicative civilizations is also small, perhaps much less than 10^3 for the whole galaxy. The corresponding estimate of the distance to the nearest such civilization is then of the order of thousands of light-years or more. On the other hand, if the more optimistic values of communicative lifetime are chosen, the number of civilizations becomes 10^5 to 10^9, and the corresponding distance is estimated at ten to a few hundred light-years.

The use of radio or other electromagnetic signals appears to be the only method accessible for communication over interstellar distances. However, only the most optimistic estimates noted above would hold out any hope for establishing communication in both directions. Straightforward detection of "intelligent" transmissions seems to hold much more promise. The efforts which have already been made to detect such signals have been quite modest in scale and it was felt that the negative results should not discourage further investigations, especially on technical improvements. Study of methods for detecting the existence of many weak signals by use of cross-correlation techniques ("civilization detection") would also appear to merit attention, since ranges of the order of 10^4 light-years may be attainable thereby. Selection of frequencies remains a problem: It was noted that the use of lasers did not appear to be advantageous over interstellar distances and in the radio spectrum the region from 10 to 30 kMc/sec seems to be preferable for maximizing the signal-to-noise ratio, but the use of the hydrogen line may ease the frequency search problem. The possibility that investigations of the sort described above might find application in other branches of radio astronomy and in space research was also noted.

The compounding of uncertainties in the type of analysis attempted is so formidable that the acquisition of any additional experimental evidence—including the negative—is almost certain to be useful in guiding the course of future conjectures. The more intensive and systematic application of modern techniques to the search for other planetary systems and the direct investigations of the nearby planets for evidence of life are examples of this sort. Similarly, the dominant effects of the evolutionary and sociological factors suggest the desirability of more profound analysis of these problems than was possible on the occasion reported here.

B. M. Oliver

29 ✳ INTERSTELLAR COMMUNICATION

Speculation as to the existence of extraterrestrial life is as old as the knowledge that other possibly habitable worlds exist. The early Greeks imagined that there might be beings on the moon. So did the astronomer Kepler and the science fiction writer Jules Verne. At the turn of the century the airless moon was no longer seriously considered a possible abode for life and attention turned to the other planets of our solar system, particularly Mars and Venus. As knowledge about the surface conditions of the other planets has increased, the possibility that intelligent life exists there has grown more remote. Today no one seriously expects to find intelligent life elsewhere in the solar system, although some feel that ammonia-based life forms may exist on Jupiter, and that there is probably primitive vegetation on Mars.

Oddly enough, as further knowledge about our solar system has shown it to be barren of intelligent life except (debatably) for earth itself, further knowledge in other fields has greatly increased our estimates of the density of intelligent life elsewhere in the universe, on planetary systems around other stars. There are of course a tremendous number of stars—about one hundred thousand million in our own galaxy, the Milky Way. And there are on the order of one hundred thousand million galaxies. The feeling that in all this vast cosmos life must exist somewhere besides on earth is very appealing and plausible, but not scientific. The real questions are: How many stars have planetary systems rich in the variety of heavy elements needed for life?, and: Given a suitable planet, how likely is life to begin and evolve?

Planets Are Plentiful

Only a few decades ago, planetary systems were thought to be very rare, the result of near collisions between two stars. On this basis, only about one star in a billion would have planets. Today planetary systems are thought to be produced as a necessary step in the evolution of a typical star (1-3). Stars begin their life cycle as huge masses of interstellar gas many times the size of the solar system. Typically, this extended mass of gas would be slowly rotating. As it condenses under its own gravity, conservation of angular momentum requires that the rate of rotation increase rapidly. By the time it has shrunk to about the size of the solar system, i.e., the orbit of Pluto or Neptune, it will have flattened by centrifugal force to a whirling lens of hot, ionized gas. In order to condense to a spherical star, the whirling gas disk must lose most of its initial angular momentum. It can do this only by casting off from its periphery satellite gas masses and imparting angular momentum to these by magnetohydrodynamic interaction. This involves acceleration of the ionized and therefore conducting satellite by the magnetic field of the ionized spinning central mass. As each satellite mass is thus accelerated into orbit, the central mass contracts further and the process repeats until the central mass becomes a star. The satellite masses then condense and cool to become planets and moons. In our own solar system over 99 per cent of the total mass is in the sun, while over 98 per cent of the angular momentum is in the planets.

Since the galaxy as a whole is rotating, typical gas masses must go through this process to condense into stars, and we conclude that planetary systems must be the rule rather than the exception. Several nearby stars show periodicities in their apparent motion which could be explained by the revolution of a planet of roughly Jupiter's mass.

The older stars, called Population II stars, formed out of almost pure hydrogen gas. It is unlikely that they produced stable planets, or if so, that life could begin on them. But these stars convert their hydrogen to heavy elements in the course of their life and when, in death, they explode as supernovae, they cast these heavy elements into space. There these elements mix with more hydrogen to form the gas masses out of which condense the second generation (Population I) stars like our sun (4). Planets of Population I stars are possible abodes for life.

Life Is Likely but Remote

A few decades ago the origin of life was a complete mystery. Life was thought to be highly unlikely unless precisely the right conditions were present. Today the right conditions are believed to be present in at least one planet of a typical Population I star (5, 6). The primitive atmosphere of a planet like the earth is believed to consist of ammonia, methane, water vapor, and other molecular gases. Upon irradiation with ultraviolet light such a gas mixture forms aminoacids, the building blocks of proteins. On the primitive earth or any similar planet, these aminoacids would rain down into the then fresh ocean to form a literal consommé covering the planet. Given a few phosphate radicals it is not difficult to visualize the formation of large quantities of the molecules out of which deoxyribonucleic acid (DNA) polymerizes. Experiments have shown that once the first DNA polymer forms, a process of self replication ensues. This is reproduction at its most basic, molecular level. Suddenly our sterile consommé has converted itself into a sea of genes, and even chromosomes. Those who have studied the origin of life now feel that, given planets only approximately like the primitive earth, life is certain to start. On perhaps 1 to 10 per cent it may develop into complex and possibly intelligent forms.

Thus, during this century, while our expectation of finding intelligent extraterrestrial life has virtually vanished for the rest of our solar system, it has grown enormously for other stellar systems. We now contemplate a universe teeming with life, but this life is so remote from us as to almost preclude our ever establishing physical contact. The nearest star, α Centauri, is 4 light-years away. By contrast our solar system is only a milli-light-year in over-all diameter. While man may roam the solar system with instruments (or even in person) during the next decades, to explore thousands of light-years into space looking for other life still seems impossibly difficult. The only means of contact that appears feasible today is some form of electromagnetic communication.

Calling All Stars

The problem of interstellar communication can be divided into three major aspects. There is the technical problem: Can we signal over these great distances, and if so, how can we best do it? There is the acquisition problem: How do we attract the attention of another race, or they ours? And finally there is the communication problem itself: How do we exchange meaningful information with a totally alien civilization?

The technical problem obviously depends on distance, and this depends upon the density of communicative races in our stellar neighborhood. A real effort to estimate this density was made last November at a conference at the National Radio Astronomy Observatory at Green Bank, West Virginia. On the basis of quantitative estimates of the numerous independent factors involved, the conclusion was reached that if we can signal out to 10 light-years our chances of contact are extremely slim, perhaps one in a million. But if we can signal out to 1000 light-years (and do so for an extremely long time) our chances of contact are good, perhaps 50 per cent. Stars likely to have habitable planets exist about 10 light-years from us. Within a radius of 1000 light-years there are tens of thousands of candidates.

The ultimate range of an interstellar communication system is determined by three factors: The energy radiated per symbol, the directive gain of the antennas, and the noise. In the simplest (and a very nearly optimum) form of modulation the "symbols" would be pulses or spaces, and the message would be encoded into these in some way. Now the limiting amplification which can be used at the receiver is determined by the noise at its input: random energy which is spread over the entire frequency spectrum. In order to "detect" a pulse, i.e., distinguish between its présence or absence, the signal energy must be comparable to or greater than the noise energy received during a pulse time. Thus the signal-to-noise (energy) ratio is a measure of detectability. If this ratio is unity, detection will be marginal and many errors will be made. If the ratio is 100 the detection will be almost unambiguous. If we double the pulse length keeping the power the same, we will double the pulse energy. We can receive these slower pulses with a receiver having twice the response time and therefore half the bandwidth. This narrower receiver will receive half as much noise power and therefore the same total noise energy during the pulse. Thus we have doubled the signal-to-noise ratio by doubling the pulse energy and using a matched receiver. Of course we can now signal only half as fast. In an interstellar channel one would presumably use the highest economically practical power and very long pulses, since the communication rate is of little importance, at least initially.

The size of the transmitting antenna (measured in wavelengths) determines its ability to concentrate the radiated energy into a beam directed at the receiver. The physical size of the receiving antenna determines how much of this energy is collected. In fact the ratio of energy received to that radiated is simply (A_T/λ^2) (A_R/D^2), where A_T and A_R are the effective areas of the transmitting and receiving antennas, λ is the wavelength, and D the distance between them. Thus the largest practical antenna should be used at both ends.

Let us now look at the spectral distribution of noise power. All bodies which can absorb and therefore re-radiate electromagnetic waves are sources of "thermal noise," i.e., black-body radiation in a single propagation mode. Resistors produce thermal noise. So do hot surfaces or gases at which an antenna may be pointed. Since thermal noise at low frequencies has a spectral power density of kT watts per cycle per second (where $k = 1.38 \times 10^{-23}$ joules/degree is Boltzmann's constant), it is convenient and customary to consider any noise source having a spectral power density, ψ, as equivalent to a thermal source at a temperature $T = \psi/k$. Figure 1 shows the effective noise temperature of three sources germane to the present problem.

Cosmic noise is received from all parts of the sky but is most intense toward the center of the galaxy (7). It is the noise which Jansky

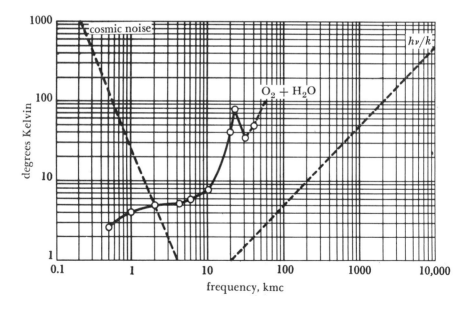

Figure 1

Equivalent noise temperatures from various sources.

(8) first heard and which started the science of radio astronomy. It falls off rapidly with increasing frequency as indicated by the line in Figure 1 (9).

Even an ideal amplifier, one without any thermal noise, is not noise-free. Quantum effects produce a noise referred to the amplifier input of $h\nu$ watts per cycle per second, where $h = 6.62 \times 10^{-34}$ joule/sec is Planck's constant and ν is the frequency, giving an effective temperature of $h\nu/k$ as shown (10). Modern masers approach this ideal quantum limited performance. (This noise source cannot be avoided by using photon detectors rather than coherent amplifiers, for then a similar "noise" exists due to randomness of photon count.)

The total noise from these two sources reaches a minimum around 8 Gc (Gc = gigacycle = 10^9 cps) of about 0.5° Kelvin. This low temperature emphasizes the importance of avoiding thermal noise sources in our receiver. Eight gigacycles would be a good frequency for interstellar communication if our receiver itself were in space. With an earth-based receiver the atmosphere radiates noise into the antenna due to absorption (and re-radiation) of energy by oxygen and water vapor (11). Taking this into account the quietest frequency range is from about 2 to 10 Gc with an effective noise temperature of 5° to 10°K. Above 50 Gc the strong oxygen, water vapor, and carbon dioxide resonances render the atmosphere opaque. When it clears up again in the infrared, $h\nu/k$ has reached several thousand degrees. Thus we have two likely regions for communication, one in the infrared and optical part of the spectrum, and a much quieter one in the microwave region.

The advent of optical masers, or lasers, has focused interest on the possibility of using optical frequencies for interstellar communication (12). Very narrow beams are possible with optical "antennas" of modest size. However, beam widths much less than a second of arc are impractical because of atmospheric turbulence and aiming problems. Such beams do not provide enough improvement over present large microwave antennas to compensate for the increased noise at optical frequencies ($\approx$20,000°K). Thus the microwave region still seems best at the present state of the art.

Figure 2 shows a performance comparison of two optical systems and one microwave system. The ordinate is the number of photons, $\bar{n}$, received per pulse for the optical systems, and the ratio of received energy per pulse to kT for the microwave system. Each of these quantities gives the signal-to-noise ratio (SNR) for the system involved, so the ordinates are comparable. The present laser with 10 joules per

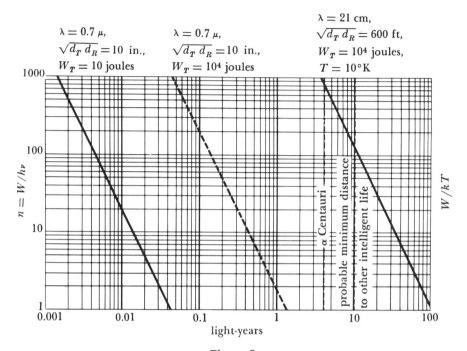

Figure 2

Comparative dx performance of laser and microwave systems.

pulse at a wavelength of 0.7 μ, and equipped with 10-inch telescope "antennas" at both transmitter and receiver, would give the performance shown by the left line. An ideal quantum limited receiver is assumed. We see that the SNR falls to unity at a distance of 0.04 light-year. Raising the radiated energy to 10,000 joules per pulse gives the performance shown by the middle dotted line: unity SNR at a little over 1 light-year. The line on the right assumes a microwave system radiating 10^4 joules per pulse at 21 cm, with 600-ft transmitting and receiving antennas, and a receiver noise temperature of 10°K. We see that unity SNR is reached at 100 light-years. At 10 light-years the SNR is 100. As a matter of fact, 10^6 joules per pulse (1 Mw for 1 sec) is certainly possible today, and this would give a SNR of 100 at 100 light-years, unity at 1000 light-years. The same results would be obtained with 230-ft antennas at 10 Gc.

We may conclude that the technical problem is barely within the present art, assuming equally dedicated cooperation at the other end!

What about the acquisition problem? How do we attract the attention of the other race, or search for their signals? This is made difficult by the dimensionality. Whether we transmit or listen, or both, we must not only search in space, star by star, but also in time, over an extended period, and possibly in frequency as well. If we could eliminate one dimension of search, we could simplify the problem enormously.

If we (or the other race) had some means of generating extremely short pulses of extremely high power, say 10^{16} watts for 10^{-10} sec, we (or they) could blanket the best part of the microwave region with energy. This is because short pulses have a very broad frequency spectrum. A very broad receiver sensitive from about 2 to 10 Gc, would then be indicated and would not require searching in frequency. Barring this, the high pulse energy can only be achieved by using the highest available power for long pulses and this requires a narrow band receiver.

Frequency search can also be eliminated, or greatly reduced, by transmitting on or near some natural frequency such as a spectral line. This is an inherent property of lasers and one of the strong arguments for their use. Project Ozma began with the ingenious suggestion of Cocconi and Morrison of Cornell (*13*) that we listen on the hydrogen-line frequency of 1420 mc (21-cm wavelength). They argued that since radio astronomers listen on this line a great part of the time, radio astronomers anywhere in the universe would be doing the same, and any intelligent race trying to communicate would choose this frequency or one nearby.

A good acquisition signal should differ markedly from all natural signals. It need not be a series of prime numbers as has often been suggested; mere pulses will do. But it should not be so efficiently encoded in the Shannon sense as to resemble thermal noise. (C. E. Shannon has shown that if the information in a signal is so coded as to make the statistics of the signal match those of thermal noise, the greatest transmission rate of information is achieved for a given power and bandwidth.) The acquisition signal can convey instructions for locating and receiving another signal more efficiently encoded, but the acquisition signal itself should be attention getting. The acquisition problem needs further study and should be reviewed in the light of each new technological development.

How should we attempt to convey meaning? Since the nearest likely stars are 10 light-years away, no answer can be received for at least 20 years. Certainly we should not waste time sending simple pulses until we get a reply. The other race would probably consider us so stupid they might not bother to answer. We should, I believe, send a repeated series of messages which constitute a course of instruction—facts about our civilization, our language, our science, and ourselves. The other race can then respond with a much more sophisticated initial message, perhaps one which would indicate some more efficient means of communication.

In constructing these first acquisition messages we are justified, I believe, in making one very important assumption about any intelligent race: that they have eyes or their equivalent. Sight is such an important sense that it is hard to imagine technological development in a race devoid of it. Further, it has developed in a very great variety of earth's life forms. Flies have eyes, so do scallops, and mice and men. Since pictorial matter provides a good, if not the best, means of conveying meaning in the absence of a common language, the initial signals should probably be pictorial. Other races would probably decide on pictorial messages for the same reasons.

In addition, certain mathematical and physical relationships would be obvious and correctly interpreted by any race whose technology was sufficiently advanced to receive the message at all. Prime numbers, for example, are prime in any numbering system. The structure of atoms does not depend on who studies them.

Using these principles, Frank Drake, of the National Radio Astronomy Observatory, constructed an imitation message which he mailed to those who had attended the meeting mentioned earlier (14). No clues for decipherment were given, yet the majority of the group successfully got most of the meaning from it very quickly. Here is a similar message to try on your friends!

Contact!

Let us assume that after years of futile listening we receive a peculiar series of pulses and spaces from ε Eridani. The message is repeated every 22 hours and 53 minutes, apparently the length of their day. The pulses occur at separations which are integral multiples of a minimum separation. Writing ones for the pulses and filling in the blanks with the appropriate numbers of zeros we get the binary series shown in Figure 3. It consists of 1271 ones and zeros. 1271 is the product of two primes 31 and 41. This strongly suggests that we ar-

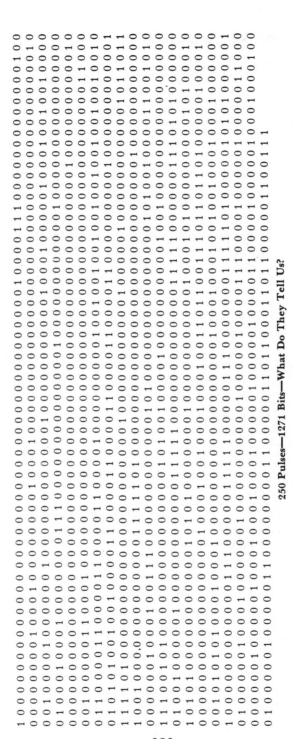

250 Pulses—1271 Bits—What Do They Tell Us?

Figure 3

An imitation message from outer space.

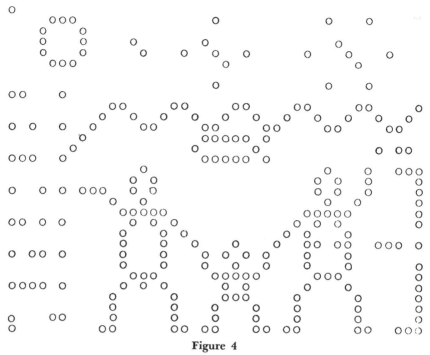

Figure 4

The same message rearranged. (We may have it reversed left to right, but we will never know unless we compare physical parity experiments with the other race or star fields visible to both of us.)

range the message in a 31 × 41 array. When we do so, leaving blanks for the zeros, and putting down a dot for each pulse we get the non-random pattern of Figure 4.

Apparently we are in touch with a race of erect bipeds who reproduce sexually. There is even a suggestion that they might be mammals. The crude circle and column of dots at the left suggests their sun and planetary system. The figure is pointing to the fourth planet, evidently their home. The planets are numbered down the left-hand edge in a binary code which increases in place value from left to right and starts with a decimal (or rather a binary) point to mark the beginning. The wavy line commencing at the third planet indicates that it is covered with water and the fish-like form shows there is marine life there. The bipeds know this, so they must have space travel. The diagrams at the top will be recognized as hydrogen, carbon, and oxygen atoms, so their life is based on a carbohydrate chemistry. The binary number six above the raised arm of the right figure suggests six fingers and implies a base twelve-number system. Finally, the dimension line at the lower right suggests that the figure is eleven somethings tall. Since the wavelength of 21 cm on which we received the message is the only length we both know, we conclude the beings are 231 cm, or seven feet, in height.

This message certainly does not exceed Shannon's information limit. Better messages from this standpoint can easily be constructed. In fact the earlier one constructed by Frank Drake used only 551 zeros and ones to convey a somewhat similar amount of information. But it is surprising how much we could learn about another race from only 250 pulses.

The likelihood of other intelligent life and the virtual impossibility of physical contact with it combine to make the study of interstellar electromagnetic communication a fascinating and possibly fruitful subject. To signal over the required distance seems technically possible. The communication of meaning appears easy. If we solve the acquisition problem (and the economic problem of mounting the sustained effort required), electronics may some day answer the age-old question: Is man alone in the universe?

References

1   O. Struve, *Stellar Evolution,* Princeton University Press, Princeton, N.J., 1950, Chap. 2.

2   H. Alfven, *Origin of the Solar System,* Oxford University Press, New York, 1954.

3   G. P. Kuiper, in J. A. Hynek (ed.), *Astrophysics,* McGraw-Hill, New York, 1951, Chap. 8.

4   J. H. Oort, in D. J. K. O'Connell (ed.), *Stellar Populations,* North-Holland, Amsterdam, 1958, p. 415.

5   C. Sagan, *Radiation Res.,* **15,** 174 (1961).

6   A. I. Oparin et al. (eds.), *The Origin of Life on the Earth,* Pergamon, London, 1959.

7   H. C. Ko, *Proc. Inst. Radio Engrs.,* **46,** 208 (1958).

8   Karl G. Jansky, *Proc. Inst. Radio Engrs.,* **21,** 1387 (1933).

9   J. H. Piddington, *Monthly Notices, Royal Astron. Soc.,* **3** (1951).

10   M. W. P. Strandberg, *Phys. Rev.,* **106,** 453 (1961).

11   D. C. Hogg, *J. Appl. Phys.,* **30,** 1417 (1959).

12   R. N. Schwartz and C. H. Townes, *Nature,* **190,** 205 (1961).

13   G. Cocconi and P. Morrison, *Nature,* **184,** 844 (1959).

14   Private communication to members of The Order of the Dolphin.

Robert Ascher and Marcia Ascher

3O ✳ INTERSTELLAR
COMMUNICATION
AND HUMAN EVOLUTION

G. Cocconi and P. Morrison have recently entertained the possibility of interstellar communication (*1*).

More recently a search for signals from other civilizations was considered by von Hoerner (*2*). In the later article it is pointed out that the potential of a search is largely dependent on the adequacy of guesses about the probability of the existence of extraterrestrial technical civilizations, the probable stage of development of a civilization which we might contact, the longevity of attempts at contact following success or failure, and the result of possible contact and exchange. Attention is given to the determination of these and other factors and some numerical estimates are suggested. Presumably this and similar investigations will form the basis for the design of listening and sending apparatus. This ambitious and expensive endeavor may benefit by using models founded on human evolution as well as extraterrestrial data, and constructed with the end of increasing the reasonableness of the guesses. This article indicates initial steps in this direction.

The use of a model or series of models which involve human evolution is necessarily based on two assumptions. We assume that throughout hominid history, since the origin of hominids and culture, there has existed sufficient curiosity to motivate attempts to contact self-conscious life forms and some means of doing so. Second, we assume that the effectiveness of the barriers which separated different populations during prehistoric times was equivalent to the effectiveness of the barrier which now separates earth civilization from possible extraterrestrial civilizations. The first assumption is supported in interpretations of the archeological and fossil hominid records and in behavioral studies of the higher primates and other advanced mammalian forms. The second assumption is tenable because for most of prehistory the only means of communication was bipedal locomotion. Extensive bodies of water, in particular, were restrictive to contact between small terrestrial populations. Both assumptions are related by opposition; curiosity encouraged contact and effective barriers inhibited it.

In order to construct the proposed models, some definitions used in the recent article in *Science* are recast. There, a technical civilization is defined by the "presence of highly advanced radio techniques"; here, a technical civilization is defined by the presence of barrier-surmounting techniques, irrespective of the barrier or the techniques. This reformulation is not only necessary for the inclusion of relevant information but is also necessary for the entire endeavor. It would be shortsighted and inhibiting to future ideas on communication to view possible extraterrestrial civilizations ethnocentrically, or rather, electrocentrically, by supposing that the highest form of communication now reached on earth is the highest form that will be reached here or can be reached elsewhere. Along with this, we substitute contact activities for contact signals. Even if within-vision devices, such as large fires, were used as contact signals in prehistoric times, they would be difficult for the prehistorian to locate, impossible to interpret with confidence, and are not directly relevant to the barrier-surmounting problems with which we are concerned. On the other hand, evidence of contact activities such as intrusive tools are the data with which the student of human evolution is familiar.

Within the context of the present problem, we tentatively divide prehistory into two technical orders and call the first early prehistory and the second later prehistory. The principal criterion for this division is the barrier-surmounting technique or techniques which existed during each order. The analogy between prehistoric contact and exchange, and hypothesized extraterrestrial contact and exchange, is suggested in the following description.

Early prehistory begins with the origin of hominids and technology more than 1,000,000 years ago and lasts until approximately 8000 years ago. At least four major hominid populations existed at some time during this era: *Australopithecus, Pithecanthropus, Neanderthal,* and *Homo sapiens.* The size of any population isolate probably never exceeded 100 individuals. These isolates, developed by budding from parent populations, microevolved (biologically and technologically) in relatively independent niches. The technological differences between isolates was never great; when contact was achieved near-equals met.

Later prehistory begins about 8000 years ago and lasts until about 1000 B.C. Only one hominid form, *Homo sapiens,* inhabited the world. For some populations, at least two barrier-surmounting techniques in addition to walking came into being, namely, the long-distance ship and domesticated riding animals. In early prehistory contact and exchange occurred between technologically similar but biologically diverse populations. In later prehistory contact was usually initiated by those populations with advanced techniques and equal exchange was rare.

The analogy is more than merely suggestive. Information from human evolution can be used to introduce additional factors into the reasons for the development and replacement of life forms possessing complex technologies over immense spans of time and large distances. The use of archeological-paleontological data in a model describing contact can refine numerical estimates for factors already proposed and add new factors with numerical estimates. The data learned from prehistory can be particularly useful in evaluating the effects of successful contacts and, therefore, the degree and results of the establishment of continuing exchange. The use of both early and later prehistory enables the testing of a contact model. Data describing a prehistoric population or populations can be substituted into the equations in the model and the indicated conclusions compared with the facts of human evolution. We grant that it would be difficult to infer the effects of unsuccessful attempts at contact from the data because such cases leave no obvious records. Nevertheless some estimates can be made on the basis of a consideration of the successful cases as contrasted with the opportunities available and the known barriers. Specific cases which can be examined in the context of the present problem include, for example, *Neanderthal-Homo sapiens* contact and transpacific exchange.

References

1 G. Cocconi and P. Morrison, *Nature,* **184,** 844 (1959).

2 S. von Hoerner, *Science,* **134,** 1839 (1961).

A. G. W. *Cameron*

3 I ✳ FUTURE RESEARCH
ON INTERSTELLAR
COMMUNICATION

The papers collected in this volume represent an important beginning in our study of the probability for the existence of intelligent species elsewhere in our galaxy, and of the possibility of communicating with such species. Undoubtedly other basically new ideas will be added as time goes on. However, the problems seem now to be well enough *defined* that we can begin to make some quantitative scientific guesses about the relevant probabilities.

Perhaps one reason for the rapid growth of scientific speculation in this field is that until recently it lacked respectability. Philip Morrison (*1*) found, prior to the publication with Giuseppe Cocconi of his pioneering paper (Chapter 15), that several of his colleagues had a great interest in the subject and had developed some of the ideas also expressed in this volume. The Cocconi-Morrison paper established the scientific respectability of the field. If this respectability is to be maintained, it is essential that further speculations be responsibly based on solid foundations of facts.

Morrison (*1*) has remarked that in a few years' time a Ph.D. will probably be awarded in this field. This is remarkable for a subject that has exactly zero data of a direct sort. Already a small scientific conference has been held to discuss the subject. This conference was widely interdisciplinary in character, and yet the participants keenly felt the absence of experts in the social, behavioral, and linguistics fields.

This points strongly to one of the most important aspects of interstellar communication. This problem challenges every aspect of our knowledge of ourselves, our society, and our environment. Consequently the entire growth of our knowledge in all fields contributes toward the guesses we can make about the nature of extraterrestrial societies. However, certain fields of research can contribute in a more direct way, and I propose to discuss some of these.

Let us start by writing down an expression for the number of sites in our galaxy where technically competent and communicative extraterrestrial social structures may be thought to exist. This number is $N = N_s f_p n_e f_b n_i f_c L_c/L_p$. Here N_s is the number of suitable stars in our galaxy, f_p is the fraction of those stars that have planetary systems, n_e is the number of earth-like planets capable of supporting life, f_b is the probability that living biological systems will develop on a planet, n_i is the number of species likely to develop on a planet having the potential for interstellar communication, f_c is the fraction of these species that is motivated to attempt communication, L_c is the lifetime of the communicative phase of such a species, and L_p is that part of the lifetime of a planet during which such species can exist. This equation is essentially the one used by Morrison (1) and is similar to the one used for the organization of the discussion at the Green Bank Conference on Extraterrestrial Intelligent Life, Nov. 1-2, 1961 (see Chapter 28). We shall discuss each of the terms.

The term N_s might have been further subdivided into probabilities. By a "suitable star" we mean one having a lifetime on the main sequence long enough for the development of an intelligent species. For the solar system this biological development took 4.5 billion years. It might well take more or less than this by a factor two on another planet. However, it seems probable that we should regard stars of spectral classes O, B, A, and early F as unsuitable.

We must also exclude as unsuitable the majority of those stars that are members of binary systems. The earlier discussion by Su-Shu Huang has shown that the probability of having life zones containing stable planetary orbits is much reduced for binary systems. This leaves for consideration perhaps about 20 per cent of the stars of spectral classes late F and redder.

There have been conflicting opinions about whether we should also exclude the faint red stars. Huang has argued that the smallness of the life zones around such stars makes it unlikely that there will be suitably placed planets. On the other hand, I have argued that the number of planets in a life zone is approximately constant down to the latest spectral classes. In practice this means down to about 0.08 solar masses. S. Kumar has recently shown that stars of still smaller mass do not start converting hydrogen into helium in the center, and hence they will cool off as degenerate stars in a time short compared to a biological evolution time.

If we include only stars of spectral classes not too dissimilar to the sun, then, using the luminosity function of Limber (2) and taking the mass of the galaxy as 1.6×10^{11} solar masses [Allen (3)], we find $N_s \approx 6 \times 10^9$ stars. On the other hand, if we include also faint stars, then $N_s \approx 4 \times 10^{10}$ stars. We have excluded the binary systems in making these estimates.

Since these "candidate" stars are all single, we must now consider f_p, the fraction having planetary systems. In order to give a number in which we could have a considerable degree of confidence, we should have a satisfactory theory of the formation of planetary systems. But the problem of the origin of our own solar system has been the major unsolved problem of scientific philosophy for more than three centuries. It is clear that many complicated physical and chemical processes were involved. Hence it is unlikely that we shall have a fully satisfactory answer in the next few years. We are now making progress in understanding the formation of stars, in determining what happens to the angular momentum of the interstellar material when star formation takes place, and in determining the physical and chemical processes that the meteorites have undergone. With the scientific exploration of the moon and planets imminent, we can expect to understand the formation and early history of the solar system very much better in a few years. My own feeling is that we should take $f_p = 1$; others would choose a lower value.

Within each planetary system, how many planets are likely to be able to support life? This depends on two principal questions: How many planets exist within the life zone and how big are they? To answer these questions we must understand even more clearly the details of the formation of planetary systems. The solar system probably has two planets within the life zone, and I have estimated in Chapter 10 that there should be an average of 1.4 planets in a life zone for any type of star. The size distribution of these is another matter entirely. In Chapter 3 I estimated that planetary sizes should probably be quite variable. As far as life support is concerned, the most important consideration is probably that the planets should be large enough to retain a decent atmosphere; there is no obvious upper limit to their size. It will be some time before we understand the physical characteristics of Venus and Mars well enough to feel that these questions can be answered with any degree of quantitative assurance. I shall guess that $n_e = 0.3$.

It is not out of the question that some further observational evidence on the matter of planetary sizes could be obtained. A few of the nearby stars have invisible companions an order of magnitude larger than Jupiter in mass. They have been discovered by means of the perturbations that they produce in the motions of their primary stars. It would undoubtedly be possible to look for smaller perturbations by using larger astrographic cameras and using modern computing methods to examine the large amount of necessary data. In principle one could also look for very shallow eclipses of a star by planets, but this is unlikely to be a fruitful possibility.

Most biologists today would say that the probability of biogenesis is unity if a planet is like the primitive earth with a reducing atmosphere. Melvin Calvin has discussed the processes of biogenesis in Chapter 5. Much progress has been made in understanding these biochemical processes, and it is likely that many of the remaining major gaps in our knowledge will be filled in a few years. However, some interesting questions remain to be posed. If a faint red star has a suitable planet in the life zone, what will happen at the point of biological evolution when the plants must develop photosynthesis in order to use the energy in sunlight? Will they be forced to get along with the much reduced intensity of light in the blue and yellow parts of the spectrum, or will some other process be discovered to make use of the overwhelming preponderance of light in the infrared? Despite questions of this sort I shall stick to $f_b = 1$. If we discover that life has originated also on Mars, our confidence regarding this point will be greatly bolstered.

About n_i, the number of species likely to develop the capability of interstellar signalling, we must be very uncertain. In the case of our earth, the number is at least 1. It is a very interesting question to ask whether any other species on earth could potentially develop a technical culture. J. C. Lilly has found that dolphins possess a somewhat complex "language" and manifest a considerable degree of intelligence. But would the dolphins, if left alone, develop technology, lacking hands? And would they be led to space exploration when their natural habitat is water? Some people think that the dolphins and several other species could develop a technological society if given sufficient time. However, it may be that no species on Mars will ever develop a technological society. Hence I shall guess $n_i = 1$.

We now come to f_c, the fraction of the technological species that wish to attempt communication. It can be argued that this fraction should be fairly large. It seems likely that the development of technology implies a considerable degree of inquisitiveness. This feature is certainly suggestive that a species will probably try to communicate once it deduces the likelihood of widespread technological civilizations within the galaxy. A preliminary look at some of the social and anthropological evidence regarding this question has been made by R. and M. Ascher in Chapter 30. Clearly this question deserves a great deal more thought. I shall guess $f_c = 0.5$.

The greatest uncertainty of all, as emphasized by Sebastian von Hoerner in Chapter 27, lies in the lifetime of a technological society after it has achieved the ability to communicate. At the same time it is likely to achieve the ability to commit suicide.

Some pessimists observe that we have had the hydrogen bomb for 10 years, and that may well be the order of magnitude of the lifetime of our society since getting the bomb. Whether this is really so, even with a thermonuclear war, is open to some question, since some analysts with the RAND Corporation believe that a society could rapidly recover its technological capability following a thermonuclear war. However, it may be that we have also passed the first major crisis of the thermonuclear age. For years the editors of *Bulletin of the Atomic Scientists* carried the picture of a clock on their cover, with the hands approaching closer and closer to the critical hour of 12 o'clock. This was taken as a measure of the time remaining before the beginning of nuclear holocaust. Recently the hands have started receding.

If a culture can survive or avoid thermonuclear destruction, then how long should it be recognizable as a culture? The greatest experience we have is probably the Chinese culture, which lasted for the order of a thousand years. It had its internal struggles during this time, but it maintained a sense of cultural continuity. But the Chinese culture was one among many on the planet, all of which were vying for supremacy. So a single planet-wide culture, that we may be gradually achieving, may be able to last much longer. How long? Species evolve on a time scale of the order of a million years. Continents change on a time scale of a billion years. Von Hoerner suggests the very important feedback effect of interstellar communication may greatly lengthen the life of a culture. But the interests of the culture may change and it may lose interest in communicating. These are the largest uncertainties with which we have to deal. I shall guess $L_c = 10^6$ years. Von Hoerner makes a more complicated and more pessimistic guess in Chapter 27.

For L_p, the lifetime of a planet following the emergence of intelligent life, we must guess several billion years. The galaxy is about 10^{10} years old and most stars were formed in the first few billion years of galactic history. So I shall guess $L_p = 3 \times 10^9$ years.

Thus my own guesses regarding these probabilities give

$$N = 4 \times 10^{10} \times 1 \times 0.3 \times 1 \times 1 \times 0.5 \times 10^6/3 \times 10^9$$
$$= 2 \times 10^6$$

This is a very respectable number of advanced civilizations.

We now wish to find the distance to the nearest few civilizations. The space density near the sun of stars I have classed as suitable is approximately 0.03 stars per cubic parsec. Hence the space density of communicative civilizations is 1.5×10^{-6} civilizations per cubic parsec. Thus we should expect the nearest such civilizations to be about 87 parsecs away (or 284 light-years). This is somewhat smaller than von Hoerner's estimate. However, all these estimates are extremely insecure.

Clearly there is much room for research in many fields of knowledge to improve the guesses that we must make for the above probability factors. The most important fields for research evidently lie in the social sciences, to determine the critical number L_c.

We should also do more research on communication techniques. A variety of suggestions have been made in this book about the relative merits of signalling with radio waves or light waves on various frequencies. We must extend our use of logic in determining where we should look for interstellar communications. Recent discussions have centered around the concept of contacting signals that will tell you where to look for a narrow communications channel. I suspect that logic can carry us much farther than it has so far. But we must always worry about the universality of the logical processes we are using.

I should like to add to the discussion of communications techniques only some thoughts regarding communications with civilizations on planets near the very faint stars that I proposed in Chapter 10 as likely to exist. For these civilizations the laser may be the obvious way of communicating, since the signal-to-noise ratio of their optical transmissions should be orders of magnitude better than that calculated for the sun by Schwartz and Townes in Chapter 23. The most logical place to transmit might well be in the hydrogen alpha line, owing to its universality as an absorption feature in all spectral types and also because it is characteristic of the most abundant element in the universe.

Some thought has also been given to the best form in which to transmit interstellar messages. This ranges from the simple transmissions of mathematical series such as prime numbers to the transmission of a complete course in linguistics to be followed by an encyclopedia. Some further research might be useful here.

Recently Hans Freudenthal (*4*) published a book entitled *Lincos: Design of a Language for Cosmic Intercourse.* In this he attempted to design a "lingua cosmica" in which he based all instruction on abstract mathematical relationships. He argued that verbal description of this sort is superior to the transmission of television pictures because we cannot tell the receiver the principle of the decomposition of the signals into a picture. One can seriously question this argument on two grounds: (1) His listener must make a very complicated chain of true-false logic come out correctly in order to understand his verbal description. One worries about the listener missing the beginning and hence being left mystified. One also worries about the degree of residual human orientation in construction of the lingua cosmica. (2) We have seen in Chapter 29 how B. M. Oliver was easily able to construct a television picture out of a series of signals of the on-off variety, and how he obtained a wealth of information from this picture despite the fact that its information content was near the saturation level (surely actual interstellar signals would outline the figures much more clearly at the expense of sending more digits). Many others were similarly successful in decomposing this and other "interstellar messages" sent out by Frank Drake.

On these grounds it seems quite likely that a television picture would be the logical way to open an interstellar conversation. But much more thought needs to be given to the question.

References

1 P. Morrison, Lecture at the Institute for Space Studies, Dec. 14, 1961.
2 D. N. Limber, *Astrophys. J.,* **131,** 168 (1960).
3 C. W. Allen, *Astrophysical Quantities,* Athlone Press, London, 1955.
4 H. Freudenthal, *Lincos: Design of a Language for Cosmic Intercourse,* North-Holland, Amsterdam, 1960.

Philip Morrison

32 ❋ OUTLOOK REGARDING INTERSTELLAR COMMUNICATION

During the few years since the topic of interstellar communication left the science fiction magazines for the scientific journals, a body of work, very well sampled in this interesting collection of Dr. Cameron's, has emerged. Perhaps the most striking feature of this work is the broad agreement which many and diverse authors have found. This is surely a favorable omen; at the same time, it would be wrong to overlook the fact that the very act of publication in so speculative a vein implies a bias of mind which may mislead. More cautious writers tend to seek an agnostic position: "I believe . . . the spontaneous generation of . . . the first living thing . . . is exceedingly improbable . . . But . . . we are certainly not in possession of all the relevant facts. It is impossible to form a judgment on this question at the present time." Thus runs the recent statement of a very thoughtful biochemist (1), one who has for 15 years considered the problem of life's origin.

It is characteristic that the more complex the process, the less well we understand it. Stellar radiation is simple enough, but planet formation, the emergence of life, evolution of complex beings, their technical development, and above all, their societal longevity, are topics for which no theory is reliable. In every case it seems plausible but never compelling to use our limited human experience as a guide. In the formation of planets, for example, it is plausible to limit our considerations to planets of terrestrial orbital size, though arguments can be made for a scaling law more like the logarithmic distribution of the orbits of our solar system. This would increase the incidence of life-supporting planets, by allowing them to exist near the many stars much cooler and smaller than the sun (2). Such arguments may serve as offsets to the unquestioned tendency for optimistic estimates of the still less secure factors.

The question of optimal signal channels is still a key one. The possibilities of the new optical masers are attractive, but they do not yet seem to better the intrinsic advantages of the low signal-to-noise ratio which the decimeter waves, so sparsely produced by nature, retain for galactic distances. But here more attention needs to be paid to the fact that this communication problem has two distinct stages: the stage of search and acquisition, and the stage of massive information transfer. The implications here require detailed study; the problem presented to our presumed sources, of multiple signal channels and of time division among them, has only been touched upon (3), and awaits closer study. A careful examination of this problem may make a rational choice of channels still more clear.

Finally, the entire point of this whole field of study is surely to make possible an empirical answer to all these attractive speculations. The first success can be looked to within the years 1964-1966, when a Mars soft-landed instrument probe should be able to settle the issue of whether life exists on that planet. If the answer is yes, as most people would now guess, the next stage of course is to see whether or not that form of life bears the marks of independent origin from that of earth. If this answer too is affirmative, it will transform the opinion that life is probable from an opinion only to a statistic. Analogous work directed at the other uncertain factors, from searches for dark stellar companions to historical investigations of the drive to technical competency, ought to replace the purely arm-chair quality of the papers in this, the first volume to survey the field.

References

1   N. H. Horowitz, *Proc. Federation Exptl. Biol.*, **21**, 687 (1962).
2   A. G. W. Cameron, this book, Chapter 10.
3   M. Handelsman, Wescon Report, 4.4, Aug. 1962, and S.-S. Huang, this book, Chapter 21.

INDEX

319